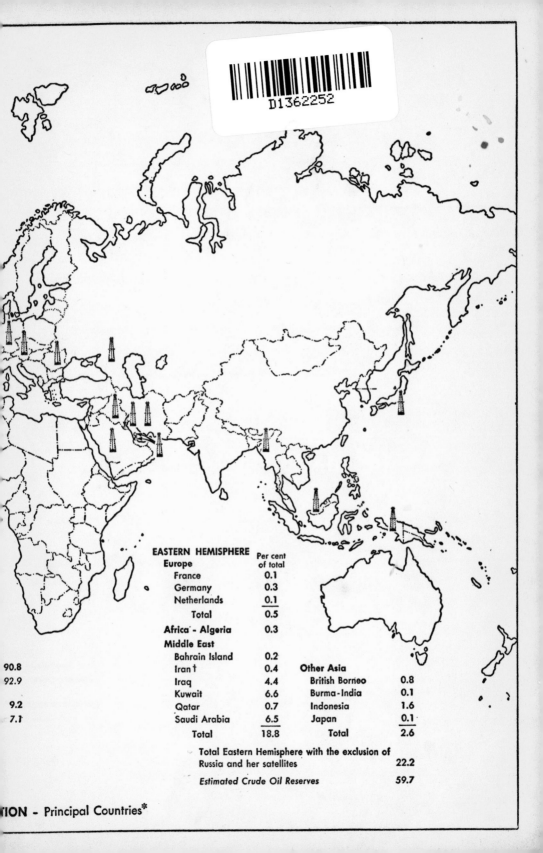

EASTERN HEMISPHERE Per cent
of total

	Per cent of total
Europe	
France	0.1
Germany	0.3
Netherlands	0.1
Total	0.5
Africa - Algeria	0.3
Middle East	
Bahrain Island	0.2
Iran †	0.4
Iraq	4.4
Kuwait	6.6
Qatar	0.7
Saudi Arabia	6.5
Total	18.8

Other Asia	
British Borneo	0.8
Burma - India	0.1
Indonesia	1.6
Japan	0.1
Total	2.6

Total Eastern Hemisphere with the exclusion of
Russia and her satellites   22.2

Estimated Crude Oil Reserves   59.7

90.8

92.9

9.2

7.1 †

TION - Principal Countries*

FOREIGN OIL AND THE FREE WORLD

FOREIGN OIL
AND THE FREE WORLD

Leonard M. Fanning

Author of "The Rise of American Oil," "American
Oil Operations Abroad," and "Fathers of Industries";
Editor of "Our Oil Resources"

FIRST EDITION

McGraw-Hill Book Company, Inc.
New York   Toronto   London

*This book is dedicated
to foreign-service oilmen
who as unsung ambassadors-of-goodwill
serve their country and the Free World
as they serve their companies*

PREFACE

This book attempts to point out the all-important contributions to the nations of the Free World made by American oil companies operating overseas. They have amply supplied—and continue to supply—the Free World with a resource which, more than ever, is vital to its economy and its defense. With a complete lack of fanfare those companies carry on their work in a spirit of good neighborliness which shows the way to economic and social progress in the nations concerned, and also enables the governments and peoples of those countries to help themselves to an extent which, even a few years ago, they did not dream possible. Diametrically and unequivocally opposed to Communism, the policies of American oil companies in foreign fields present a formidable barrier to the spread of Kremlin-dominated statism. American oil operations abroad, in short, provide many different and sturdy buttresses to the Free World.

Yet the problems of, and the pressures exerted upon, foreign oil development are many and diverse. Some are in the nature of the extraordinary costs incurred abroad as against those inherent in domestic operations. Others are met in such extracurricular activities as providing housing, hospitals, health and utility services and roads for public, as well as for company, use. Still others comprise political risks. These involve degrees of nationalism and nationalization—the xenophobia that brought about the ruinous three-year shutdown of Iranian oil was an extreme case—and Communist intrigue. Additional pressures relate to the natural urge of every nation to develop ready sources of crude-oil supply and refinery capacity so that it may bolster and safeguard its economy and its security.

In broad perspective, however, both the immense problems and the equally immense promise of petroleum development are the common concern and interest of every Free World nation. Thus the necessity for an international oil policy and, above all, for a public understanding of what foreign oil *means* to the Free World.

In the pages that follow we have taken the position that present American foreign oil operations could best be sketched against the background of their evolutionary development. Necessarily we have had to dip our brush in the palette of history, and in so doing we have been afforded the pleasure of renewing friendships with many oilmen —some in the forefront of today's stirring advances, some, so-called old-timers who, not long ago, were in the van. If, to any extent, we have succeeded in capturing and preserving information of value about these men and the events which they helped to forge, we shall be content. The American oil industry is approaching its centennial, and, for that occasion, some fitting record should be made of the pioneers who opened so many frontiers in the world of oil at home and abroad. Though their ranks are thinning and their memories fading, collectively these old-timers constitute a rich, primary source of invaluable information.

We wish to point out that this book contains facts and figures which heretofore were not available and which were contributed by various companies on request from us.

Credits for photographs go to Arabian American Oil Company, California Texas Oil Company, Creole Petroleum Corporation, Gulf Oil Corporation, Interprovincial Pipe Line Company, Kuwait Oil Company, Standard Oil Company of California, Standard Oil Company (New Jersey), The Texas Company and Trans Mountain Pipe Line Company.

Our sincerest gratitude goes to Harold R. Manakee for assistance in editing. For typing manuscript drafts, to Alice V. Farrington an accolade, and our thanks also to Charlotte L. Price and Beatrice B. Fisher.

We have inscribed the book to foreign-service oilmen. Our dedication speaks for itself.

Leonard M. Fanning
Saugatuck, Connecticut

CONTENTS

PART FIVE. PROBLEMS AND PRESSURES
AND POLICY NEEDS

APPENDIX I. STATISTICAL SECTION

APPENDIX II. GENERAL

LIST OF ABBREVIATIONS

AEOF	Anglo-Egyptian Oil Fields
AIOC	Anglo-Iranian Oil Company
API	American Petroleum Institute
APOC	Anglo-Persian Oil Company
Aramco	Arabian American Oil Company
Calarabian	California-Arabian Standard Oil Company
Caltex	California Texas Oil Company
GA	General Asphalt Company
IPAA	Independent Petroleum Association of America
IPC	Iraq Petroleum Company
MAORT	Magyar Amerikai Olajipari Rezveny Tarsasag
NIOC	National Iranian Oil Company
NPC	National Petroleum Council
NNGPM	Nederlandsche Nieuw Guinee Petroleum Maatschappij
PAD	Petroleum Administration for Defense
PAW	Petroleum Administration for War
Pemex	Petróleos Mexicanos
PIWC	Petroleum Industry War Council
PRC	Petroleum Reserves Corporation
Socal	Standard Oil Company of California
Stanvac	Standard-Vacuum Oil Company
SVPM	Socony-Vacuum Petroleum Maatschappij
TPC	Turkish Petroleum Company
VOC	Venezuelan Oil Concessions, Ltd.
YPF	Yacimientos Petrolíferos Fiscales

PART ONE

HAZARDS OF FOREIGN OPERATIONS

Chapter 1

WORLD OIL—A VITAL NECESSITY

World War I first focused attention on petroleum as a strategic material of the highest priority and as a vital need to an industrial economy. In so far as oil was concerned, World War II was a gigantic underscoring of the lesson of the first conflict. Unfortunately, the postwar era scarcely has been one of peace. Constantly facing Russian aggression during that time, the Free World has been occupied with rearmament, national defense and mutual security.

Under such circumstances, the fact that petroleum should figure in international as well as in national politics is natural and unavoidable. The seriousness with which a country regards the oil question is dictated by the degree to which that nation is, or is not, blessed with the resource either within its boundaries or in readily accessible locations. War, the threat of war or, simply, the ever-present consideration of national defense creates a situation of almost permanent urgency with respect to oil supply.

Nevertheless, the petroleum expansion of the last few decades is not entirely a war phenomenon. Rather it has a sound basis in peace and in the efforts of many peoples to raise their standard of living. In a very real sense the Industrial Revolution—begun in the late eighteenth century—still rolls outward from its beginning centers in England and the United States, and the dynamics of commerce, industry and science now are just reaching the so-called underdeveloped nations of the world.

Few people fully realize the wide influences of petroleum and its products on their daily lives. In modern industrialized countries, dependence on that much-sought-for liquid at least approaches a breathtaking universality, while underdeveloped countries have a present

3

interest and perhaps thrilling future in oil. Petroleum fuels power the engines of automobiles, buses, farm tractors and trucks as well as those of fishing craft, merchant ships, passenger liners and airplanes. Petroleum cutting oils make possible much of the drilling and grinding that are basic operations in mass production. Too, petroleum fuels heat homes and buildings. No engine or motor, including those of the major home appliances, could operate without the use of petroleum lubricants. Petroleum asphalt helps build our modern highways.

Either by self-consumption or by generating electricity, petroleum illuminants still supply many people of the world with artificial light. The almost endless uses of petroleum also include synthetic fibers for clothing; synthetic rubber for tires and other uses; cleansing agents, such as soaps and detergents; paints and plastics; and numerous ingredients used in fertilizers, food processing and many medicines. Such peacetime applications of petroleum multiply almost daily as scientists find new uses for the liquid's by-products. A whole new industry has grown out of petroleum chemistry—the petrochemical industry.

Moreover, if petroleum is necessary in peace, it is vital in war. Essentially, modern warfare is based on movement, and petroleum powers and lubricates airplanes, tanks, trucks and ships of all classifications. Petroleum yields, in addition, many specialty war products such as toluol, an ingredient of TNT; waterproofing greases essential to amphibious operations; inflammables for flame throwers; and, last but not least, fuel for rockets and jet engines.

In peace or war, then, no modern factory could operate without petroleum. Without it no machine products turned out by factories could perform the tasks for which they were made. If petroleum has become a necessity of life as we live today, it has become, as well, the promise of a better way of life for all the world tomorrow.

These facts place petroleum in its proper perspective. The spotlight on oil does not focus brightly merely when war comes or is threatened and then black out when the time of danger is past. Always that spotlight burns with intense and restlessly searching rays, for, now and in the future, perhaps no material is so vital to the peoples of the world as oil. Moreover, given a copious flow of the raw material, oil expansion is one of the wizardries of science, for ever it creates new products which, in turn, give birth to new industries and new employment.

The growing indispensability of oil makes its availability imperative. The mounting demand for it makes its production and distribution an attractive commercial proposition. Thus the struggle for oil —which has existed since Edwin L. Drake drilled the first well in 1859—continues and intensifies with the years. Never has it been more seething than it is today.

"Subject to change without notice" might be an appropriate label to hang on the world struggle for oil. Indeed, not only is the factor of change always present and operative, but, from time to time, fundamental differences merge in the pattern of change.

Change and oil ever have gone hand in hand. Claiming the headlines on one day was Texas' Spindletop, on another Mexico's "Golden Lane"; on the next day the great Mid-Continent fields of the United States; then California; on another day Venezuela's Maracaibo Basin; and on still another East Texas. More recently, the wonder of Middle East oil has captured the attention of the world, and, now—already in actual production and admittedly capable of a great, though undetermined, potential—Canada looms on the horizon. Who knows what new producing areas of major importance will fill tomorrow's headlines and change the face of the world oil map?

The first great factor of change is physical or operational and has to do with the so-called "fickleness" of discovery. Discovery may favor one country as against another or one company as against another. But always it stimulates and intensifies the eternal scramble for oil.

The second great factor is political and divides into national and international phases. On the national level each nation seeks its own oil security. In the international arena the struggle of various powerful nations for oil is known popularly as a "Power"—or "Great Power"—struggle. It is truly that. But today the Great Power struggle holds new meaning.

For, since World War II, significant change has entered the oil picture.

An aftermath of World War I was a determined effort by Britain, France and the Netherlands—acting individually or in certain areas in concert—to shut out Americans and other foreigners from their

controlled and mandated territories in the Middle and Far East—
the "closed-door" policy. Only the State Department, backed by capital furnished by American oil companies, finally was able to open
that door. Aftermaths of World War II, however, were the Marshall
Plan and the North Atlantic Treaty Organization. In other words,
European nations joined in a pact with the objective of establishing
not only military safety but also basic economic security. To NATO
countries oil is militarily and economically vital. Likewise it is essential to all the eastern and western nations of the Free World which
are engaged in the struggle against Communist aggression.

Could any change be more striking than this sharp contrast between today's policy of inclusion and yesterday's policy of exclusion? Could anything be more certain to produce changing
pressures in the world struggle for oil than to remove that commodity from a basically individual international power struggle to
one of mutuality of interest? Today, though denied by logic from
thinking in terms of "one world," nevertheless we can and do think
in terms of the "Free World." Therefore, the importance of postwar political combinations immediately is evident as affecting the
international operations of oil companies of various nationalities.

The third influence of change upon the world struggle for oil
has to do with social concepts—the lifting of underdeveloped nations
to higher living standards. In this field is the Point Four Program
of the United States government. If confined to what the American
taxpayer can contribute in direct taxes, the latter is a delimited and
fallacious handout policy. But, in its design to help nations to help
themselves, to justify and stimulate home and foreign investment and
to provide the world's people with more extensive and profitable employment in agricultural and industrial projects, Point Four becomes
a potent force.

With reason the operations of American oil companies in certain
foreign countries have been called a "Private Point Four," and in certain countries the transformation induced by oil is occurring before
our very eyes. Generally speaking, however, this social change is
largely one of vast future prospect.

Inevitably each one of these factors of change—(1) physical or operational; (2) political, (*a*) national (*b*) international; and (3) social—
bears heavily upon the foreign operations of American oil companies.

World oil before and after World War I is an amazingly contrasting picture with world oil before and after World War II! Before World War I, oil lived in the Kerosene Age. Though Russia and Rumania had petroleum industries before Drake sparked the American industry in 1859, enterprising Americans stole the show, and rapidly the United States became the world's greatest producer and consumer of oil products. In less than a decade after Drake had drilled his well in western Pennsylvania, Americans were exporting kerosene. Within another 10 years John D. Rockefeller introduced the lamp to China, and Standard Oil and independents in the Pennsylvania region were vying with each other for foreign business in practically every port of the world.

At the turn of the century, painfully but energetically, Edward L. Doheny with Californian and Mexican oil and J. S. Cullinan and others with Texas oil introduced the Fuel-oil Age by way of railroads, ships and industries. Even more significant, Henry Ford was beginning to market his "Tin Lizzie"—the car for the multitude—to give spur to the Gasoline Age. The Fuel-oil Age and the Gasoline Age—not to forget the Age of Petroleum Lubrication which overlapped both of them—delineate the period which saw oil take its place as a basic commodity in the culminating phases of the Western World's Industrial Revolution—the age of power and speed in industry and transportation.

Even before World War I the United States consistently was producing well over 60 per cent of all the world's oil and possessed probably 85 per cent of the world's refining capacity. Though American oil products were marketed in every country of the globe, only in Mexico and Rumania—in the former extensively, in the latter less so—had Americans entered into the production of oil abroad. And most Mexican oil was brought to the United States for refining, since the United States was the refining center of the world.

Following World War I a shortage scare touched off American exploration ventures in virtually every country considered promising, provided that Americans could gain access to them. In other words, old as was the American tradition of foreign investment in oil, most of this investment—except for the previously mentioned Mexican and Rumanian production—was in the marketing department. Now Americans invested heavily in searching out and developing oil sources abroad.

When World War II began, in so far as vital oil products were concerned, the United States was prepared. As had been the case in the first world conflict, this country supplied the large bulk of the oil products needed by the Allied forces confronting Germany and Japan. But this time Venezuela, instead of Mexico, was the chief reinforcement to the United States supply.

Yet, even before the war, a new factor in world oil was making itself felt—the promising source of the Middle East. Here, it may be said, hostilities at once stimulated and interrupted a trend. The conflict made oil from this strategic source more urgently needed, but difficulties of transportation, of obtaining steel for drilling and for building pipelines, as well as the lack of refineries and the time necessary to construct new ones, all held back development of the area. After the war, the trend began where it had left off. Indeed, it rushed on so fast and so conclusively as to put an entire new face on the oil map of the world.

Then, during the postwar period, came the swelling world consumption of oil—intensified or affected by shortage scares, existent or imaginary—by the cold war, the Marshall Plan, Point Four, the "little hot war" in Korea and the culminating rearmament of the Free World. All were pressures involving not only the position of the United States as a consumer, but also the nation's economic well-being and its security.

Investments of American oil companies abroad at the end of 1919 totaled around $400,000,000. By the end of 1929 the figure had reached $1,400,000,000—a jump of a cold billion in 10 years. And, despite the long depression of the thirties, another billion in foreign oil investment was added in the decade of 1929 to 1939.[1]

Today the operations of oil companies abroad rank second only to manufacturing in point of direct American investments in foreign countries. Of the country's $14,800,000,000 aggregate direct investment abroad at the end of 1952, $4,600,000,000, or 29 per cent, comprised money spent by American companies for the production, transportation, refining or marketing of oil (see Chapter 19, Does Foreign Oil Pay?).

From the first recorded commercial production of oil, which began in Rumania in 1857 and in the United States in 1859, until the end of 1936, man had tapped the earth for petroleum to the extent

[1] Fanning, *American Oil Operations Abroad*, 1947, p. 9.

of more than 29,125,000,000 barrels, with the United States yielding more than 18,694,800,000 barrels, or nearly 64 per cent of the total. In 1900 an annual production of less than 150,000,000 barrels filled the world's needs; in 1919—after World War I had greatly expanded industrial and transportation oil-consuming agencies—production had risen to 555,000,000 barrels per year. Within seven years world production had doubled to more than 1,000,000,000 barrels in 1926, and within another 11 years it had redoubled to more than 2,000,000,000 barrels in 1937.

As impressive as they are, these accelerations were nothing compared with what was to come.

From 1857 through 1953, world cumulative oil production was 79,082,000,000 barrels. In other words, in the 16 years between 1937 and 1953 world cumulative output increased 49,957,000,000 barrels compared with the aggregate of 29,125,000,000 barrels during the 79 years 1857 to 1936. In 1953 the commercial production of oil was under way in 46 countries, as compared with 35 in 1937. World production in 1953 was 4,755,000,000 barrels, or more than double the 2,000,000,000 barrels of 1937 and more than quadruple the 1,000,-000,000 barrels of 1926.

But, vastly important, whereas United States production accounted for 70 per cent of world production in 1926 and 63 per cent in 1937, its share in 1953 was only 50 per cent.

These statistics strikingly reveal (1) the tremendous growth in world production; (2) the gradual recession of the United States from its dominant position, though it still is the world's foremost oil-producing country; and (3) a profound change in the traditional flow of oil in the world's markets.[2]

After 1940, because of the expansion of development in old areas and the discoveries of new regions, estimated oil reserves were revised sharply both as to location and extent. As of January 1, 1954, estimated world crude-oil reserves reached the huge total of 136,-877,482,000 barrels.[3]

Shortly after World War II, the United States yielded first place in estimated petroleum reserves to the Middle East. As of January 1, 1954—so fast was the Middle East's rise—the respective figures were

[2] See Appendix I, Table 1—World Crude-oil Production by Countries.
[3] See Appendix I, Table 2—Estimated World Crude-oil Reserves.

29,007,482,000 and 79,075,000,000 barrels. The 1954 total for all countries outside the United States was 107,870,000,000 barrels as compared with 12,597,000,000 barrels back in 1928.

As it relates to the position of the United States, this picture of
world production and world reserves is not complete, however, and
might be misleading if dropped without further explanation. The
fact is that by the 1950's the United States oil industry no longer
was merely national in scope, but had become a world-wide industry productively operating in most of the oil-producing areas not
controlled by the USSR. American companies operating abroad were
accounting for a substantial percentage of the oil produced outside
the United States. United States owned companies in those countries produced 40 per cent in 1923, dropped to 24 per cent in 1938,
but regained and fortified their position to 53 per cent in 1953. Moreover, in 1954, of the 90 million barrels of reserves in foreign countries
exclusive of the USSR, American companies controlled an estimated
50 per cent.

Today, then, as a result of widespread and profound world changes,
the United States oil industry irrevocably is a world industry. National boundaries increasingly have been wiped out of the supply-
and-demand picture. Today, so far as interdependence is concerned,
oil *is* one world.

The fact is not difficult to understand nor even entirely new. In
a sense it is the logical result of a trend. Just before the twenties, California was an isolated oil area, but within the next decade its prolific
supplies were coming through the Panama Canal to bolster the hard-
pressed output of the Mid-Continent, the Gulf Coast and the East.
The movement spelled the beginning of the end of isolated markets
within the United States and made every producing territory a part
of the whole.

Similarly, the modern trend toward foreign operations by U.S.
companies began in Mexico. The movement spread to Venezuela, Colombia and Peru and, in the Far East, to the fields of Indonesia. More
recently, the prime example of such extension has been the Middle
East, and now it is Canada. Whether for better or for worse and regardless of their own wishes in the matter, all producing countries
are interrelated through the necessity of world demand and by the
desire of every major company to have a share in every major source

of production. Given a favorable political climate, no country is too remote to be excluded. All are interrelated by the urgency of the world demand for oil. No field is too remote not to be included in the relationship.

Strikingly revealed in this picture is the fact that no great industrial nation of today—except Russia—is self-contained as to oil, *not even the United States*. Actually, the United States has not been totally self-sufficient at any time since World War I. Our supplying the bulk of demands in two world wars removed the possibility of obtaining self-sufficiency during those eras. Despite its huge production, its large reserves and its tremendous refining capacity, in 1954 the United States was less self-contained in petroleum than ever before.

In 1920 Sir Edward Mackay Edgar, a British promoter, declared that, "the Americans have dealt with their [oil] resources . . . in the pioneer spirit of sheer, unmitigated pillage." They "had squandered in 60 years," he wrote, "a legacy which, properly conserved, should have lasted . . . for at least a century and a half." He painted the United States as the great "have nation" in oil, but hell-bent to become a "have-not nation." Sir Edward merely was trying to sell Venezuelan oil shares. But he touched off one of the greatest of all periodic shortage scares—the "John Bull scare" of 1920. Vying with each other, Washington officials pronounced that the country was running out of oil, that the foreign oil combines—Royal Dutch–Shell and Anglo-Persian (Anglo-Iranian) Oil—were taking the ball away from the vaunted Standard Oil and independent oil industry of this country.[4]

By referring to the United States as being less self-contained than ever before, we are not saying that at long-last Sir Edward's prophecy has, or is about to, come true. The United States is far from being a "have-not" oil nation. Despite vastly larger consumption, Sir Edward's shocking 1920 prophecies have not materialized. As American demand has increased, American domestic production also has increased. Home output has been supplemented in recent years by increased imports. And despite the huge annual withdrawals in the form of production, United States reserves have shown continual growth.

But the United States' position as to self-sufficiency is not a matter of simple statistical computation based upon present demand or projected consumption in relation to domestic production and reserves.

[4] Fanning, Case History of Oil-shortage Scares, *Our Oil Resources*, 1950, p. 336.

The reason why the United States is less self-contained today than ever before lies in the changed picture of international politics. In a divided world this nation has had leadership thrust upon it. Therefore, supply sources of such strategic materials as oil must be considered in relation to total war and the preservation of the Free World. But in a world at peace the development of petroleum resources—wherever they exist or may be found in the future—can go forward efficiently, which in oil parlance means with full regard to conservation, in the interest of improving national and world living standards. In the Free, if not in the global, World each source can take its proper place in the economic scheme of things.

Chapter 2

HIGH STAKES ON A WORLD-WIDE TABLE

Most old-time oil men were good and inveterate poker players. They favored table stakes. The table could be anything or anywhere—a roughly hewn plank in a shack called the National Hotel at Borger, Texas; interlocking Pullman tables in "Josh" Cosden's or Harry Sinclair's private car; or a regulation felt-lined poker table with chip shelf, provided by eager bellhops in "Bill" Skelly's room at the Vanderbilt Hotel on Park Avenue, New York. But no matter where the old-timers set up their tables, always their chips were the same—white, red and blue. And considering the company they priced their chips modestly.

In a mixed game, supposedly the odds overwhelmingly favored the oil men. In the popular mind, at least, money meant nothing to them—all oil men were supposed to be millionaires. Certainly they were gamblers—else why were they in the oil business?

Actually, however, the old-timers played their cards close to their vests—as if their lives depended upon each hand, each draw, each bet—for they loved poker as a card game. At once students and masters, they nursed its essential element, gambling. To a visitor, an innocent little game with old-time oil men could be a terrifying experience.

Today, oil men still are good poker players, but on a modern basis of scientific, calculated risk. Let us concede, however, that they are not all millionaires. Less frequently are they seen in oil-boom towns, which are themselves less numerous. And when they visit strange cities, most likely they fill their evenings with consultations between their staff entourage and the field representatives, in strict application

13

to the business at hand. Modern oil men have little time for poker. In a way they are a different breed of cat from the old-timers. Science and efficiency have replaced the instinctive "nose for oil," the ready inclination to "take a chance."

Yet scarcely would we say that oil men have lost the instinct for handling chips, particularly those men responsible for companies engaged in foreign operations. The last thing in the world they would want to be called is "gamblers," and we would be the first to defend them from such a charge. However, considering the risks and the height of the stack of chips necessary to engage in the pastime, we cannot help but look at today's foreign operators as being cast in the same mold as the poker players of the past generation—with one important difference. Now they use only blue chips. The white and red ones have gone out of circulation. It costs real money to "sit in" on foreign oil operations.

Involving, as it does, great risk, foreign oil is a game of calculated venture based on modern science and efficiency and absolutely requires large capital. The risks are divided into political hazards, such as various degrees of nationalization—including the drastic form employed by Mossadegh in Iran in March, 1951—and unusual operating conditions far more hazardous than those encountered domestically.

As to the latter, when oil companies engage in foreign exploration and production, often the country is remote and favorable territory is isolated and highly inaccessible within the country. Perverse Nature, in other words, often ordains that choice oil sources should be located at places far removed from supply centers and markets and, perhaps equally often, in areas either lacking human habitation or only sparsely populated. Men, tools and supplies must be brought in and highways constructed. Camps—which sometimes grow to veritable cities—must be built and provision made for all the facilities of community life, such as houses, commissaries, industrial buildings, water, light, sewage, hospitals, schools, movie theaters and other recreational facilities.

Largely, then, foreign oil is a "big-company" operation. It has to be. The risk and cost are too enormous for most small companies to assume. Even larger companies have found the risk and cost mounting to a point which taxes their individual capacities, and, in many undertakings, they have been forced to combine their efforts.

These cooperative operations usually take the form of joint-ownership companies engaged in a particular area or field of activity. Their existence is no secret, and the principle involved is one of long standing. Because of the large and ever-mounting costs and a human and pragmatic desire to hedge on possible losses, oil men have formed jointly owned companies or joint ventures to explore and operate given leases or concessions since the earliest days of the industry.

In this connection, the old-timers' saying comes to mind, "Everybody hears about the successes, the 'gushers'; nobody hears about the losses, the dry holes." Oil men have been using that truism since the beginning of the industry, and they repeat it today. Successful operations get the headlines; unsuccessful ones are passed over. An interesting commentary on their present, generally successful operations in the Middle East, for instance, is the fact that The Texas Company and the Standard Oil Company of California—the original discoverers of the fabulous oil riches of Saudi Arabia—suffered heavy losses in Mexico, and one company or the other also has gone into the red in India, Egypt and other countries of the Eastern Hemisphere.

A recent estimate shows a company whose name must be withheld to have recovered only a small percentage of nearly 40 million dollars spent in oil exploration and development in Eastern Canada, Spain, Argentina, Colombia and several other South American nations.

Between 1937 and 1949 Standard of New Jersey spent $12,327,000 in Egypt—a total loss. It dropped another $12,159,000 in Ecuador from 1943 to 1947. In partnership with Shell Oil in another Ecuador operation between 1948 and 1950, Standard of New Jersey spent $4,995,000 and the Shell company laid out a like amount in addition to $24,842,-000 expended before 1948. Individually or jointly neither company struck oil.

Another company reports an over-all expenditure in Egypt between 1936 and mid-1953 of $22,000,000 against a total recovery of $19,320,-000. Though the company still is operating, production is small and declining, with $2,698,000 still unrecovered. Over a period of seven years another unnamed company spent $1,674,000 in Egypt and recovered only $71,000 for a loss of $1,603,000.

Still another company, which must be nameless, reports a total investment in Cuba of $4,527,000 from 1946 to 1952 without result. In Panama an unnamed company put up $1,974,000 for concessions and drilling without striking a drop of oil.

The Beacon Sun Oil Company spent $6,487,000 in Venezuela and did not take out a cent. After sinking $2,545,000 in dry holes, an unnamed company relinquished a concession in Colombia. In Argentina, Standard Oil of California dropped $1,463,000, and another company, which must remain anonymous, lost $3,119,000.

In the southern llanos area of Colombia an American company operating over a period of 10 years expended $7,653,000, all of which was lost since it found no oil. Another unnamed American company shows a red-ink entry of $7,233,000 in Colombia.

At least 10 million dollars, it has been said, must be spent today by any company merely in assessing the possibilities of finding oil in a nonproducing country. The cost, of course, could run much less or much more, but the 10-million-dollar average seems to be borne out by returns received from a questionnaire sent out by the writer and by other data.[1] Moreover, in connection with the examples given below it should be borne in mind that for the greater part these expenditures were 100-cent dollars and not the depreciated dollar we know today.

Between 1944 and 1948 Creole Petroleum Corporation expended 22 million dollars in exploring the Barbacoas and Tamanaco concessions in Guarico, Venezuela, an area of over 317,000 hectares, or 783,-000 acres, in the northern part of the state. Because of the remoteness of the area, Creole built a "city" with modern living accommodations for its workers, schools for their children, a hospital and an airport. Also the company contributed heavily to the construction of a 200-mile highway from the concession to the seaport of Puerto La Cruz. Its drilling activities were unsuccessful. Not one well produced oil.

Another American company—the name of which must be withheld—operating in Venezuela since 1926, has spent a total of 96 million dollars. As of the end of 1952 it had taken out 35 million dollars. Its operations show a deficit of 61 million dollars.

A company which prefers not to be known reports expenditures of $8,498,000 in a European country between 1938 and 1952. By the end of 1952 it had drilled 14 wells without success.

Another company has conducted exploratory and occasional drilling operations in many parts of the world—in remote Sakhalin, in Portu-

[1] See Appendix I, Table Series 3 and 4.

guese West Africa, in Central American countries—and is reported to have spent in excess of 25 million dollars, with no discovery of commercial production.

During World War II an American company made a heroic effort to find oil in England by drilling several deep wells. The task proved futile and cost $2,107,000. Before the war Standard of California spent $1,234,000 in the Philippine Islands, and an unnamed company paid out $3,135,000 in New Zealand, each with a negative result.

So it has gone in many other countries which Americans have tried to tap without success—Cuba, San Domingo, the Barbados, Costa Rica, Guatemala, Ecuador, Ethiopia, the African coast from the Gold Coast to Somaliland, Madagascar, Palestine, India and China—to name only some.

Mexico stands as a classic example of heavy losses (see Chapter 3, Mexico—Prelude to Crisis).

So much for a partial exhibit which tends to support the lament of oil men who keep repeating, "Nobody hears about the dry holes!"

Second in significance only to "losses" is the "time lag" between beginning exploration and earning revenue, if any. Before presenting the following examples, we should emphasize that these time-lag figures by no means tell the whole story. To say that a company spent on a concession 1 million dollars or 50 million dollars from the time it started exploration to when it first loaded oil into a tanker might give the impression that at this point profits finally begin for the undertaking. The company oftentimes has months and years of additional investment and of development of suitable markets before it actually goes on a profit basis and begins to get its investment back. Moreover, to stay in business it generally must continually reinvest and commit itself to additional expenditures for the maintaining of its operation on a profitable basis.

The discovery well of the Iraq Petroleum Company—jointly operated by an international group, in which the American companies are Standard Oil of New Jersey and Socony-Vacuum—was completed in 1927, after preliminary work extending over two years. But not until 1933 was a pipeline completed across the vast deserts and rugged mountains from the producing fields near Kirkuk to the ports of Tripoli in Syria and Haifa in Palestine. In the period 1925 to 1934, before one barrel of oil reached the market, the Iraq international group expended for all purposes approximately $62,000,000, of which the American share was $14,400,000.

Between the time of first investment in 1915 to the day of first commercial marketing in 1926, International Petroleum, a subsidiary of Standard of New Jersey, and its predecessors spent an estimated $48,-400,000 on the De Mares concession in Colombia.

In Eastern Venezuela two American companies jointly paid out 44 million dollars over the 15-year period of 1924 to 1939 before the first barrel of crude oil was delivered aboard ship.

Exclusive of its Lake Maracaibo parcels, Creole spent $48,335,000 on its Venezuelan operations between the day of first investment in 1920 and the day in 1930 when it first commercially marketed oil.

An American company originally invested in the Puerto Boyaca area of Colombia in 1926. Before its first oil discovery in November, 1946, it had spent $7,252,000. Not until over two years later, however, and an additional expenditure of $704,000 did it commercially market oil from the area.

A company operating in Egypt made its first investment in the Land of the Nile in 1936 and waited out the war before discovering oil in 1946. It spent $3,900,000 before the oil could be commercially marketed, and at the end of 1947 its total investment in Egypt had risen to $7,400,000.

A classic example of persistent effort against terrific odds and of a lengthy time lag in revenue is provided in the development of the Barco concession in Colombia. From October, 1916, the date of the first investment, to March, 1933, the date of oil discovery on the concession, there were 17 years of exploration and development, costing about 21 million dollars. Then building a pipeline over the Andes Mountains and developing wells to fill it required another 6½ years and an additional 39 million dollars, all before the first oil could be commercially marketed. In other words, 23½ years elapsed and an aggregate of 60 million dollars was spent before a penny of revenue came (see Chapter 4, The Barco Concession—A Case History).

In the Middle Eastern countries American oil companies poured millions of dollars into exploration and development in such places as Iraq, Bahrain Island, Saudi Arabia and Kuwait before a barrel of oil moved to the markets. The Arabian American Oil Company—first owned solely by Standard of California and Texas—made its first investment in Saudi Arabia during August, 1933, and spent 5 million dollars before discovering oil in March, 1938. Until the company marketed its first oil in September, 1938, it had expended another 3 million dollars. But the sums cover only the first chapter of an oil epic. To date Saudi Arabia has absorbed a total investment of more than 500 million dollars, over 200 million dollars of which is represented in a pipeline system which makes it possible to transport oil to the Mediterranean Sea, thereby saving long tanker hauls around the Arabian Peninsula (see Chapter 5, The Middle East—A Recent History).

The activities in Indonesia of Standard-Vacuum Petroleum Maatschappij, wholly owned subsidiary of Standard-Vacuum, date back to 1912. In 33 years (30 years prewar and three postwar) of exploration risks the company drilled 187 wildcat or exploratory wells at an average cost of $156,000. In this total were 169 dry holes, costing $26,-418,000 and 18 successful wildcats representing $2,814,000, a total expenditure of $29,232,000. This does not include the development costs after the field discoveries were made. In the over 40 years that SVPM has searched for oil in Indonesia, it has found five commercially useful fields, which are being depleted at the rate of 22 million barrels a year, and the company is seeking additional areas for testing. Exploration in Indonesia takes much more money today. SVPM now estimates the cost of one wildcat, including seismic, geological and gravity-meter work as well as drilling, at $630,600.

New Guinea—both Netherlands and Australian—provides a classic example of time lag. The Nederlandsche Nieuw Guinee Petroleum Maatschappij, a company in which the American interest is 60 per cent (Standard-Vacuum Oil Company, 40 per cent, and Far Pacific Investments, Inc.—a Caltex affiliate—20 per cent) obtained exploration and development rights in 1935 in Netherlands New Guinea on land totaling about 40,000 square miles. The first exploration well was "spudded" in May, 1936, and the first discovery was made in the Klamono field in 1937. Three years later, the Wasian and Mogoi fields were discovered. Bataafsche Petroleum Maatschappij, Shell affiliate which holds the remaining interest, has the technical management.

When war conditions brought a halt to development activities, 14 wells had been drilled, eight proving productive. But it was not until December, 1948—13 years after the company's formation—that the first crude oil came out of New Guinea. With the postwar resumption of activities in 1946, NNGPM discovered that 90 per cent of its equipment had been destroyed. Thereafter 2 years were consumed to set up a new supply base at tidewater and construct a 30-mile road and pipeline through dense jungle from the Klamono field to the port of Sorong. The Wasian and Mogoi fields in another section of Netherlands New Guinea did not begin commercial production until April, 1954, when a 46-mile pipeline was completed to Muturi.

The total investment between the time of the company's formation in 1935 and the end of 1937, the year of the first discovery, was $4,205,000. At the time, 11 years later (December, 1948) when they loaded the first tanker with crude, the two American and one European participants had sunk $50,000,000 into the venture. As of December 31, 1953, this gross investment figure had mounted to $103,000,000, the American share being $62,000,000. In terms of production the Klamono field in 1953 delivered an average of 4,700 barrels per day. Even with additional production which became available on April 1, 1954, a good many years will elapse before the original investment can be recovered.

In Australian New Guinea (Papua and mandated territory), Australasian Petroleum Company, an exploration company, was formed in 1938 by subsidiaries of Standard-Vacuum, Anglo-Iranian and Oil Search (Australian capital). The American participation is approximately 45 per cent. At the end of 1953, the gross investment in the venture by all participants was more than $22,500,000. Postwar operations were resumed in 1946. Six dry holes have been drilled, and a seventh wildcat test, known as Omati No. 1, was drilling at a depth exceeding 13,000 feet in May, 1954. The exploration activity was continuing with three seismic, two gravity-meter and three geological parties at work and two strings of wildcat tools operating. All the drilling has been in Papua.

Island Exploration Company, formed in 1936 by Stanvac and Anglo-Iranian subsidiaries, also holds exploration rights in Australian-controlled New Guinea. Oil Search has since acquired a 10 per cent interest. The gross investment by all partners as of December 31, 1953, amounted to $6,792,000. There had been no oil discoveries.

Australia had a 50-year wait before repeated attempts to find oil met success. After spending half a century and 15 million pounds (33 million dollars), Australia struck oil beneath the red dust and spinifex of a lonely place called Rough Range late in 1953. The lonely site is 650 miles north of Perth, capital of Western Australia. The well lies in the southwestern corner of a 200,000-acre sheep ranch on the western shore of Exmouth Gulf.

In 1925 this area was adjudged an unlikely oil region. Later surveys showed that surface rocks were not so unpromising. In 1945, Dr. Harold Raggatt, head of the Commonwealth Bureau of Mineral Resources, returned from a visit to the United States impressed by the similarity of formations in Western Australia to certain oil-bearing areas in America. He said they merited detailed examination, and the government agreed. As no Australian company had the resources to make the necessary surveys and as overseas companies were not interested, the government itself made preparations for drilling.

Ampol Petroleum, an Australian oil and gasoline distributing company, became interested and subsequently acquired prospecting rights on the western and northern coastal areas of Western Australia. In 1949, Ampol sought the help of Caltex in exploring these rights. After much geological and geophysical work in collaboration with the government, an operating company, Western Australian Petroleum Pty., Ltd., was formed in 1952. Caltex has an 80 per cent and Ampol a 20 per cent interest in this company. The operating company chose Exmouth Gulf as its first drilling site because of its comparative accessibility to water transportation. The drilling plant had to be brought to Western Australia from California, lightered ashore and hauled 20 miles to the site. The surrounding country is completely undeveloped, has no roads, no railway system.

A rig capable of drilling to 15,000 feet was erected in August and began drilling on September 5, 1953. The drilling team included 30 American experts. At 3,600 feet shows of oil were encountered. The well was tested and flowed waxy oil for 25 hours at a rate of 23 barrels hourly.

Tremendous excitement swept Australia when the discovery was announced on December 4, 1953. Dr. Raggatt Waudcoop, associated with the search for oil in Australia for many years and in 1954 head of the Commonwealth Government Department of National Development, said that probably a large important field had been discovered. Caltex, owned half by The Texas Company and half by Standard of California, is not predicting. They first began geological work in

Western Australia in 1939. As of May, 1954, the company still was conservative about the possibility that a field existed here, stating that months, perhaps years, will elapse before the commercial value of the venture can be determined. However, nothing could stop Australia's oil "rush." The Rough Range well all but stole the show from Queen Elizabeth's visit.

Standard-Vacuum has done exploration work in Australia, without result. With Anglo-Iranian and the Zinc Corporation, an Australian mining company, in 1947 it organized the Frome–Broken Hill Company, the American investment as of June 30, 1947, amounting to $100,000. Exploration permits covering 159,000 square miles were obtained in the Bonaparte Gulf and Desert Basin areas where activity was confined to geological reconnaissance. In addition the company did gravity-meter and magnetic surveys in the Frome basin for the Zinc Corporation which held mining permits there. No exploratory wells were drilled, and the company became inactive in 1949. But early in 1954 the Frome–Broken Hill Company was reactivated, its authorized capitalization was increased and exploration permits were granted in several areas of the Commonwealth.

Money has been sunk for oil in New Zealand since the 1880's without turning up commercial oil. The first full-scale search by foreign interests was undertaken by the New Zealand Petroleum Company, in which the American interest ranged from 70 to 80 per cent. During the period from 1938 to 1945, the company invested well over $3,-000,000 in geological, seismic, gravity-meter and test drilling extending over an area of 600,000 square miles on the North and South Islands. No oil in commercial quantities being found, in 1945, after eight exploratory wells had been drilled, the effort was abandoned. One of the wells approached 12,000 feet, which at that time was the deepest test south of the equator. American investment in the effort, shared equally by Standard-Vacuum and Caltex, amounted to $2,540,000. New Zealand and Australian capital, identified as Shale Oil Investigations, contributed the remainder of the funds. The New Zealand Petroleum Company's activities was the first large-scale search by foreign capital. Subsequently three additional test wells (two of them with Australian government support) were drilled by foreign interests without success.

Efforts to develop commercial oil in Canada—which since 1947 has been having the oil industry's greatest boom—date back to the days before Drake drilled the well that touched off the United States industry in 1859. During and after World Wars I and II, activities were pressed persistently; yet no world-shaking discovery came. In the three decades before 1947—when the Leduc well became a producer in Alberta—it is estimated that 125 million dollars had been spent with relatively small results. Since then another 600 million dollars has gone into exploration and development and an additional 200 million dollars into pipeline transportation. The end of the expenditures is nowhere in sight (see Chapter 16, Canada on the Horizon).

Between losses and time lag, either of which can run into blue chips, foreign oil is obviously a game for titans.[2]

Yet the stakes are not to be evaluated merely in terms of a commercial game of gain and loss. Foreign oil is a game in which the stakes also are of the kind significantly to involve the economic well-being and the military security of the United States and the Free World.

[2] For statistics supporting many of the above summaries see Appendix I, Table Series 3 and 4.

Chapter 3

MEXICO—PRELUDE TO CRISIS

As compared with domestic operations, those in foreign fields always have involved infinitely more risk and much greater cost—as evidence, Mexico.

In 1900 Edward L. Doheny—a forty-one-year-old one-time New Mexican mining prospector who, with his former sourdough partner, "Charlie" Canfield, already had launched California's oil industry—paid $600,000 in United States gold for what he believed to be fee ownership of the Ebano hacienda on Mexico's eastern coastal plain near Tampico. He "took particular care" to secure mineral rights as well. Too, before he bought his Mexican lands, he was careful to secure the blessing of President Diaz on his venture.

For almost 10 years the partners sank money into drilling wells with such indifferent success that, finally, their chief backers would not put up another dollar. Doheny, thereupon, risked his own newly acquired California oil fortune and bought out the timid souls. Only Canfield and a few others stuck with him. "All of the earlier borrowings of the company [Mexican Petroleum Company] were made from two of the principal stockholders, Mr. Canfield and myself, who advanced a large part of the $3,000,000 which we invested at Ebano before our income began," Doheny related in after years.[1]

Doheny then bought the fee title and mineral rights to the Juan Casiano farm about a hundred miles south of Ebano. Thoroughly convinced that he could find good wells on this property, he built a 70-mile-long pipeline from the port of Tampico through the jungle to the well site and also constructed a tank terminal at the seaport.

[1] *Mexican Petroleum*, Pan American Petroleum & Transport Company, New York, 1922, p. 1.

All this before he drilled in a single well. Not including what he was putting into his wells, Doheny was taking a 2-million-dollar gamble.

Ralph Arnold, veteran oil geologist of Los Angeles—whose experience has run the gamut of American pioneer oil development in Mexico, Venezuela and other foreign countries—rated this example of industrial daring and confidence as unequaled in oil to this day. But Doheny's reward was Casiano No. 7—one of the world's biggest wells. The gusher roared in on September 7, 1910, and the same day oil rushed into the line.

For years Casiano No. 7 flowed at the rate of 60,000 to 70,000 barrels daily. Surviving revolution and hijacking raids by revolutionary and bandit guerillas, it continued to discharge its precious liquid until November, 1919, when it went to salt water. In nine years the well had produced 85 million barrels.

Told in brief fashion the venture sounds simple enough. Doheny gambled, and he won. When he struck his oil, he already had his pipeline and storage facilities. But Doheny had used his head and had profited by the experience of the British Pearson interests, who, a few years before, had brought in Dos Bocas in the same general remote and inaccessible region, only to have a wild well on their hands. With no tanks and no pipeline connections, the Pearson people had no way to capture the oil even if they could have brought the well under control. Dos Bocas caught fire. Flaming oil touched off the dense forest, turned trees into giant torches and rivers to roaring roads of blazing destruction.

For 40 days oil surged from the underground reservoir only to go up in flame and smoke. Around the well the earth's surface collapsed. Finally, all that remained of Dos Bocas was a charred crater covering several acres. An estimated 100 million barrels of oil—the entire content of the underground reservoir—had burned. Doheny had remembered and wanted no repeat performance at Casiano.

But there is much more than a production venture in the Doheny saga in Mexico. The oil man's accomplishment of getting his Casiano oil and piping it to his hastily built tanks at tidewater meant little unless he could transport it to the United States for refining. The era, moreover, preceded the day of oil-burning ships and factories and was a decade before the heyday of the automobile. Where was his market?

Still in the Street are a few men who remember Doheny and Canfield peddling their Mexican wares to Wall Street bankers. The literate
Doheny—short, slender, dapper, with red hair, an oddly pinkish walrus
mustache and a ruddy complexion—peered myopically but alertly
through steel-rimmed spectacles and did the talking. The unschooled
Canfield—handsome, gracious, powerfully built, with a handle-bar
mustache and gold-nugget tie pin—furnished the window dressing and
exemplified confident support.

Wanting proof of Doheny's fabulous claims, the bankers sent Ralph
Arnold to Mexico to investigate. His report painted the owner of
Casiano No. 7 as a dreamer. A gusher, yes; but how long? Challenging
Arnold, Doheny dared the bankers to come and see for themselves,
thus inaugurating his Mexican promotion trips which were to become
celebrated. The bankers came, they saw, Doheny conquered!

Dating from—if not before—Arnold's report, Doheny had a low
opinion of geologists, though later he relied on the services of several.
Yet, said Arnold later, nobody *could* believe what Doheny claimed
for his Casiano properties, for at the time no scientific basis existed
for such statements as he made. "We, the geologists, were wrong," he
admitted afterward. "Doheny proved that with his Casiano No. 7
well. He could say he knew what he was talking about, and that we
didn't. He made monkeys out of us. His kind of figures don't lie."
Further to confound the geologists, in 1916 Doheny brought in Cerro
Azul No. 4, the world's largest oil well, never since topped. It was
gauged on February 19, 1916, as flowing at 260,858 barrels a day.

Doheny and Canfield got the money they needed to charter, buy
and build tankers and to construct terminals and refineries while Doheny carried on a one-man supersales campaign. Almost singlehanded
he created the Fuel-oil Age, though World War I gave him a powerful boost. Doheny's commodity—Mexican oil—gave the Allied navies,
merchant marines and industrial plants a superiority which speeded
the victory.

Doheny had been invited to Mexico by A. A. Robinson, American
railroad pioneer, whose Mexican Central Railway traversed the oil-
seepage country of the eastern coastal plain. Since the country had
no coal, Robinson conceived the idea of converting his wood-burning
locomotives to oil—Mexican oil. His selection of Doheny and Canfield
was natural, since as an outlet for their California oil discoveries, they

had persuaded the Santa Fe Railway in the United States to change to oil. They were the men that Robinson wanted.

Doheny succeeded in supplying Mexican railways with oil. More than that, he paved the streets of many Mexican cities, including the capital, with asphalt, built miles of asphalt roads into the country and made cheap fuel oil available to various national industries. In the economy of Mexico, oil skyrocketed to become the country's greatest asset, briefly even superseding her mines. This bonanza came not from the limited domestic use, however, but from the taxes the government received on the huge production and export. Not only had Doheny made good in supplying the Mexican railroads, but also he fueled the giant Cunarders, the *Aquitania, Lusitania* and *Mauritania*. President Diaz desired that Mexico be self-contained in oil, but Doheny and Pearson and other developers made Mexico not only self-sufficient but second only to the United States as a supplier of the world's oil markets.

Doheny created a great oil empire in Mexico. So, after his tragic Dos Bocas overture, did Pearson. England rewarded the latter with a title, and called him Lord Cowdray.

Even before Doheny and Cowdray, bold men had failed to find oil in Mexico. A Cecil Rhodes organization had dropped £160,000 in the region south of Tuxpam. And an American ship captain had been so unsuccessful as to commit suicide.

As the pioneers, the "early birds" Doheny and Lord Cowdray did well in Mexico. They did far better, in fact, than the "latecomer companies," as they were called when in 1917 they participated in Mexico's "Golden Lane"—one of the most famous oil rushes in history.

During and immediately following World War I the fame of the "Golden Lane"—a 25-mile-long mile-wide path in the humid land of the Huastecas—entranced the world. The name implied that those who trod upon it found, by some beautiful magic, their pockets lined with gold.

But Al Watts, a veteran oil man who was there and saw it through, says that "Golden Lane" had a much different meaning. The sliver of land received its colorful appellation, he declares, from a disillusioned oil producer who said of the latecomer companies, "We're spending enough to cover with 20-dollar gold pieces the whole producing structure from the Juan Casiano field in the north to the Toteco field in the south, and this *golden lane* never will return the amount of money it's being lined with." [2]

Whatever the name's origin, the venture proved to be more doleful than happy. Most of the companies which followed the pioneer concerns into Mexico lost heavily. In 1919, "Golden Lane" wells began to go to salt water, and many already laid pipelines never had a barrel of oil pumped into them. Numerous refineries, built at the cost of millions, never produced a gallon of petroleum. One oil company which had constructed a freight and passenger railroad between Tampico and Panuco sold it for scrap.

One latecomer was the Atlantic Lobos Oil Company, organized in 1919 and controlled by the Atlantic Refining Company. With the money from its $25,696,000 issued stock, the company acquired and developed acreage in the "Golden Lane" district and built refineries and pipelines. In August, 1921, Amatlan—the entire production area where the company's wells were located—was invaded by salt water. By developing its Aquada tract outside the "Golden Lane" district the company tried to recoup. Its fate hinged on 14 wells already being drilled, and despite the best geological advice and the utilization of geophysical apparatus, then just being introduced to oil exploration, results were negative. At the time of its involuntary dissolution in 1933, Atlantic Lobos Oil Company had a deficit of about $25,000,000. Every cent that it had put into Mexico was lost.

During the 1917–1926 decade of intensive development, one could scarcely name an oil company that did not take a whirl in Mexico: Royal Dutch–Shell and British Cowdray interests represented foreign holdings and among the American interests were Doheny's Mexican Petroleum, Standard of New Jersey, Standard of Indiana, Standard of California, Sinclair, Pierce Oil, Gulf Oil, The Texas Company, Magnolia Petroleum, Atlantic Refining, Atlantic, Gulf and West Indies, Island Oil & Transport, National Oil, New England Oil, Marland Oil, Tide Water, General Petroleum, East Coast Oil (Southern Pacific Railway), Cities Service and Warner-Quinlan. Reaching a top production of 180 million barrels in 1922, four years later Mexican oil exports had dropped to 90 million barrels, only half of the peak, and were tobogganing fast.

[2] *American Petroleum Interests in Foreign Countries*, Government Printing Office, Washington, D.C., 1946, p. 235.

The next decade was one of company liquidation and absorption as exports fell to 23,215,000 barrels by 1936.

Risks other than operational had attended foreign companies developing Mexican oil. When the Carranza Constitution of 1917 proclaimed the nationalization of the subsoil, preconstitutional companies, like Doheny's, which had bought Mexican land in fee from the surface owners just as they did in the United States, challenged the legality of this section of the constitution. They were apprehensive as to the security of titles acquired prior to nationalization, while postconstitutional companies were up against procrastination on the part of the Mexican government in making available to foreign operators sufficient and promising acreage.

For years Doheny fought tooth and nail for what he considered his legal property rights in Mexico. Joined by other American interests, he led the opposition against nationalization which in his mind violated those rights, meantime, through successive revolutions, managing to operate his properties. Political and social upheavals below the Rio Grande were not conducive to the development of ideal conditions in the oil camps, but Doheny's Ebano camp was considered a show place of its kind, was equipped with good housing, hospital and recreational facilities. Doheny—and the other companies—employed men from the United States for skilled jobs, Mexicans largely for common labor, but gradually the nationals were learning the business and he paid high wages. Nevertheless, old-timers are apt to say that if Doheny and the others had been on their toes, or had recognized a social revolution when they saw it and had made greater efforts to meet the change halfway, foreign oil interests would still be operating in Mexico.

The government, meantime, hiked production and export taxes to the point where, exclusive of other general taxes, imposts alone amounted to 46 per cent of the value of oil exports. Then, beginning in 1923, a series of labor strikes at Tampico—out of which Lombardo Toledano in the 1930's gained his present decisive position in radical Latin-American labor circles—provided a third element in the prelude to expropriation.[3]

[3] *Lombardo Toledano*—profession, lawyer. Born in the town of Teziutlán, Mexico. Began studies in Mexico City in 1910. In 1917, elected secretary of the student group "Universidad Popular Mexicana." Soon afterward became a pro-

Of 22 major American oil entities operating in Mexico in the early 1920's, seven had definitely retired by the 1930's: The Texas Company, Atlantic Refining, Island Oil & Transport, National Petroleum, English Oil, Tide Water and General Petroleum. With perhaps one exception, all had sustained severe losses.

Certain companies purchased and absorbed the Mexican holdings of nine others. Standard of New Jersey bought Standard of Indiana's holdings—Indiana having previously acquired Doheny's empire. These properties Jersey consolidated with its own large holdings in Transcontinental and also took over the leases of other companies being driven out of the country by the salt-water invasion, high taxes and radical labor. Jersey then maintained operations in Mexico for years under conditions which probably no other company—certainly none without huge resources—could have endured. No new foreign companies ventured into the country. And, after the 1938 expropriation, the government's agency, Petróleos Mexicanos (Pemex), took over virtually everything.

The story of Mexican oil up to the time of expropriation may be summed up briefly. In the early era of discovery and development, company after company failed to strike oil in paying quantity, or could not raise enough capital for the expensive development work necessary. These folded. Those which staggered through the pioneer era produced enormous quantities during the boom period, but most of them entered the fruitful era with large deficits due to heavy expenditures which the richer revenues of a few years could not offset. Oil men who followed the Mexican story more or less all the way agree on two points: (1) only three or four companies consistently

---

fessor of philosophy, then a representative in the National Congress. In 1933 organized the Mexican Confederation of Laborers and Farmers (Confederación de Obreros y Campesinos de Mexico), which by wage and benefit demands on the oil companies and by forcing the action politically and in the courts, almost singlehandedly threw most of the foreign oil concerns out of the country. At one time, the Confederation claimed membership of about 1 million men. In 1938 he called the meeting of the first Inter-American Labor Congress in Mexico City at which was born the Confederación de Trabajadores de America Latina (CTAL), with himself as president. In that capacity he toured the other Latin-American countries, visiting Venezuela in 1944. His followers consider him as the greatest of the Latin-American labor leaders. In 1946, after returning from a visit to Moscow, Toledano applied for and was denied a visa to visit the United States.

made money; (2) taken all in all, American companies in Mexico as a group just about broke even.

Four American companies certified the value of their Mexican holdings in 1938 at $104,363,000. At that time when their properties were expropriated, their compensation totaled $23,710,000. Hence the estimated net loss of these four companies alone was $80,653,000.[4]

The end of Mexico's preeminence was not simply the fact that her wells went to salt water, for such losses business ventures must be, and are, prepared to accept. Far more important from the standpoint of foreign investment were the political and social changes which occurred there. Scarcely had Casiano No. 7 come in and been announced to the world than President Diaz was overthrown after a dictatorship of 27 years. Two decades of frequent and turbulent revolution followed.

In the preface to his *Democracy in America*, De Tocqueville says, "There will be found on every page a solemn warning that society changes its forms, humanity its condition, and that new destinies are impending." In Mexico, society was changing its form, humanity its condition and new destinies indeed were impending. Throughout the world similar changes were imminent. They were vitally to affect foreign oil operations.

[4] *American Oil Operations Abroad*, p. 82.

Chapter 4

THE BARCO CONCESSION—
A CASE HISTORY

The Barco concession in Colombia stands as a classic example of revenue time lag in foreign oil operations.

Four distinct phases have marked Barco's history: (1) the creation of the grant and its static character while the concessionaire vainly tried to interest capital; (2) its promotional phase in which more was said than done in bringing about actual development; (3) a twilight time during which the Colombian government sought to revoke the grant on the ground of lack of activity; and (4) its development era, entailing the investment of men, money and skills.

In 1905, General Don Vergilio Barco, venerable hero and political figure of Cúcuta in Norte de Santander, acquired the concession to which his name was given from the Colombian government. A continuous stretch containing 600,000 acres, though the land was reputed to contain promising oil seepages, for at least 10 years the general tried in vain to enlist capital for its development. Though located in Colombia, the concession lay on the eastern slope of the rugged Cordillera Oriental of the Andean Mountains and adjoined the Venezuelan boundary. Thus the area was walled off from most of Colombia proper. Historically, the franchise may be said to have been more closely related to those granted during this period by President Castro of Venezuela than to Colombia. Indeed, the only entrance to and egress from it was through Venezuela.

The second phase began in 1916, at about the time that Doheny was emerging as America's premier foreign oil operator. In that year Carl K. MacFadden, an American promoter, appeared in Wall Street with his Carib Syndicate, Ltd., organized around the Barco concession, and

32

virgin jungle and traversed by numerous clear streams, some of which were navigable throughout the year.

MacFadden reported the discovery of many oil seepages on Barco and backed his claim with numerous photographs. To reach the seeps, the party often had to hack its way through the dense jungle tangle. On one occasion, at least, trail blazers fought a lively skirmish with a wandering band of Motilone Indians, who, about 75 miles from their usual stamping ground in the Colombian-Venezuelan mountain land to the north, evidently were on a hunting expedition. Of this adventure the promoter wrote as follows:

"These savages are stated to be perhaps the most uncivilized in South America and although armed only with bow and arrow are not to be despised as warriors. In the initial brush one of the natives, employed by the expedition in cutting a trail to an important seepage, was struck down by two large wooden arrows. One entered the shoulder, breaking the collarbone, the other entered the back and, going almost entirely through the body of the victim, passed through the lung and caused the death of the man. The two arrows were removed from the body of the dead man. Eight or ten arrows were found in the forest at the point of attack, rather gruesome exhibits of this feature of the trip.

"The Colombian government at once provided the party with a company of sharpshooters for protection and no further evidence of Indians was found, nor does the company anticipate any difficulty in future operations on the property, for former experiences with the tribe by the Colon Development Company, an English company operating in Venezuelan territory nearby, points to the Indians' keeping a safe distance from the white settlers and their camps and habitations."

The party then explored the possibility of access to the Barco concession from the west, in other words, a route within the confines of Colombia. With a 20-mule pack train on a 200-mile trip they crossed the Andes at elevations as high as 10,000 feet and endured "interesting experiences in fighting intense cold." Upon reaching the warm and humid valley of the Magdalena River, however, they met with opposite climatic conditions and many insect pests not encountered on the higher ground of the concession. Aboard a river steamer, they made the 250-mile trip to Barranquilla, and thence proceeded to Cartagena

announced that its seepages were similar to those which had
Doheny to Mexico.[1]

Returning from a trip of inspection and exploration to Bar
Fadden brought back trophies of his adventurous trip—arr
from the bows of savage Indians. More graphically than his b
trophies, however, his account of the expedition portrayed
accessibility of the isolated tract which was to become pr
only after the most arduous experiences of several American
panies.

According to MacFadden the trip had come about when the
of Carib Syndicate had decided to make a careful inspection
area with the intention of instituting active development. Acco
ing the promoter were W. E. Griffiths, J. E. Burnett and
Fyfe, Americans, along with General Barco, José Murillo,
Dubois and a number of Colombian engineers.

Leaving New York early in March, 1917—where the ailing G
Barco had been under medical treatment—the party sailed to
caibo, Venezuela, took a shallow-draft river steamer to the mo
the Catatumbo River on the southwest side of Lake Maracaib
then proceeded about 40 miles up that stream to Encontrados.
because of extreme low water, the group transferred to boats of
lower draft before continuing upstream to the Zulia River up wh
pushed another 55 miles to Puerto Villamizar, Colombia. To assis
sweating, straining polemen in the long trip against the current,
4-horsepower outboard motors had been attached to a dugout c
of native construction. With the canoe towing a larger barge, con
ing the baggage and passengers and a heterogeneous assortment
freight and mail, the party made a record trip.

During the few days necessary to complete the outfitting of the
pedition, the party visited picturesque Cúcuta, deliberately built w
low buildings and wide streets as safeguards against earthquakes, si
a severe tremor had destroyed the city some 30 years before. T
capital of the state of Norte de Santander, Cúcuta later was to beco
the headquarters of companies which operated the concession. The
reinforced by a large number of native woodsmen, the expedition b
gan the final 70-mile trek afoot.

Containing no white inhabitants, the land was covered with thic

[1] *Oil Trade Journal*, June, 1917, pp. 64, 66.

from which the American members of the group sailed for the United States.

Such, briefly, was MacFadden's story. Obviously, General Barco had found a promoter, and, again obviously, MacFadden, or Carib Syndicate in which the general had a stock interest, possessed a promising property. But where was the money coming from to develop it? World War I was in full swing, and the demand for petroleum had boosted oil securities into the class of the "war babies." Given impetus by sensational gains in the quotations of Doheny's Mexican Petroleum and other companies with foreign holdings, Carib stock skyrocketed to a high of $5,800 a share in 1918. On paper MacFadden was a millionaire. In 1919 the stock began to "hit the skids."

It was one thing to possess a successful speculative promotion and entirely another to interest oil people in putting up the hard cash needed for development. Yet, MacFadden proved himself equally adept in each field. He interested Henry L. Doherty, utility magnate turned oil operator with Cities Service Company.

In 1918 MacFadden transferred the concession to the Compania Colombiana de Petrolea, three-quarters owned by Henry L. Doherty & Company and one-quarter by the Carib Syndicate. By this deal MacFadden temporarily checked the tobogganing of Carib stock.

Though Doherty controlled Barco, his development of the concession lagged, and in 1925 he sold his interest to Gulf Oil which negotiated a new concession owned by Colombian Petroleum and South American Gulf Oil Company, a wholly owned subsidiary of Gulf. So ended the second, or promotional, phase of the grant.

Then, in 1926, on the ground that the required amount of development work had not been accomplished, the Colombian government canceled the concession and the third phase began—the twilight time in the grant's history.

Though General Barco had died in the early twenties, his heirs backed Gulf in its long court fight against the cancellation. In 1931 the company finally gained an understanding known as the Chaux-Folsom agreement which granted a contract to the Colombian Petroleum Company for the exploration and development of the Barco concession and gave authority to the South American Gulf Oil Company to construct a pipeline to tidewater.

Thus, the company held its concession—but at a stiff price. Back in

1905, when oil had not yet come of age, the terms of the original grant had been comparatively liberal. Now Colombian, Gulf's subsidiary, would hold Barco only on the government's terms. The concession would cover 400,000 hectares, or 988,000 acres. Exploration work requirements were specific and rather on the drastic side. Test wells had to be drilled before prescribed dates. By 1936 the franchise holders were required to select for development at least 50,000 hectares, in blocks of 10,000 hectares each, and by 1941 sufficient additional blocks to bring the total to 200,000 hectares, or 494,000 acres. Then, except for necessary right of ways, the remainder of the concession would revert to the government. Within three years after production reached 3,000 metric tons or about 21,000 barrels per day, a pipeline had to be laid, and when output arrived at 4,000 metric tons or approximately 28,000 barrels daily, a refinery must be built on the concession. The pipeline, furthermore, had to extend entirely through Colombian territory, a requirement which debarred the company from using the nation's natural backdoor through Venezuela and posed an immense construction project over the Andes.

For the nation and for the company the third phase was most critical. The Colombian government sought not only to secure revenue for itself in the way of royalties, but also to bring about the establishment of an industry. The concession would revert to the government 50 years from August 24, 1931. The Colombian Congress ratified the Chaux-Folsom agreement which continues in effect today.

Gulf then proceeded to populate an uninhabited land with workers to carry on explorations and put down test wells. On March 5, 1933, it drilled a discovery well in the Petrolea field—not a great gusher but, at least, a producing well. Incidentally, this well blew out, caught fire and, until extinguished by Myron Kinley, burned for weeks in the jungle. It was never actually completed as a producer. From October, 1916, the date of the first investment in Barco, $21,-387,000 had been expended and now, at last, there was a promising prospect of oil.

But, with transportation lacking, not a drop of petroleum could be taken out. Gulf finally decided that the development was a strain on its resources and, early in 1936, sold its entire holdings in the Colombian Petroleum Company and in the South American Gulf Oil Company, which held the pipeline rights, to The Texas Company and

Socony-Vacuum Oil Company. Later, the new owners also acquired the interest of the Carib Syndicate in Colombian Petroleum. Except for a few shares, then, Colombian Petroleum now is owned in equal parts by Texas and Socony-Vacuum while South American Gulf is wholly owned on the same basis. Acquiring control of the Barco concession involved the payment of 12½ million dollars to Gulf.[2]

Several fields had been discovered on the Barco concession, the original one being the Río de Oro field at the northern end. The first to be fully developed, however, was the Petrolea field at the southern end. Later, Tibu, about 30 miles north of Petrolea, became the major producing area.

Development work in the fields presented many difficulties, since the whole area was virgin jungle which had to be cleared for roads, camps and drilling sites. Though the original estimate of the concession's development cost was about 21 million dollars, actually over 47 million dollars has been spent. The company brought in thousands of tons of machinery and supplies by way of Lake Maracaibo and shipped them up the Catatumbo River on barges. Materials for Petrolea went up the Tarra and Sardinata Rivers to Puerto Reyes or by railroad to Puerto Leon and thence by road to Petrolea. The developers moved equipment for Río de Oro up the river of the same name. Airplanes supplied almost all communication and moved most of the personnel back and forth. Airports sprung into being at both Petrolea and Río de Oro, and within the concession itself the company laid a light railway and miles of surfaced highway to connect important points.

The new owners authorized a survey for a pipeline route and actually began construction of a 260-mile 12-inch line to Coveñas on the Caribbean in February, 1938. Soon it became apparent that the project would be one of the most difficult pipeline construction jobs ever undertaken until that time. The whole central section had to cross jungle territory which was barren of towns, roads or transport facilities, and the eastern section had to climb over an Andean mountain range.

Originally, at least, planes transported most of the pipeline materials, and the Barco line had the distinction of being the first ever constructed in which a great part of the equipment was conveyed by

[2] Amended Answer of The Texas Company, U.S. District Court, Southern District of New York, Civil Action No. 86-27, September 21, 1953.

air. Ten freight planes flew in a total of 11 million pounds of materials. Several suspension bridges—each 350 feet in length and weighing 176,000 pounds—were especially designed and prefabricated for air transport. For one bridge alone the air lift made 240 separate trips, carrying 8,000 bags of cement, bridge steel, concrete mixers and other machinery. The total distance flown in the course of the construction work was more than 1 million kilometers, or 621,000 miles. About everything except line pipe was brought in by air.

Over terrain previously untouched by either wagon trail or foot-path, the pipeline ascended the Cordillera Central to a maximum height of 5,200 feet and then rapidly fell to the sea level of the Magdalena Basin, terminating at the port of Coveñas on Morosquillo Bay about 75 miles south and west of Cartagena. At its own expense the company constructed a road—open to the public—along the pipe-line right of way from the concession to the Magdalena River.

Assisted by thousands of Colombians, hundreds of Americans, skilled in the methods of pipeline construction, finally brought the difficult project to a successful completion. And on November 1, 1939, the first barrel of Barco oil was delivered aboard a tanker at Coveñas on Morosquillo Bay.

Until that moment, without receiving a cent of revenue, American companies had spent 60 million dollars from the time that MacFadden had secured the concession, as shown by the following summary: [3]

BARCO CONCESSION REVENUE TIME LAG

A. Date of first investment . . . . October, 1916
B. Date of first Petrolea field discovery . . . . . . March 5, 1933
    Total investment between *A* and *B* $21,387,000
C. Date of first oil commercially marketed . . . November 1, 1939
    Total investment between *A* and *C* $60,310,000

Later, in anticipation of the concession requirements, the company also built a refinery at Petrolea.

But the story of the Barco concession is not complete with a bare recitation of the physical development of its production and its cost. The human element also stands out—the story of the men who have seen the job through. C. O. Isakson, Colombian Petroleum's manager

[3] *Report of Group on American Petroleum Interests in Foreign Countries,* Special Committee Investigating Petroleum Resources, U.S. Senate, 75th Congress, First Session, Government Printing Office, Washington, D.C., 1946, p. 227.

at Cúcuta—a solid, serious-minded American, formerly with The Texas Company and Cities Service—reached Colombia in 1937 by way of Mexico and Argentina. In May, 1946, when we talked with him in his Cúcuta office, he told us several of his problems. The war had slowed work on the concession almost to a standstill because priorities on oil-well supplies did not embrace out-of-the-way Barco. Though the pipe-line had been designed to carry a capacity of 45,000 barrels daily, runs never had reached much more than 27,000 a day. At that time, how-ever, even though Barco never had come up to expectations, activities were being intensified. Further exploration and a stepped-up drilling program had been authorized. A major camp change on the conces-sion, long in the blueprint stage, was under way. Later, housing facili-ties for both labor and technical personnel would be moved from Petrolea to Tibu where a new refinery and a gas-absorption plant were to become an integrated installation, including the main pipe-line pump station, tankage, machine shops, commissary, laundry, ice plant, offices and radio station. Concentrated efforts to increase produc-tion and runs were near at hand. Shortages of oil-field equipment and housing building materials still worried Isakson. But his worst problem by far was the labor demands instigated by syndicates or unions.

Tall, lean William Hightower, Colombian's aviator, flew us in the company Lockheed from Cúcuta to Petrolea. He, too, had been with Colombian Petroleum since 1937, serving as a one-man air lift by shuttling men and supplies between the concession and Cúcuta and Barranquilla. The landing field at Petrolea was a thin rectangular clearing laid out in the direction of prevailing winds in a dense forest that spread out below as far as the eye could see in any direction. Yet he flew passengers and freight into and out of Petrolea three or four times a day.

At Petrolea we inspected the encampment, company field quarters, a small refinery and the hospital. Then we went on to Tibu to see the projected new camp. From Petrolea to Tibu we drove the road that followed the pipeline. A broad oiled strip of winding hill and dale with frequent river crossings, the 35-mile-long highway might have been considered a good secondary suburban road in the United States except for the lack of traffic, the utter void of wayside life and habita-tion and the impenetrable depth of the surrounding forest. Sometimes, we were told, wandering Motilones took pot shots at passing cars.

Our thoughts leaped back to MacFadden's expedition of exploration, to his Indian arrows.

Tibu was a giant clearing in the vast jungle where safety was a main consideration. Acres of land beyond what was necessary for the buildings—under construction or projected—had been divested of timber. Clearings a hundred yards in diameter ringed each well location. The drillers carried arms, and at night searchlights played on the surrounding cleared areas. All for protection against the Indians. Incidentally, the casualty toll from arrows since 1936 stands at 42 employees and 1 nonemployee injured and 13 employees killed, the last attack having been on September 8, 1953. Yet scarcely was the feature of danger convincing, for here was modern life, a bustling community, rumbling industry and fairly busy roads. Were we really deep in the jungle of Norte de Santander? Less than a generation ago MacFadden and General Barco had reached this land only by virtue of their woodsmen's machetes. That day it was our familiar world.

We remained several days on the concession before Hightower flew us out. We sat on a box up forward. Behind us empty acetylene gas bottles were piled high, and anxiously we thought of the tonnage that Hightower's twin-motor Lockheed had to lift over the mountains to get us to Barranquilla. But he showed us the usual courtesy given to visitors by flying out of his course over a Motilone village which lay completely deserted in its clearing. Seldom had a flyer been able to glimpse those wary savages.

Still managing the job at Cúcuta in 1954, Isakson faced a more pleasing prospect than he did in 1946. The major shift from Petrolea to Tibu was all but completed. About 40 houses occupied the laborer area, eight dwellings stood in the foremen-clerk section and about 24 houses were in the technical quarter. Each space had its clubhouse and sports field. A fine, new, direct highway covered the 16 miles between Petrolea and Tibu as against the old 35-mile winding road. Instead of getting supplies by way of Venezuela, all materials came in through Barranquilla, were shipped up the Magdalena River by boat to Puerto Sagoc, then by truck over the improved pipeline road—a busy, truck-packed public highway.

Still on the job, too, was Bill Hightower. But Bill's air lift had been strengthened by two more pilots, and instead of a single Lockheed the company had three Douglas DC-3's, of which two were kept in regular service flying passengers and freight to the fields daily except Sunday, twice a week to and from Coveñas, and every day except Saturday and Sunday to and from Barranquilla. Their cargoes included regular shipments of groceries and fresh vegetables. The casual raids of the Motilones had ceased, and sometimes the Indians were visible from planes flying over their villages.

In 1954, Colombian Petroleum and South American Gulf had some 2,600 employees of whom all except about 150 were Colombians, but because of its isolation the Barco concession always has presented, and still does present, a tough management and development problem. Employees' homes still were in Cúcuta, where living conditions are infinitely better than on the concession. A part of the technical personnel is flown out to Cúcuta and back over week ends and another part during mid-week. In staggered groups laborers also regularly were transported to and from their homes at Cúcuta over the railroad connecting the concession and the city.

On the outskirts of Cúcuta, Colombian had built and financed two housing projects costing a total of approximately 2 million dollars. By early 1954 the projects contained 350 houses available to all classifications of eligible employees, who were permitted to purchase them through a plan by which monthly payments were deducted from their salary. The amortization period ran from 10 to 12 years, and no interest was charged. The projects included paved streets and sewage, water and lighting systems. The houses were in such demand that the waiting list was long for additional houses being constructed. Finally, the labor headache had eased.

Isakson's first deep sigh of relief, however, came in 1947. In that year Colombian Petroleum Company began its first substantial payments to its parent companies, to whom it was more than 50 million dollars in the red. These have continued.

As of June 30, 1953, the total expenditures of the present ownership amounted to $206,824,000. Meantime, the income from the sale of Barco crude and refined products had reached a total of $188,336,000, leaving $18,488,000 unrecovered—a deficit shared equally by The Texas Company and Socony-Vacuum to the tune of $9,244,000 each.

Production averaged 25,200 barrels a day in December, 1953, and, though the output is on the decline, it is expected to be maintained at such levels as to pay out the concession eventually—probably in about five to six years. Whether or not the parent companies can be repaid in the estimated time—or at all—depends largely on meeting extensive current expenditures. In 1952 and 1953, for instance, the major shift of operations and quarters from Petrolea to Tibu together with a new refinery and gas-absorption plant cost Colombian 6 million and 5 million dollars, respectively. The building program, which was to include a new $210,000 hospital at Tibu, had not been finished at the time of this writing.

After 38 years of promotion and development it does look as if Barco will pay out. But only 27 more years remain before the concession reverts back to the government on August 24, 1981.

Incredible faith and tenacity have kept Barco alive all these years. In the depths of a jungle an industry has been built. One might say that Carl MacFadden's early dream had come true in a measure.

By way of postscript, a brief contrast between Doheny and MacFadden:

As oil pioneers, Doheny and MacFadden are not comparable. Before or since his day, Doheny probably personally discovered and produced more oil than any other man in the world. With justice he must be ranked as a true industrial pioneer—one of America's greatest. Doheny also was a builder—an "empire builder," we used to call them proudly. He made a fortune in oil and died a multimillionaire. MacFadden was a promoter; he was bold, even audacious. He made a fortune, but lost it. His name today is forgotten. But by keeping the Barco concession alive and by interesting an American company in the area, he earned a place for himself in the story of United States foreign oil operations.

Chapter 5

THE MIDDLE EAST—
A RECENT HISTORY

At about the time that Doheny went to Mexico, William Knox D'Arcy, an adventurous Britisher, who had made a considerable fortune in gold mining in Australia, looked at Persia—today's Iran—with a commercial eye. In Persia, Herodotus recorded, the conquering Alexander the Great found oil seepages about 325 B.C. In a very real sense oil in the Middle East is ancient history, for as far back as Biblical times the area saw the first commercial use of petroleum when an asphaltic product was sold for house and ship construction.[1]

Old as is the Middle East's oil story, it is the great modern event in world petroleum.

And D'Arcy was the man who started it all. A description of the oil seepages by de Morgan, the French archaeologist, had attracted the alert Britisher's attention, and so impressed was he that, in 1901, he obtained from the Shah a concession covering about a half-million square miles in Persia. Three years later he secured from the Turkish Grand Vizier the promise of another concession in Mesopotamia—today's Iraq—then a part of the Turkish Empire.

At that time underdeveloped, Turkey ruled many Arab lands in this region of the world. The Middle East also had been lifted to the international stage as the center of a two-power almost century-old struggle—a colonial tug of war between Britain and France. And in recent years Germany—another Western power growing in military might and ambitious for a "place in the sun"—also had entered the lists.

Though contemporary in time and though both pioneers were attracted by oil seepages and by the growing importance of oil, the

[1] Fanning, Petroleum in the Ancient World, *Think Magazine*, June, 1953.

stories of D'Arcy and Doheny differ in significant particulars. Doheny's moves to win oil were entirely commercial; he dealt with private land-owners. While D'Arcy's efforts, too, were commercial, he had to deal solely with government heads. For a price he received his huge con-cession in Persian territory, and, in return, he signed a contract "to search for, obtain, exploit, develop, render suitable for trade, carry away and sell natural gas, petroleum, asphalt and ozocerite through the whole extent of the Persian Empire, with the exception of the five northern provinces." D'Arcy's franchise, in other words, was a con-tract to explore, develop and operate, with the government retaining ownership of the subsurface oil. After 60 years the contract would ex-pire.

Doheny, on the other hand, was invited to Mexico by a railroad man intent on cutting his fuel bill. From large landowners Doheny bought property outright, including rights to develop the subsurface oil. He asked President Diaz's blessing on his project only as the pre-cautionary move of a businessman ready and willing to invest in a foreign country. In each case, however, the method was in keeping with the existing law and practice of the nation concerned. As it transpired, another great difference was Doheny's rapid development of his properties. Mexican oil was a fact as well as a factor in World War I.

In Persia, D'Arcy faced an inhospitable landscape, roadless and comfortless, a bleak and baking expanse of empty hillsides and in-escapable sun. Because of transport difficulties he did not begin drilling until November, 1902. Six months later he formed his First Exploita-tion Company, and by the year's end he, personally, was £300,000 out of pocket, with only two moderate wells to show for his loss. Years of unsuccessful and expensive exploration followed until, rich man though he was, D'Arcy was unable to continue his quest single-handed. Eventually the Burmah Oil Company, a British concern with a long record of successful operation in India, took over.

Drilling went on near Haft Kel in the foothills of the Zagros Moun-tains in southwestern Persia and also at Maidan-i-Naftun, about 50 miles to the north-northwest. After surmounting immense difficulties, and at a time when funds nearly were exhausted, Burmah Oil brought in a giant gusher in the latter area. It spouted valuable light (high-grade) oil. The date was May 26, 1908, almost exactly 7 years after the grant of the concession. As a result of this first discovery of oil in the Middle East, in April, 1909, the Anglo-Persian Oil Company was formed. (Its name was changed to the Anglo-Iranian Oil Company in 1935.)

Soon APOC was challenging the Royal Dutch–Shell Company whose star was rising out of the Netherlands East Indies and spreading over the world, including the Middle East. In APOC's behalf, D'Arcy pressed his Mesopotamian claim which was counter to a concession already granted the Turkish Petroleum Company, owned half by German interests (the Deutsche Bank) and half by British-Dutch interests (Royal Dutch–Shell). But so powerful was the British government's intercession that when the controversy was settled on March 19, 1914, the TPC and D'Arcy claims were merged, with the up-and-coming APOC receiving a half interest in TPC and the original owners splitting the remainder and surrendering 50-50 control.

In Persia, meantime, at Abadan, a barren mud flat on the Shatt-al-Arab River, the APOC chose a site for a refinery and connected it by pipeline with the Maidan-i-Naftun oil field in June, 1911. Though possessing an annual capacity of 400,000 tons of oil—about 3 million barrels—the refinery did not function normally until 1913. Twelve long years of costly hard work had elapsed from the moment that the D'Arcy concession was signed to the time when refined petroleum products from the Middle East flowed into world markets.

Then, in May, 1914, two epochal developments vitally affecting APOC occurred: (1) By order of Winston Churchill, First Lord of the Admiralty, the Royal Navy officially converted from coal to oil and (2) entered into a long-term contract with the company for fuel oil for the Navy, the British government investing 2 million pounds in APOC to become the controlling—56 per cent—stockholder.

Four months later the world was aflame with war.

Though Middle East oil was far beyond the dream stage, its role in World War I was restricted, for Turkey was an ally of Germany. Hostile forces menaced the oil fields, the pipeline and the refinery. Communications were hindered, material from Britain became increasingly hard to obtain. But, at the war's end, Germany was eliminated from Middle East oil.

Adventurous Americans, meanwhile, had not wholly overlooked the Middle East. Before the war a certain ex-admiral had been bidding for a Turkish concession, but the Turkish Petroleum Company held the plum—the Mesopotamian concession with its ancient oil seepages and its rights throughout the old Ottoman Empire. At the end of hostilities, Iraq (Mesopotamia) became a mandate of Great Britain, and Syria, to the west of Iraq, became a mandate of France. In the San Remo Agreement of 1920, Britain and France arranged a Middle East oil monopoly which would freeze out the United States. To understand the full implications of the San Remo Agreement, it is necessary briefly to review the oil background of the time.

World War I had been won with United States oil, assisted by Mexican oil. Tanks, trucks and airplanes—all new to war—had left the great powers exceedingly oil-conscious. Now a world-shortage scare was in full cry.[2] But a vignette of history, only recently revealed, shows that American oil men were alert to the danger of being frozen out of the Middle East. In 1919 the energetic, astute Walter C. Teagle, president of Standard of Jersey, heard rumors of an Anglo-French plan to reorganize the Turkish Petroleum Company—apparently the beginning of the developments that led to the San Remo Agreement. Through John Bassett Moore, then advising the company on matters of international law, Jersey informed the State Department of the possibility of a freeze-out and pressed the issue with a formal memorandum prepared by Moore. Then, through the State Department, Jersey attempted to secure permission from Great Britain to send geologists to Iraq. Britain refused. Only a few months later, on April 24, 1920, Great Britain and France signed the San Remo Agreement dealing with petroleum reserves in Rumania, Asia Minor and French and British colonies.

So far as the agreement concerned Iraq, it accorded the French government a 25 per cent interest in any private petroleum company which would develop Iraq oil fields, in consideration for which France agreed to permit the construction of pipelines through French spheres of influence to the Mediterranean.

Simultaneously, the British took the position that, except for TPC, no Iraq concessions were available to other companies in view of the blanket terms of the prewar grants from the Turkish Sultan. Teagle called the British position to the attention of Secretary of State Bainbridge Colby and, at the same time, made it clear that, if the Iraq

[2] A Case History of Oil-shortage Scares, *Our Oil Resources*, p. 329.

field were opened to American capital, Jersey would take steps to participate.[3]

Standard of Jersey's interest stemmed from its extensive foreign marketing operations, from severe competition with Royal Dutch–Shell and Anglo-Persian Oil and from the threatened oil shortage. Closely interested, also, were Socony-Vacuum—then Standard Oil Company of New York and the Vacuum Oil Company—and Atlantic Refining, each with a long tradition in foreign trade. Then, too, a lengthy list of older independent American companies, such as Pure Oil and Cities Service, engaged in foreign trade, and the newer independent companies, like The Texas Company, Gulf Oil Corporation and Sinclair Oil Corporation, all were entering the field of foreign oil development.

Alarmed because of a possible oil shortage, Washington told American companies, in effect, to "go out and get foreign oil." And to Britain the State Department called for an "open-door" policy in the Middle East. The resultant American participation—wherein APOC split its interest in the Iraq Petroleum Company (the former Turkish Petroleum Company) with an American group—is a striking instance of United States government sponsorship of American joint oil operations abroad. It came only after 7 years of diplomatic and commercial negotiations. At first, under the original Group Agreement of 1928, the participating American companies comprised Standard of Jersey, Socony-Vacuum, Gulf, Pan-American Petroleum and Transport Company (Doheny) and Atlantic Refining, but subsequently the three last-named withdrew. From 1934 to the present writing the American interest has been held by Jersey and Socony through the 50-50 controlled Near Eastern Development Company. Iraq Petroleum Company ownership now is split 23.75 per cent Anglo-Iranian; 23.75 per cent Royal Dutch–Shell; 23.75 per cent Compagnie Française des Pétroles, in which the French government has a 35 per cent interest; 23.75 per cent Near Eastern Development Company (American); and 5 per cent Participations and Investments, Ltd. (C. I. Gulbenkian, fabulous international magnate of Armenian descent).[4]

[3] *Joint Oil Producing Ventures in the Middle East—Their Status under United States Antitrust Laws*, Standard Oil Company (New Jersey), December 31, 1953, pp. 7–10.

[4] See Appendix II, Section 1, Concessions in the Middle East.

The importance of the American breakthrough in Middle Eastern oil development cannot be overemphasized. IPC was not merely a local company with its operations confined to the boundaries of Iraq. Rather it ranged throughout most of the nations and sheikdoms which the old Ottoman Empire had held in Europe and Asia, except those administered by the Egyptian government, that of the Sheik of Kuwait and the "transferred places" on the Turko-Persian frontier—territories which at the time embraced all the known "likely areas" for new oil discovery in the Middle East. Moreover, because of a long series of treaties which the British had entered into with the various sheiks around the Persian Gulf, those chieftains could make no contracts for the development of oil without the approval of the British. Such a relationship existed even with Ibn Saud who was freed from it only by the Treaty of Jidda in 1927.[5]

IPC—directly, or through subsidiaries, holding oil concessions covering all of Iraq and the "trucial coast" (see Chapter 15, A Middle Easterner Looks at Oil)—proceeded successfully to develop its original Iraq concession. It began drilling operations in April, 1927, and completed its first well on the Kirkuk structure in October. Coming in out of control, the well flowed at an estimated 100,000 barrels a day. Subsequent drilling operations proved the existence of a field of great proportions, and before exports commenced in the fall of 1934 American engineers constructed a pipeline to the Mediterranean, 620 miles distant, at an outlay of 62 million dollars.

But IPC's development of the rugged Kirkuk field—far inland and separated from an outlet by mountain and desert—could not compare with the Anglo-Iranian's (Anglo-Persian's) strides in Iran.

During the years 1921 to 1923, AIOC's capital expenditure amounted to approximately 30 million pounds, or 120 million dollars. With the money, the company built more pipelines in Iran, expanded the Abadan refinery, constructed the first major refinery in Britain—in South Wales at Llandarcy, named after the redoubtable D'Arcy—launched a great tanker fleet and made the company a world marketing organization. Widely separated geographically as they were, these undertakings aimed to build the company into one of the world's most effectively integrated oil organizations.[6]

---

[5] See Appendix II, Section 2, Treaties with Middle Eastern Countries and Sheikdoms.

[6] *Fifty Years of Oil*, Anglo-Iranian Oil Company, 1952.

By 1935 Iran's production had risen to 156,000 barrels daily as against Iraq's 76,000 barrels, and within a few years it still further outstripped the output of its neighbor.

Entirely different in character from AIOC, IPC was controlled by companies of world-wide operational scope—Royal Dutch–Shell, AIOC and Jersey Standard and Socony-Vacuum. Moreover, IPC essentially was an oil-producing development company and not integrated in character. Important as was the United States' achievement in getting a share in IPC—and thus a toehold in the Middle East—a fly was in the ointment so far as the two final American participating companies were concerned. This was the "red-line agreement."

Originating back in 1912 in the document which merged British, German and Royal Dutch–Shell interests in the newly named Turkish Petroleum Company and deriving its name from a line drawn on a map to define specific areas, the "red-line agreement" provided that the participating groups should confine their operations in the Middle East to the old Ottoman Empire of Europe and Asia—except in Egypt, Kuwait and the "transferred places" on the Turko-Persian frontier.

At this point, upon the Middle Eastern stage entered Standard Oil Company of California—unshackled by commitments of any kind.

In 1930 Standard of California acquired a concession covering about 156 square miles of Bahrain Island, lying in the Persian Gulf, within eyesight of the great desert country of Saudi Arabia. Earlier, Gulf Oil had been approached by Frank Holmes, an Englishman, who originally had secured the Bahrain concession as a result of drilling for water for the sheik of the island. At the same time, Holmes also had obtained from Ibn Saud a concession in Saudi Arabia which later lapsed. At that time Gulf was one of the American group in IPC and thus was signatory to the "red-line agreement." Though its attention had been called to this agreement, Gulf nevertheless offered the concession to IPC which turned it down—not because of the "red-line agreement," but because its geologists recommended rejection on the basis of lack of promise. Gulf then was asked to dispose of the concession and did so to Standard of California—Gulf subsequently withdrawing from the American IPC group. Before Standard of California could obtain a transfer of the concession, it had to—and did—obtain approval of the British authorities. The Bahrain Petroleum Company, Socal's Canadian-incorporated subsidiary, drilled a discovery well in June, 1932, and soon after constructed a refinery on the island. By 1939 Bahrain output averaged in excess of 20,000 barrels daily.

In the early thirties, meantime, King Ibn Saud had employed Karl S. Twitchell, an American mining engineer, to try to interest American mining and petroleum companies in Saudi Arabia, but Standard of California, currently exploring in Bahrain, already had considered approaching the neighbor king. A meeting between Twitchell and representatives of Standard of California led to negotiations which, on May 29, 1933, resulted in the company's obtaining from Ibn Saud a concession on over 200 million acres in Saudi Arabia.

Four months after the signing of the grant, a party of Socal geologists landed at Jubail, on the Persian Gulf coast of Saudi Arabia, where few Arabs ever had seen an American or a European. Desiring to minimize the strangeness of their presence, the geologists had grown beards and accustomed themselves to native Arabian dress. The region where they landed contained only primitive facilities. Summer temperatures reached 125 degrees.

The company's first wildcat test well was started on nearby Dammam Dome in April, 1935. Early efforts were disappointing. That it might share the risks and financial burden involved in further development, in 1936 Standard of California sold to The Texas Company a half interest in both Bahrain Petroleum and California-Arabian Standard Oil Company (Calarabian). The last-named was a Delaware concern, which held the Saudi Arabian concession. It also sold Texas a half interest in Socal's N. V. Nederlandsche Pacific Petroleum Maatschappij, which, in turn, owned concessions and rights in Sumatra and Java, as well as a half interest in Socal's 20 per cent holdings in the Nederlandsche Nieuw Guinee Petroleum Maatschappij, which held a concession in Netherlands New Guinea. For these interests, Texas agreed to pay 3 million dollars in funds with no strings attached, plus 18 million dollars in amounts based on the quantities of oil and other products—if and when—actually produced from these concessions. And Standard of California acquired a half interest in Texas' marketing facilities in the Eastern Hemisphere outside West Africa. For the latter operations The California Texas Oil Company (Caltex), equally owned by the two companies, was formed.[7] In 1944 the name of

[7] Amended Answer of The Texas Company, U.S. District Court, Southern District of New York, Civil Action No. 86-27, September 21, 1953.

California-Arabian Standard Oil Company was changed to Arabian American Oil Company (Aramco).

By the end of 1937 Calarabian had spent millions of dollars in drilling 10 wells without getting enough oil to warrant moving it to seaboard, only 6 miles away. Refusing to give up, the men drilled deeper. The turning point came in March, 1938, when they penetrated the so-called "Arab Zone"—a good oil-bearing limestone of substantial thickness—in the Dammam field. At last oil in commercial quantity had been discovered. Up until that time the company had spent 8 million dollars and was to expend another 7 million dollars before getting its oil to market. In 1940 and 1941 the company completed wildcat wells which discovered two more oil fields at Abu Hadriya and Abqaiq and in 1940 completed a small 3,000-barrel-per-day refinery at Ras Tanura.

The modern pioneers of Calarabian built a materials-receiving pier, brought in a vast variety of equipment, constructed houses, developed a water supply, set up repair shops for motor vehicles, established medical facilities and telephone communications and built miscellaneous shops and warehouses. Everything with which they worked had to be imported from the United States, halfway around the world from their desert outpost.

Then, as in Iran, World War II began to interfere greatly with oil operations. When the United States entered the conflict, however, American officials saw in Bahrain Island and Saudi Arabia sources of oil which, if developed, were ready-made for future military undertakings in the Far East. Accordingly, they sought expansion of the operations by assisting in obtaining priorities on materials. As a result, in about 1942 at the request of the United States government and in the face of the German drive in North Africa, the Bahrain refinery made a substantial increase in its capacity and installed facilities for the manufacture of aviation gasoline. Only a small part of the cost was financed by a 17-million-dollar loan from the Reconstruction Finance Corporation. Since the new facilities meant that the refinery could accommodate more oil than the Bahrain field could supply, additional wells were drilled in Saudi Arabia and a sea pipeline was laid from the Arabian mainland to Bahrain. In 1944, again at the urging of the United States but without any government financial aid, a new

50,000-barrel-per-day refinery was begun at Ras Tanura. Including housing and additional wells, the project involved a total cost of about 65 million dollars. Though the refinery did not commence operations until September, 1945, just after V-J Day—it contributed substantially to the postwar operations of Allied naval and military forces in the Pacific.[8]

Meantime, Gulf Oil, after having relinquished its participation in IPC, as early as 1926 had sought an oil concession in the little sheikdom of Kuwait, lying between Iraq and Saudi Arabia on the Persian Gulf. Kuwait, however, was a protectorate of Great Britain, and the treaty creating the protectorate provided that the sheik could not grant oil concessions to non-British subjects without the consent of Great Britain. Simultaneously Anglo-Iranian—controlled by the British government—engaged in similar independent negotiations with the Kuwait Sheikdom. The dilemma was resolved in 1933, when, with equal stock ownership, Gulf and Anglo-Iranian organized Kuwait Oil Company to which, with the consent of the British government, an oil concession was granted.[9] Just before the war the Kuwait company discovered oil on its concession, and the sands tapped promised to be as rich or richer than the producing formation in Saudi Arabia. Because of the war, however, Kuwait did not achieve commercial production until 1946. Thus, at the war's end and within a few years, Bahrain Island, Saudi Arabia and Kuwait, the latter two being highly potential oil-producing areas, appeared on the oil map outside the "red line."

At this stage, definite pressures clearly influenced the actions of American companies in this area. Jersey and Socony—to protect their markets, to share in the expected growth of consumption in Europe and Asia and to meet the competition of the two great foreign oil companies, Royal Dutch–Shell and Anglo-Iranian—were caught in IPC with only an insignificant share of Middle East oil reserves. Standard of California and The Texas Company, joint owners of Aramco, felt the twin pressures of a great oil potential and of Ibn Saud's need for oil revenues.

[8] Amended Answer of The Texas Company, U.S. District Court, Southern District of New York, Civil Action No. 86-27, September 21, 1953.

[9] Answer of Gulf Oil Corporation, U.S. District Court, Southern District New York, Civil Action No. 86-27, September 1, 1953.

The end of the war signaled great increases in world oil consumption, particularly in Europe, and, naturally, Europe looked to the nearby Middle East for a supply. But, because of war conditions, Ibn Saud had suffered serious financial embarrassment when Aramco production—and consequent royalties—had been curtailed and when pilgrim traffic to Mecca and Medina—historically one of the principal sources of government revenue—had been restricted. Now he demanded greater oil activities and revenues. From where were the funds coming to provide for expansion, one important phase of which would be to build a pipeline to convey oil to the Mediterranean to expedite the flow of oil to Europe? The huge expenditures involved would have strained even the substantial resources of Aramco's parent companies.

Simply put, this was the situation. On the one hand, Standard of New Jersey and Socony-Vacuum had markets and faced the need for more oil; on the other hand, Standard of California and Texas had the oil and invited Jersey and Socony to participate in Saudi Arabian development. But Saudi Arabia lay within the "red line."

A solution was at hand. After World War II, Standard of Jersey's British counsel advised it that the original Group Agreement of 1928, including the "red-line agreement," had been frustrated and dissolved in 1940 because, under British law, two of the parties—Compagnie Française des Pétroles and Gulbenkian—had acquired enemy status following the German occupation of France in that year. In December, 1946, Jersey and Socony-Vacuum formally notified the other parties to the group of this conclusion. At the same time, they announced that, in principle, they had arrived at an agreement to purchase a stock interest in Aramco. In January, 1947, Compagnie Française des Pétroles instituted suit in the British courts against the other parties to the 1928 group agreement, seeking a declaration that the "red-line agreement" was binding. The suit was settled, and on November 3, 1948, all parties entered into a new agreement governing the IPC venture.

The Agreement of 1948 completely replaced the original Group Agreement of 1928. All provisions dealing with the "red-line agreement" were eliminated entirely. Also, in a separate document, the participation of Jersey and Socony in Aramco was stated not to be a

breach of any agreement between the parties, and it was agreed to
terminate the pending litigation.[10]

On March 12, 1947, meantime, Jersey and Socony had executed contracts with Aramco by which, in 1948, Jersey acquired a 30 per cent
and Socony a 10 per cent interest in Aramco and Tapline, the latter
being the company formed to build a trans-Arabian pipeline. The joint
ownership of both companies now comprises Standard of California,
Texas and Jersey, each with a 30 per cent interest, and Socony with a
10 per cent interest. For the shares which they acquired, Jersey and
Socony paid 102 million dollars in cash. Together with Standard Oil of
California and Texas, they also guaranteed loans aggregating 125 million dollars to construct the trans-Arabian pipeline. These two transactions alone involved the risk in 1947 of an investment amounting to
approximately a quarter of a billion dollars.

These highlights of recent Middle Eastern oil history, then, present
a classic example of the problems which can create the necessity for
additional investments and of the need to spread the risk. By the end
of 1946 Texas and Standard of California had invested great amounts
in Aramco, Texas alone to the tune of 62 million dollars. That huge
sum notwithstanding, clearly much larger commitments would be
vital if Saudi Arabian production were to be expanded as required.
A listing of just some of the investments, which were made from 1946
to 1952, strikingly illustrates the magnitude of the problems confronting the earlier Aramco owners. Oil-handling facilities, product pipelines and local marketing facilities required capital totaling 70 million
dollars. Expansion of the refinery at Ras Tanura cost 16 million dollars. The construction of housing, roads and general plant facilities
totaled 140 million dollars. For drilling new wells an expenditure of
15 million dollars was necessary. Over and above all these investments
was the cost of the trans-Arabian pipeline, running over a thousand
miles from the producing fields in Saudi Arabia to the Mediterranean.
Originally estimated to cost 125 million dollars, by the end of 1950
when the line had been completed more than 200 million dollars had
gone into its construction.

One of the fundamental reasons for operating abroad in joint producing ventures is the necessity for sharing political and economic

[10] *Joint Oil Producing Ventures in the Middle East—Their Status under United
States Antitrust Laws*, Standard Oil Company (New Jersey), December 31, 1953.

risks, which either do not exist in the United States or are of such magnitude as to be out of all proportion to similar risks in domestic operations. The expansion of Aramco from a two-party to a four-party venture represents a clear instance of this economic truth. The dangers peculiar to foreign oil operations made it prudent business judgment for Standard of California and Texas to invite Jersey and Socony into the venture to contribute financially to the Aramco expansion program and so to spread the risk of loss among four companies instead of between two. Moreover, by having Jersey and Socony join the venture, Standard of California and Texas made a profit from each barrel of oil lifted by the former companies.

The rise of Middle East oil has been nothing short of fabulous. Producing 825,000 barrels a day by 1952, Aramco had become the leading oil producing company not only in the Middle East but in the world.[11] With estimated crude oil reserves of over 28 billion barrels, the company alone possessed reserves equal to all those of the United States.

So, at this point, it might be said that the twin pressures of great oil potential and the Saudi Arabian government's need for oil revenue had exerted their combined influence. Obviously, with a mounting crude production in Saudi Arabia and an increasing demand in the Western Hemisphere, the crude supply for Eastern Hemisphere markets would shift from South America to Middle East sources. In 1952 over 90 per cent of the crude oil shipped to European markets came from the Middle East as compared with less than 50 per cent in 1926. And the Saudi Arabian government recouped its financial position, for its aggregate receipt of taxes and royalties from oil increased from 10 million dollars in 1946 to 60 million dollars in 1950 and to about 150 million dollars in 1952.

Scarcely less spectacular than the Saudi Arabian oil development was that of tiny Kuwait in which American interests (Gulf) hold a half share. Though the entire country is less than 2,000 square miles in area, its Burgan field became the richest single producing field in the world.

Reviewing briefly the rise of Middle East oil, immediately before World War II production in this area amounted to about 330,000 barrels a day in a world total (excluding Russia) of approximately 5

[11] See Appendix I, Table 1, World Crude-oil Production.

million barrels daily. The output constituted only a minor supplement to the great quantities of oil fed into the markets of the world, largely from the United States, Venezuela and other Western Hemisphere countries. During the war, Middle East production increased greatly but in 1946 still was less than 700,000 barrels daily. Then the dynamics of the area caught fire. By 1953 the Middle East was producing 2,424,-000 barrels a day, out of a world production totaling 13,116,000 barrels daily. The Middle East had replaced Venezuela, whose output averaged 1,766,000 barrels a day, as the second largest producing area in the world. As of January 1, 1954, the Middle East's proved crude-oil reserves soared to 79,000,000,000 barrels, in an estimated total world reserve of 136,877,482,000 barrels.[12]

So much for the statistical picture.

However, the human elements in the drama of Middle East oil and the bearing that a commingling of East and West in commerce have on world tensions cannot be omitted from the picture. Even before Mossadegh clamped down on the Anglo-Iranian Oil Company in 1951, American oil men had taken the lead over Britain in Middle East oil development.

Had it not been for the initiative and keenness of Walter C. Teagle in the twenties and for the pioneering of Standard of California, Texas and Gulf in the thirties, American interests in the Middle East oil area—so vital to the economy and safety of the Free World and to the United States itself—might be infinitesimal today.

Aggressiveness and business acumen, a willingness and a capacity to take great risks have given the American companies an interest in concessions covering over half of the estimated 136 billion barrels of proved reserves. More than that, their careful cultivation of the good will of the governments and peoples of Middle Eastern nations has gained for them a high level of respect—not an inconsiderable factor in promoting understanding and in aiding the orientation of the Middle East toward the West during the troubled present and, for that matter, what may well be a troubled future.

Then, too, the Middle East provides a striking example of the effect on the fortunes of companies and nations of the "fickleness" of oil discovery (see Chapter 1).

[12] See Appendix I, Table 2, Estimated World Crude-oil Reserves.

Depending on the point of view, the effect on companies can be good or bad. The first company, Anglo-Iranian Oil—long the area's leading producer not alone because of its large and exclusive production in prolific Iran but also because of its 23.75 per cent interest in Iraq Petroleum and one-half share in Kuwait Oil—found itself challenged by the American Aramco. Iraq Petroleum, which at the time of its formation was thought to have sewed up for itself all the likely Middle East oil areas outside Iran, though acquiring additional concessions in Iraq and other parts of the old Turkish empire, has succeeded in developing production outside Iraq only in the trucial state of Qatar.

The effect of the "fickleness" of discovery on the Great Powers can be far-reaching and highly important. The obvious result of the success of American oil enterprise in the Middle East has been the enhancement of the United States' position at the expense of Great Britain. Moreover, British prestige suffered an additional body blow when, in 1951, Mossadegh "nationalized" Iranian oil and forced AIOC to close down the oil fields as well as the Abadan refinery, the largest oil refinery in the world. From early in 1946 until its shutdown in 1951, Abadan operated near its maximum throughput of 25 million tons, or 187 million barrels, a year. In large part the company could and did recoup its supply loss by turning toward and drawing upon Kuwait's immense reserves and by diverting its great tanker fleet from Iran to Kuwait. Inevitably, however, the damage to British prestige remained.

One might be tempted to observe that the British government's participation as a shareholder in oil operations may have hurt rather than helped. The French position has not been elevated by virtue of the French government's participation in Middle East oil development. American oil people generally opposed proposals made during World War II that would have sent into the Middle East the Petroleum Reserves Corporation, a United States government-owned company, empowered to build a pipeline across Arabia and to engage in refining and other operations. The oil people disliked the plan not merely because they did not want their government to engage in the petroleum business, but because they saw no need of—and extreme danger in— the United States entering directly into the politically explosive Middle East. Mainly because of their strenuous opposition the Petroleum Reserves Corporation project was killed, and the wisdom of their judgment has been amply demonstrated by subsequent events.[13] (See Chapter 25, Why Not an International Oil Policy?)

At this writing, meanwhile, it would seem the Middle East's recent oil history is about to complete a full cycle of change. Following a three-year paralysis, early in 1954, near-agreement loomed on a plan to revive Iran's oil industry. According to the projected plan, a consortium of leading international oil companies would take over operations on the following basis: Anglo-Iranian, 40 per cent; five United States companies—Standard of Jersey, Socony-Vacuum, Standard of California, Texas and Gulf—8 per cent each, or 40 per cent as a group; Royal Dutch–Shell, 14 per cent; and the French government-controlled Compagnie Française des Pétroles, 6 per cent. While emphasizing that the United States government had not been directly involved in these commercial negotiations, Secretary of State John Foster Dulles expressed satisfaction that they "will have as their purpose the resumption of large-scale oil production in Iran on terms consistent with reasonable safeguarding of foreign capital within the structure and rights of the national sovereignty." He observed further that the interruption to oil production seriously had hindered Iran's own efforts toward social and economic progress.[14] (See Chapter 25, The Iranian Oil Settlement.)

Is not this just about where we came in? Does not this turn of the wheel harken back to 1928 when Iraq Petroleum Company's internationalization was revised to include a joint operating group of United States oil companies having the full approval and blessing of the United States government?

[13] A Case History of Oil-shortage Scares, *Our Oil Resources*, p. 352.
[14] *The New York Times*, April 11, 1954.

Chapter 6

VENEZUELA—THE WELCOME MAT

So far we have discussed largely the economic or operational costs and risks which are far greater abroad than in domestic operations. To the list of hazards not found at home must be added political risks, consisting chiefly of unstable governments subject to sudden coups, and also the trend toward nationalization. Mexico's expropriation of foreign oil properties fairly represents the extremely high price that can be paid on the second count by both the nation and the oil companies involved. The companies simply wrote off their losses and departed. Production dropped sharply. Yet oil people claim without qualification that Mexico still could be a high-ranking producer. Under its government operation the industry never has staged a real comeback.

In all Latin-American countries, following an old Spanish custom, ownership of the subsoil is in the state. That is, a fundamental principle of old Spanish law was that the Crown—and hence succeeding governments—inherently owned certain minerals. However, in Mexico prior to the constitution of 1917, the owner of the land from whom the oil companies bought or leased property did own the oil and gas rights which went with the sale or lease. But these rights were doomed after the adoption of the Carranza "nationalization" constitution of May 1, 1917 [1] (see Chapter 3). Nevertheless, there are still exceptions as to government ownership of the subsoil in some lands owned in Mexico and Colombia.

Nationalization of oil received its biggest boost in the Western Hemisphere from Mexico's 1917 Constitution and from subsequent expropriation in 1938. But the policy was not altogether new. As early

[1] *American Oil Operations Abroad*, p. 28.

as 1912 Argentina withdrew lands which had been discovered and developed by an American oil company and with its government-owned Yacimientos Petroliferos Fiscales—subsequently incorporated by an Act of the Argentinean Congress in 1932—succeeded in obstructing private operations to the extent that the status of foreign oil companies deteriorated steadily. Bolivia's seizure on March 15, 1937, of the properties of the Standard Oil Company of Bolivia (Standard of New Jersey) and its formation of the government-owned Yacimientos Petroliferos Fiscales Bolivianos drove foreign companies out of the country. Chile and Uruguay substantially have curtailed foreign oil investment by nationalization, and Brazil will not permit foreign capital to participate in the search for oil.[2]

In all these countries oil prospects are high, but government operation has retarded and thwarted development, even to the extent in certain cases of the nation's inability to meet its own requirements.

Nationalization—or "creeping expropriation" as Dr. Milton Eisenhower calls it—is at large in many Latin-American countries to the discouragement of the investment of foreign capital.[3] Among the countries resisting this trend thus far, though their subsurface oil is owned by the government, are Venezuela, Colombia and Peru. Indeed, Venezuela is pointed to today as a shining example of how laws favorable to foreign investment can mutually benefit a host nation and its foreign guests in trade.

"An almost classic example of economic cooperation between two free world nations, to the benefit of both, is afforded by Venezuela and the United States," says the Paley report.[4] "By developing her rich materials resources, mainly with the aid of private investment capital and technical know-how supplied by the United States, Venezuela has achieved in a short span of years an almost unparalleled record of economic and social advancement. . . . It has achieved a balanced budget, with oil revenue supplying over 90 per cent of foreign exchange; a low income tax rate; enormous foreign trade; rapid industrial growth, and broad national development and social benefits. . . . Venezuela thus

[2] *American Oil Operations Abroad*, pp. 17–36.

[3] Dr. Milton S. Eisenhower, *Report to the President on Latin-American Relations*, November 19, 1953.

[4] The President's Materials Policy Commission report, *Resources for Freedom*, June, 1952.

presents an outstanding example of growth based on development of materials resources, to the advantage of her own people and other free nations. Furthermore, Venezuela and the investing corporations have worked together to develop a climate that assures mutual benefits, a sound working basis for operation, and a resulting incentive for additional foreign capital to make its contribution to the development of the country. . . . As an example to underdeveloped countries with aspirations for their own development, Venezuela affords some interesting and valuable lessons."

Venezuela came into petroleum prominence in the late teens and twenties when salt water, revolution, taxes, radical labor and nationalization were combining to drive foreign oil companies out of Mexico. In a well-timed action President Juan Vincente Gómez put out the welcome mat, and the "foreign play" switched to Venezuela.

But oil wells had been drilled in that country long before the twenties. Even at the turn of the century when General Cipriano Castro, Gómez's predecessor, came into power, an American named Horatio R. Hamilton held a 99-year concession he had received in 1883 which permitted petroleum development. Covering an area of 12 square miles, it contained bubbling springs of thick asphalt known as the Bermudez Asphalt or Pitch Lake, situated near Guanoco in eastern Venezuela. Two years after obtaining his grant, Hamilton had assigned it to the New York and Bermudez Company of Albany, New York. Though the company had worked it for many years, in the period immediately following Castro's ascent to power, it continued to do so at great inconvenience, because a revolution to overthrow the president surged in the area where the property was located. One of Castro's first acts was to try to relieve the New York and Bermudez Company of its holdings—an action which, with the sequence of subsequent events, is of interest because it draws a contrasting picture of conditions at the time when Venezuela's oil industry was born with those of today.

Castro charged that the company had financed General Manuel A. Matos' abortive "liberating revolution" of June, 1901; that the company had bought the steamer *Ban Righ*, had fitted it out as a warship, had loaded it down with weapons of war and that, while carrying none other than General Matos himself, the vessel had appeared off the Venezuelan coast where it had made piratical history. All this the company vehemently denied in the Venezuelan courts.[5] However, several former employees, among them Amzi L. Barber, an American promoter of asphalt companies who owned the title of "Asphalt King," filed affidavits supporting Castro's allegations, and the courts canceled the Bermudez Lake concession. Whether or not Americans financed this particular revolution, the point is that such illegal things did sometimes happen in those old days. In December, 1908, while Castro was visiting Europe, Gómez, as Venezuela's vice-president, closed the door on him and began the fabulous Gómez dictatorship which lasted until the day of his death in 1935.

Gómez proceeded to confer concessions on relatives and friends. In the State of Zulia Dr. Andres J. Vigas received a grant covering the whole District of Colon, running from Lake Maracaibo to the Colombian border. General Antonio Aranguren pocketed a concession embracing the Districts of Maracaibo and Bolivar. Francisco Jiminez Arraiz was handed a tract encompassing parts of the Districts of Silva, Zamora and Acosta in the State of Falcon, all located in western Venezuela. The concessionaires promptly sold their grants to British promoters.

Gómez, the President, returned the Bermudez Lake concession to the General Asphalt Company, which in 1902 had acquired the New York and Bermudez Company. President John M. Mack of General Asphalt, believing that the birth of a vigorous "Fuel-oil Age" was imminent, already had drilled several expensive dry holes in Trinidad where the company operated asphalt properties. Now he sent geologist A. C. Veatch to Venezuela to examine the bubbling seeps on the Bermudez concession. In the following year Ralph Arnold replaced Veatch, and on the second geologist's recommendation, General Asphalt organized the Caribbean Petroleum Company to carry on its oil operations. Almost immediately the company acquired a second grant—to become known as the Caribbean concession—which covered all Venezuelan lands not in existing grants.

In 1912 near Bermudez Asphalt Lake in eastern Venezuela, the company drilled its first well and followed up with others. Though they were shallow and disappointingly small, and though they were not the first oil wells ever drilled in Venezuela, they were the first to attract

[5] Seizure of Property, Statement by the New York and Bermudez Company submitted to the State Department, 1906(?).

attention. But still under the spell of the "Asphalt Age," General Asphalt's directors reacted violently against their president's foray into petroleum. They replaced him with Arthur W. Sewall, an experienced asphalt man, and used Arnold's final report to sell Caribbean Petroleum to Royal Dutch–Shell, with GA retaining a 25 per cent stock interest which it relinquished in 1922 for a one-eighth royalty interest.[6]

Meantime, two British companies, Venezuelan Oil Concessions, Ltd., and Colon Development Company, had acquired the Aranguren and Vigas concessions, respectively. As early as 1915, reportedly both companies had drilled producing wells and promptly had capped them. The "mystery" wells were rumored to be of great capacity. Impressed by the gigantic British concessions and by the shut-in wells—together with the British concession held in Persia or Iran—Americans listened to the hue and cry set up about the oil pinch following World War I and took stock of the piercing utterances of Sir Edward Mackay Edgar, VOC's vocal publicity man, who predicted oil plenty for the British, but saw only oil starvation for the United States because of its past and continuing profligacy.

In Venezuela, meantime, Gómez had seen that the time was ripe for a new law. The result, the petroleum law of 1920, required the renewal of old concessions in complete conformation with the new law and opened up fresh areas for exploration concessions. By these means Gómez hoped to reward friends and relatives, attract American and other foreign companies and, furthermore, build a fire under the British with their capped wells which produced not a penny of revenue. A law unto himself, President Gómez saw a great national and personal opportunity if he could attract foreign oil capital from Mexico where it was being hounded. The decline of that country's "Golden Lane" and the shortage scare following World War I played into his hands, and the oil companies came. Though under Gómez's petroleum law of 1920 the oil industry was classified as a public utility, it enjoyed many of the rights of eminent domain and so could condemn lands required for the construction of pipelines, refineries and railways. An appraisal board was set up to settle disagreements between oil companies and landowners. Royalties ranged between 7½ and 15 per cent for an average of 10 per cent. Some of Gómez's legendary 84 children were represented among the concession holders, and the

[6] *Report of American Petroleum Interests in Foreign Countries*, p. 360.

rich concession in Lake Maracaibo, originally acquired by Lago, was given to Gómez's son-in-law.

Gómez's plan exceeded his own expectations. Between 1913 and 1918 not one American-controlled company had owned a concession in the Maracaibo Basin. But by 1925 so eagerly did Americans avail themselves of Gómez's welcome that 20 American companies held extensive areas in both western and eastern Venezuela and at least 11 were classified as operating—that is, actually drilling. The others were turning over their lands to drilling companies in return for a bonus and an overriding royalty. Even Doheny, Mexico's oil pioneer, was represented with Lago Petroleum. Six British companies were on the scene, with five of them operating and controlling the "cream." Royal Dutch–Shell soon absorbed Colon Development Company and VOC with their capped secret wells, as it already had taken over Caribbean, and began active development of the properties.

But American companies sprang a surprising coup by gambling on underwater concessions in Lake Maracaibo. Certain of these grants offset some of the proved VOC shore holdings. Venezuelan Gulf Oil Company (Gulf Oil Corporation) and Creole Syndicate—an American stock promotion of J. S. (Josh) Cosden and others—went to work on concessions in the Maritime Zone, an offshore strip 1 kilometer wide in the large and shallow lake. Lago Petroleum Corporation (later acquired from Doheny by Standard Oil Company of Indiana) started overwater drilling on its holdings comprising all the rest of the lake. Then on December 14, 1922, VOC's Barroso No. 2 well—in the La Rosa field on the east side of the lake—drilled itself in and flowed wild for nine days at the rate of more than 100,000 barrels daily before finally sanding up. The Venezuelan oil boom began in earnest. Soon VOC made other important discoveries at La Paz and Concepción west of the lake.

Standard of Jersey, which has played a leading role in Venezuela, started drilling operations in that country with its Standard Oil Company of Venezuela as early as 1921 but met with poor results. Indeed Standard of Jersey's Venezuelan entrance may be said to have been by way of Mexico. With its Cia. Transcontinental de Petroleo, Jersey, at that time, was a rather large producer in Mexico. With labor and production conditions going from bad to worse, Doheny meanwhile had sold his Pan American Petroleum & Transport Company—with

Lago Petroleum Corporation thrown in—to Standard Oil Company (Indiana). Jersey now acquired from the Indiana company for about 146 million dollars—48 million dollars in cash and the balance in stock— all its Pan-American foreign holdings. When, in 1931, the deal was made, Lago Petroleum's Venezuelan production of 31 million barrels was the largest in the Maracaibo Lake area. Thus, in one stroke, Jersey became a large producer in that country, while adding the old Doheny holdings and Indiana's acquisitions to its Mexican properties.

Also Jersey acquired Lago Oil & Transport Corporation and Lago Shipping, respectively operating a 115,000-barrel-a-day refinery on the island of Aruba, D.W.I., off the Venezuelan coast, and a fleet of shallow-draft tankers carrying crude oil from the lake fields to the island. Previously, in March, 1928, Jersey had acquired a controlling interest in Creole Syndicate—the Cosden promotion—had changed its name to Creole Petroleum Corporation and had made it the holding company for all its Venezuelan subsidiaries, including Standard Oil Company of Venezuela which became the operating company for all units. Then, in 1932, Jersey put its newly acquired Lago properties into Creole, thereby making it one of the largest producing companies in Venezuela.

In the light of history the deal by which Standard of Jersey acquired Standard of Indiana's foreign properties is considered a sensational bargain. Certainly it was Jersey's great good fortune to have obtained the Lago bonanza in Venezuela. But the Standard of Indiana deal also rendered irrevocable Jersey's decision to stick it out in Mexico during a most difficult period—with results which later proved invaluable to it in policy matters in Venezuela. Jersey literally poured money into Mexico to protect its investment and became, by all odds, the most important operating American oil company in that country. It raised the level of the industry's social and labor relations while it fought the battle against expropriation practically singlehandedly. Jersey tried hard and learned much from the politico-social conflict in Mexico and carried many valuable lessons to Venezuela.

As to operations in Venezuela, for years Jersey's Creole ranked first among the oil-producing companies of the world. Its 1953 daily average production of 794,000 barrels was exceeded only by Arabian American, whose Saudi Arabian production averaged 825,000 barrels daily. Creole's annual report for 1953 showed a net income of 229 million dollars and total current assets of 360 million dollars.

The Creole figures, of course, mirror Venezuela's rise as an oil-producing country. The nation's first recorded production—an average of 600 barrels daily—came in 1917. At that time the United States, first ranking producer, was averaging 919,000 barrels; Russia, in second place, 173,000 barrels; and Mexico, third, 152,000 barrels. While Venezuela's production remained insignificant and Russia's nose-dived because of the Soviet revolution, in 1921 Mexico registered its all-time high of 508,000 barrels, almost half of the United States' 1,294,000 barrels, and sat firmly in second place. By 1928—within the short space of seven years—Mexico dropped to 137,000 barrels daily, and Venezuela rose to 289,000 barrels, thus capturing second place for the first time. The United States still led with 2,469,000 barrels, while Russia showed 240,000 barrels. But not until 1943 did Venezuela securely win second place over Russia. The following comparative figures may be found interesting:

DAILY AVERAGE CRUDE OIL PRODUCTION

(In thousands of barrels)

Year	United States	Vene-zuela	Russia	Iran	Saudi Arabia
1939	3,466	563	602	203	11
1946	4,751	1,064	457	401	164
1950	5,407	1,498	752	664	547
1952	6,262	1,805	935	28	825
1953 *	6,455	1,745	1,040	28	845

* Preliminary.

In 1954 authorities estimated that—after interim production of over 7 billion barrels—Venezuela possessed proved oil reserves of about 10 billion barrels and rated the Lake Maracaibo Basin, or Bolivar Coastal Area in western Venezuela, as one of the richest oil deposits in the world. In retrospect, therefore, Sir Edward Mackay Edgar's prophecies have come true. Venezuela had the oil. But no concurrent decline in United States' output accompanied Venezuela's rise. In other words, as Venezuela has become a "have nation," the United States has not become a "have not." Moreover, in 1954, American interests accounted for over 75 per cent of Venezuela's production.

In Venezuela, the world's second largest producing country, oil operations began and remain on a private-enterprise basis. The welcome mat still is out. Yet occasionally there have been signs indicating that there, too, time might run out for private enterprise, in favor of nationalization. No one can say, however, that Venezuela's petroleum laws which permitted and welcomed foreign private capital have not justified their original and continuous objectives: to determine the existence of and to develop the country's oil resources.

Attaining such success has been no painless achievement, nor has profitable petroleum development brought an end to the problems faced by either Venezuela or the foreign oil companies operating there. Recognizing the adverse pressures already overcome and in store in the future as well as existent problems due to an unbalanced oil economy, Venezuela's *great experiment* becomes the more impressive.

PART TWO

EVOLUTION OF THE "50-50"

Chapter 7

VENEZUELA STARTS IT

With increasing frequency Venezuela is cited as the outstanding example of an underdeveloped country attaining development and material advancement through its policy of encouraging foreign investment. Often a rose-colored picture is painted of a government-industry partnership in petroleum development as the key to the nation's well-being. This conception, of course, is based on Venezuela's 50-50 profit-sharing law—a requirement that under certain conditions oil companies' profits must not be more than the government's "take."

Venezuela's 50-50 clause has spread, and may become universal. With modifications, the principle of 50-50 sharing has been written into the concessions and laws of Saudi Arabia, Iraq, Kuwait, Peru, Turkey. Incidentally, it has been said that its adoption might have saved Iran from its costly experience in petroleum nationalization. The basic principle involved—ostensibly of 50-50 sharing—has had and in all probability will continue to have profound implications upon oil development in the Free World. This being the case it might be well to examine the "50-50." How did it come about? What is meant by 50-50 profit sharing?

The processes that brought about the "50-50" were entirely evolutionary. The "great experiment," if you will, that is Venezuela has two prongs, one economic, the other social—more specifically, the petroleum laws and the labor laws. And, in chronological order, perhaps the latter branch should be considered first.

Until his death in December, 1935, Gómez had exercised dictatorial control for 27 years. As a result of his policies, certain basic conditions affecting the social and economic life of the entire country prevailed. He objected to the education of his countrymen. Eighty per cent of

71

the population was illiterate. Most of the few schools in existence were in the cities, whereas the majority of the oil fields were buried in the remote interior often in areas where malaria, dysentery and smallpox were endemic. Throughout the country sanitation facilities were extremely low, if, outside the cities, they existed at all. Venezuela's mortality rate was deplorably high. Generally, the masses were underprivileged, and their development was retarded.

The population was agricultural. Except for the Federal District containing Caracas, the capital, little industrial activity prevailed until the start of the petroleum industry in the early 1920's. Wages were barely enough to exist on. Few workers had skills beyond those related to simple construction or fishing. And as he had quashed opposition political parties, so Gómez suppressed all labor organizations. Even the most elementary social legislation received little attention until the passage of the 1928 Labor Law which dealt almost entirely with industrial accidents, and even then unconcern for proper enforcement characterized the law. Such was the Venezuela that the United States' oil companies first saw upon entering the country.

At first, the internal policies of foreign companies naturally reflected the basic conditions and the government policies. The last thing a foreign oil company wanted to do was to risk any action that might run counter to the prevailing attitude of the government. Since the nationals lacked industrial experience, only unskilled workers were available, and those were illiterate. To carry on necessary operations, large numbers of North American workers of all categories had to be imported. The use of nationals involved a tremendous training problem, but the companies began programs, starting with such simple lessons as how to use a wrench or how to drive a truck. They gave little attention to industrial relations, however, or, for that matter, to public relations. The concern of the oil men was to maintain good relations with the government. As an oil man expressed the situation, "It is apparent that during the period up to 1935, when Gómez died, an extremely poor foundation was laid for industrial and public relations."

Long before Gómez's death, however, foreign oil companies operating in Venezuela had built and were managing various permanent camps as the communities, established by the companies near major oil fields, came to be called. When commercial oil first was found in western Venezuela, the companies brought in North Americans, built houses, provided food and other necessities of life for them and thus gave birth to the "oil camps." National workers they recruited from fishing villages, such as Cabimas and Lagunillas on the eastern bank of the lake, or from Maracaibo, second largest city, on the opposite side.

In the early days of the Venezuelan oil industry—even where the operation was not far from small towns as was the case in the Lake Maracaibo development—persuading nationals to move into an oil camp was not easy. The people preferred their own villages, their own way of living. Though the move meant leaving a one- or two-room shack without lighting or plumbing and swarming with people and domestic animals for comparatively pleasant quarters with modern conveniences, the nationals had to be "sold." The village was their community. Its ways had been their ways for generations. Gradually, the change was made, however, and as the industry and camps grew, the companies provided not only "bachelor" quarters but houses for married couples.

As with the bachelors, married employees often resisted moving. Camp life involved not only environmental change but also certain restrictions and obligations. Families acquired definite responsibilities as to personal, household and community cleanliness. No chickens or pigs in the house—not even in the yard! The pioneer families in the oil camps constantly fought this battle of change within themselves and had the battle brought home to them by company officials charged with creating a physically healthy, strong and steady labor force to work in—and to learn—the oil business.

Except for its coastal towns, eastern Venezuela was either an un-inhabited jungle or an equally deserted *llanos*, or plains country, tree-less, roadless and flat to all horizons. The approach to the Quiriquire field, the first in eastern Venezuela, was by way of the Gulf of Paria and up the San Juan River by motorboat and barge. When in 1927 Gulf Oil sent geologists into the *llanos* country in the northern part of the State of Anzoategui, the only ingress was by a slow 1,000-mile river-boat route up the Orinoco to Soledad; yet actually the Oficina field was only 150 miles from the Caribbean coast. Not until a road—along with a pipeline—was built from Oficina to Puerto la Cruz was this field accessible except by the Orinoco River or by air.

Gradually, company permanent camps took on the aspect of sizable self-contained towns. The permanent camps had modern utilities, hospitals and schools. Companies such as Standard of Jersey, Shell and Mene Grande (Gulf) were applying what they had learned in Mexico to good advantage. By 1935 certain of these camps, though far from being what they are today, were introducing a new way of life to some 15,000 Venezuelan petroleum workers and their families.

Today some of the older camps—the oldest ones are at Cabimas and La Salina on the eastern lake shore in western Venezuela—provide an interesting study in contrast with the newer ones, such as Creole's Caripito and Mene Grande's San Tome in eastern Venezuela. Compared with the modern housing projects complete with landscaping, they resemble our suburban developments of the twenties somewhat showing their age. In the older settlements, the labor camps are not so neat. They have gone a little backward, and sometimes the prohibited pigs root and grunt in the yards. The workers are older, many of them second-generation oil employees, for Creole first built up its skilled and semiskilled labor supply along Lake Maracaibo and drew heavily on this source when it began expanding its eastern Venezuelan operations.

Inevitably, whenever new fields were being developed, native towns mushroomed close to company camps—and still do. As often as not they were "squatter" communities on company concessions, though sometimes nearby villages which formerly had held a few hundred persons suddenly expanded to many thousands. Often the villagers' water supply came to them only through the bounty of the oil companies. Sanitary systems were lacking in the towns, but they had their stores, their liquor and their pitiful honky-tonks. These settlements were the bane and the progressive migraine of the oil companies from the standpoint of keeping company workers on the job and out of trouble. Moreover, because the government seemed powerless to do much about them, they often became the responsibilities of the oil companies. Indeed, the local authorities and the people of these towns soon took it for granted that the companies would help them, and before the companies quite realized it, they were drilling water wells and supplying water, helping out with lighting systems and caring for the sick not just in their permanent camps, but in the villages as well.

Some of these towns grew to considerable proportions. El Tigre—

which appeared near Mene Grande's Campo San Tome—for instance, soon had a population many times that of the camp from which Mene Grande used to run its entire operations in eastern Venezuela. El Tigre planted itself on Mene Grande's concession and has grown to be eastern Venezuela's second largest city. At one time, in a valiant effort to clean up El Tigre, Mene Grande laid out an entire new modern townsite and, with government help, tried to persuade the people to move into it. One can still see the asphalt streets, but not a single house ever was built along them. The government-company effort was abortive. The people were satisfied with El Tigre—then a squalid, tough, frontier community.

Similarly, when Lagunillas—an early oil-boom town partly built on piling at the side of Lake Maracaibo—burned down, the government laid out Ciudad Ojeda, a new village. Standing a short distance back from the lake, the modern town was complete with houses, a school and a church, but the people would not move into it. A new kind of ghost town—not deserted, because never occupied—Ciudad Ojeda stood for years while Lagunillas rebuilt itself in its old frontier image over the charred remains of the former town.

As a final example, in 1930 Caripito was a little fishing and farming community of about 80 persons lying in the tropical jungles on the banks of the Río San Juan in eastern Venezuela. When Creole began to build its Caripito camp close by, the town grew three times faster than the camp. Creole cooperated in the life of the village by furnishing water fountains, fire protection and dump trucks for collecting refuse. Though the company refurbished an obsolete electric lighting plant, only a few of the shacks were electrically lighted, most of the people preferring kerosene lamps or candles. Creole also provided a clinic and maternity hospital.

The oil companies in Venezuela, then, constantly found themselves in an increasingly paternalistic situation. It was thrust upon them, first, by their own labor needs and, second, by the inability of local governments in those early days to care for the staggering number of camp followers and their towns.

Meantime, the industry boomed. By the time of Gómez's death in 1935, Venezuela's oil revenues alone aggregated more than its entire expenditures in 1908. As a corollary to the welcoming hand that the dictator extended to foreign investors, he saw that the government paid its external debt. But Gómez did not pass on to his poverty-stricken people the profits or benefits from petroleum. Deadened by a background of over a century of oppression, civil strife, graft and peonage, the masses accepted their lot. Those who resisted or objected, Gómez promptly jailed. But before the dictator breathed his last, social unrest stirred the people. Labor ranks became sources of seething agitation. Throughout the country outbreaks began with Gómez's death. The world was changing.

When General Eleazar López Contreras, Minister of War under Gómez, took over as President in April, 1936, the Venezuelan people achieved their first taste of freedom since Bolivar. Their liberation was of a new type and not wholly political. They demanded social reforms, and they got them. To eliminate the possibility of another dictatorship, the Presidential term was reduced from seven to five years without the right of immediate succession. López Contreras also announced a program of public-utility improvements, expansion of school facilities and improvement of public health and sanitation. Gómez had shackled labor. But his successor endeavored to quiet the workers and to anticipate threatened future outbreaks with the reform Labor Law of 1936. While sponsoring his enlightened labor program, the President nevertheless kept a firm hand on the government at all times by certain restraints on opposition political parties, on press reform and on the right of free assembly.

Even by today's standards the Labor Law of 1936 was a liberal document. It borrowed from, and went further than, Mexico's labor legislation. But, of particular note, the oil-company policies in hiring, housing and caring for their workers and their families—already achieving good results—were a decided factor in the development of that country's labor legislation and have continued to be. International labor agencies credit the program as being among the most advanced social legislation in the world, and certainly at the time of its passage the 1936 law was far in advance of the commercial and industrial development and social thinking of most Venezuelans. Placing full responsibility for administration under the Ministry of Labor, the law covered every phase of work relationship, including wages, hours, working conditions, employment of women and minors, industrial accidents, obligatory social insurance, labor organizations, governmental agencies for administering the law and methods of handling labor disputes. Among its more advanced provisions were requirements to build modern sanitary housing for company workers in permanent field camps, to furnish primary education for workers' children, to grant scholarships to employees and members of workers' families and to establish complete company medical care for workers. The law also provided for the payment of service indemnities upon the termination of employment without cause on the part of the workers, for annual vacations and for employee participation on an annual basis in the company's profits. An extremely modern and complete body of labor legislation!

The law included many provisions which in other countries usually are subject to extensive collective bargaining and covered by collective contracts. From the workers' viewpoint, therefore, no need existed for collective organizations to secure benefits, already guaranteed by law. The organizational setup of the Labor Ministry furnished a sound framework for administration and enforcement. Under numerous labor inspectors, regional offices were subdivided into district offices under labor commissioners. Separate labor courts handled mediation, arbitration and judicial review.

Though the law provided for the formation of syndicates or unions by employees and employers, it subjected syndicates to definite obligations and controls. To become legally established, they were required to submit copies of their articles of incorporation and bylaws to the appropriate labor authorities for review and approval. Every six months syndicate directors were obliged to present to their members a complete and detailed accounting of income and disbursements and to send a copy to the labor authority concerned. In addition, the syndicates had to furnish any additional information requested by government labor authorities and, semiannually, to submit complete listings of their memberships.

In the light of subsequent developments, a provision in the law to keep syndicates out of politics—and politics out of syndicates—is of outstanding interest. Whether formed by employees or employers, syndicates were prohibited from federation with any political parties, national or foreign.

Worker syndicates, which could be industrial or professional, received the right to represent their members before the labor officials and in collective-bargaining conflicts, especially in conciliation and arbitration procedures. Upon attaining 75 per cent of the total labor force as members, the syndicate could make collective contracts with employers.

Venezuela's labor law came during a period of labor strife and reform in the United States, and naturally the policies of American oil companies in meeting domestic labor reforms were reflected in their Venezuelan policies. Unionization—whether open or *sub rosa*—already had occurred in every Venezuelan oil camp. Indeed, labor agitators concentrated on the oil industry, since it was the nation's largest employer and the payer of the highest wages. Since no syndicate had attained the necessary 75 per cent membership, however, the new labor law required no company to recognize or deal directly with any union, and none did. But, because the law authorized the unions to represent worker members in presenting cases before labor authorities, the companies had no alternative but to deal indirectly with unions.

The Labor Law Regulations of 1938 together with judicial interpretations arising from labor cases contributed to a clarification of the legal obligations imposed by the law. By experience, labor authorities became more proficient in administering the law. And the companies found that they had to give more attention to industrial relations. Until this time, industrial relations largely had been confined to interpreting the law and building up a basis of standard practice for compliance. Now, in western Venezuela—where the three largest oil companies, Shell, Creole and Mene Grande—carried on their main operations—one company had to submit to what it considered onerous terms simply because of syndicate pressure, and the unions used this victory gained as a lever on all companies. Generally speaking, however, industrial relations were not a pressing problem. Most complaints against the companies were for failure to comply with the labor law.

The major companies met the requirements of the Labor Law of 1936 to the full—except perhaps for housing. They lived up to all terms involving wages, pensions, vacations and *utilidades*—the annual employee bonus based on company profits. Already they had established schools for workers' children and hospitals or clinics for the complete care of employees and their families. No longer was the Venezuelan merely a laborer. In the classroom and in the field he was obtaining the skills necessary to such employment as machinist or driller's assistant and even was taking over some jobs hitherto held only by North Americans. In a word, he was learning the oil business. The companies also were giving scholarships so that nationals could take over such technical jobs as petroleum engineer and geologist. One or two companies consistently exceeded the requirements of the liberal Labor Law of 1936.

Since in the United States Standard of New Jersey had pioneered in promoting industrial relations, it is not surprising that Creole, its Venezuelan subsidiary, reflected Jersey's policies. To the extent that cooperative relations with the other companies would permit and in recognition of certain basic worker needs, Creole consistently adopted various policies which provided for more liberal conditions than required by the labor law. The company, for instance, extended medical service without cost to workers' families. It established a thrift plan providing for joint company-employee contributions. On a scale beyond the law's terms, it made primary education available to workers' children and adults. And voluntarily the company established in its permanent camps such community facilities as commissaries, markets, clubs, sports fields and churches.

These outlays, of course, were expensive. Only extremely profitable enterprises could afford them. And as oil emerged as Venezuela's primary—almost its sole—industry, a highly paid, highly company-subsidized labor group came into being. The rise of living standards among national oil workers notwithstanding—and perhaps at least partially because of it—the oil companies became targets of radical labor and political agitators, as did the López Contreras government which had sponsored the liberal Labor Law of 1936.

However, during this period the seeds of a kind of government-industry partnership had taken root. But the growth and very survival of the plant was to be sorely threatened on both political and labor fronts.

Chapter 8

SHADES OF MEXICO!

To determine the political motives behind the sudden shifts of power that have occurred in Venezuela since 1944 is outside the scope of this book. We are concerned only with stating facts and analyzing consequences as they have affected that nation's oil development and as that development relates to the Free World. Shortly before the war and again since the war Venezuela has followed the pattern of many Latin-American countries—the pattern of political unpredictability, if not instability. This incontrovertible fact cannot help but be a factor weighed by foreign investors. On the other hand—and vitally important after the nation's recent political upheavals—Venezuela has held the line against petroleum nationalization which is at once the *bête noir* of the oil men and the black shroud draping petroleum development in many countries today. Often mistaken for the banner of independence, nationalization spreads or hangs threateningly over certain underdeveloped nations which are striving for the very goals that a vigorous, free enterprise handling of their petroleum resources would go a long way toward attaining. And Communism, parading under false colors, always is ready and willing to drape the last folds of the shroud and act as pallbearer for the victim.

Even during Gómez's rule petroleum laws underwent significant modification. But unchanged to this day are the basic principles that the government owns the subsoil, that the government does not operate oil properties, that the government grants concessions to private individuals or companies and receives its revenue from the oil developed through royalties and taxes.

Though Gómez's first petroleum law was passed in 1920 (see Chapter 6, page 63), the first really workable petroleum code was enacted in 1922. This provided that exploration concessions could be granted up to a maximum of 10,000 hectares (approximately 25,000 acres) and that at the end of three years the concessionaire had the right to select exploitation parcels up to one-half of that area. The area not selected for development reverted to the country's national reserves which, in large part, later were acquired under concessions by the companies. The exploitation concessions had a life of 40 years, and the exploitation tax, known as royalty, was 10 per cent of the market value of the oil in the Venezuelan port of embarkation. Concessions situated more than 100 miles from the sea and those covered by water, as was the case in Lake Maracaibo, paid a reduced exploitation tax of only 7½ per cent because of greater development costs. In 1925, 1928, 1935 and 1936 the nation enacted further petroleum legislation which slightly modified the principal provisions of the 1922 law and continued to encourage Venezuela's thriving oil progress, for they fully protected foreign interests and gave the oil men the flexibility they needed to develop the properties.

After López Contreras became President in 1936, his reforms included a new petroleum law by which the government would get a higher participation in oil profits. Enacted in 1938, the new legislation provided that the exploitation tax be increased to 15 per cent when concessions covered government lands and 16 per cent when they covered privately owned or municipal lands. The law also contained a number of conditions which the oil people found onerous. A requirement for continuous drilling and development, for example, practically stopped progress on new lands, with the result that under this law the companies took out no new concessions.

Though López Contreras' constitution prohibited the President from succeeding himself, it did not call for popular elections. In order to continue his rule after his term ended, López Contreras handpicked his Secretary of War, General Isaías Medina Angarita, who became President in 1941 in the face of violent denunciation by the major opposition parties which were of leftist and Communist stripe—namely, Acción Democrática (AD) and Unión Popular Venezuelano (UP). But the election results did not still the opposing parties who cried that the foreign oil companies were making excessive profits and were mulcting the Venezuelan government and people. Immediately Medina announced his dissatisfaction with the government's participation in the profits of the oil industry and initiated a drawn-out series of negotiations with the companies previous to submitting legislation to Congress.

As a result of the economic dislocation caused by the war—and particularly following the entrance of the United States into the conflict in December, 1941—the Venezuelan government faced various major economic and political problems directly affecting the daily life of all its people. In spite of efforts at price regulation, the cost of living gradually increased. The oil companies and Venezuelan industry generally recognized the need to increase wages because of higher living costs, but dared not do so, for unannounced government policy strove to stabilize wage levels to avoid inflation from this source. In June, 1942, a war measure suspended constitutional guarantees and gave the government virtual dictatorial control of the country's economic life. Then, seeking popular support, the administration launched a period characterized by a more liberal government attitude toward labor. Medina also permitted more press freedom and removed some of the restraints on opposition political parties.

As submitted to Congress, in 1943 the new petroleum act increased the exploitation tax to 16⅔ per cent and provided that the companies could convert all concessions obtained under prior laws to new ones good for 40 years; this substantially increased the life of the contracts. In presenting the act, the government exhibited calculations tending to show that the exploitation tax, or royalty, of 16⅔ per cent, together with other taxes imposed, would give Venezuela a participation equal to the net profits of the industry.

This was the initiation to the world of the 50-50 profit-sharing principle.

The act was bitterly opposed by Romulo Betancourt, teacher-socialist, and Perez Alfonso, brilliant, young lawyer delegate—both Acción Democrática leaders—who declared that, while under *existing* price and cost conditions the government *might* get its 50 per cent, a fixed royalty would not bring about the same desideratum under different price and cost conditions and in times of extraordinary profits. Nevertheless, the Petroleum Law of 1943 was passed.

In addition to the 16⅔ per cent royalty, the legislation imposed excise taxes on refined products at the rate of 50 per cent of the import duty on imported products and a tax of 2½ per cent on tariff charged to third parties for transportation. Then there was an income tax on a graduate scale ranging up to 27 per cent of profits. In sum the 1943 law and income tax represented an increase of 70 per cent in revenue from the oil industry, and at that time oil men considered that a maximum readjustment of profit division had been made.[1]

Thus, a joint product of protracted government-industry negotiation—eventually to become known as the 50-50 law—appeared for what authorities believe to be the first time. Here was introduced a novel pattern, a new principle which, in conjunction with labor legislation, was evolving from the oil men's experiences in Mexico, from their appreciation of changing times and of the social responsibilities thrust upon them by the unique character of their enterprise in underdeveloped foreign countries. Though fully recognized as a law of considerable significance to Venezuela, this petroleum legislation still had to undergo further development before becoming a true 50-50 government-industry profit sharing.

Until this time the Communist party had been outlawed in Venezuela. Now, in pursuance of his liberal policy, Medina relented, and in May, 1945, a constitutional amendment was passed legalizing the party. Thenceforth, though prohibited from doing so by law, the syndicates entered increasingly into political activities, affiliated themselves with AD and UP, the two major opposition parties, and, instead of functioning as bona fide labor organizations, became political labor instruments devoting their major activities to political objectives. The government made one weak attempt to discipline the syndicates of Unión Popular by dissolving them for their adoption of a political resolution at the March, 1944, National Worker Congress in Caracas, but they subsequently were reestablished and legalized.

Newspaper columns were full of syndicate activities, and it soon became apparent that, by using the oil-worker syndicates as nuclei, outside influences were attempting to form a single national federal organization. Unión Popular leaders were in periodic contact with Communistic labor leaders in Mexico and other South American countries, and in December, 1944, at Cali, Colombia, they attended the Second Annual Convention of the Latin American Federation of Labor, presided over by Lombardo Toledano.

---

[1] Ruth Shelden, Venezuelan Oil Policy May Affect World Situation, *World Petroleum*, July, 1946, p. 36.

Shades of Mexico! Would Venezuela stage a repeat performance? How successful would the Communist syndicates be in Venezuela? Their activities followed the familiar Communist pattern employed in all Latin-American countries. But the convention's attempts to form a central federation foundered on the rocks of internal dissension.

Meantime, the leftist AD's and the Communist UP's agitation for wage increases gathered steam. Since the government was not in favor of wage adjustments to meet the increased cost of living, in May, 1944, Creole, Shell and Mene Grande adopted a plan of subsidizing commissaries and selling basic necessities to workers at March, 1940, price levels, a program from which employees derived substantial benefit. Nevertheless, with prices mounting, the syndicates brought such strong pressure to bear that in November, 1944, the government suddenly formulated a decree granting a Bs 2-per-day, or 60-cent-per-day, wage hike for a one-year period to oil workers earning less than Bs 600 per month. Though the companies voluntarily extended this increase to all workers earning less than Bs 1,000 per month, the syndicates got the credit, and the companies' prior action in subsidizing the commissaries was given none.

With constitutional guarantees suspended, the government departed from the normal procedures provided by the labor law. Often it issued decrees to settle labor disputes. Frequently syndicates bypassed local authorities and dealt directly with the Labor Minister, who, in turn, negotiated directly with the top management of the companies on an increasingly political basis. Failing to adopt firm policies or principles on basic labor problems, the government consistently made expedient decisions based on immediate political needs. In 1944, Congress made various changes in the labor law which were to become effective in May, 1945. The various liberalizations included enlarging the scope of syndicate activities and granting job protection to members of syndicates' boards of directors.

In June, 1945—as a result of political labor agitation originally instituted by Acción Democrática, with the later support of Unión Popular—a serious labor situation involving Creole, Shell and Mene Grande erupted in the Maracaibo district. Acting as mediator, the Labor Minister wrote an agreement by which the companies recognized the syndicate organizations as the representatives of their members—the first occasion when companies formally recognized the oil-workers' syndicates. Since the labor law reforms of May, 1945, required such recognition if 75 per cent of the groups were unionized, the step was inevitable. But a request for the deduction of syndicate dues upon individual authorization of the worker members was refused. Believing that similar agitation by syndicates in other sections of the country was only a matter of time, Creole took the initiative by granting recognition to all the local oil syndicates in its area of operations. Other companies subscribing to the Maracaibo agreement resisted for a time, but soon extended similar recognition *because* of local syndicate agitation. Eventually, newcomer companies followed suit.

Syndicate activities increased in the summer and early fall of 1945. They formulated and widely publicized an elaborate bill of complaint, the apparent purpose of which was to build membership on the basis of potential benefits to be secured through syndicate efforts—a political device to disturb the over-all labor situation and bring pressure on the government.

The Labor Minister formally proposed to company representatives a six-month extension of the Bs 2-per-day wage increase with the understanding that the syndicates would raise no new issues during the period. The alternative? A government decree containing the same provisions! After securing company acceptance the official, using the same device, obtained the agreement of the labor syndicates. The government claimed that the step was an effort to assure labor stability through and after the pending Presidential election.

The elections did not materialize. Instead, came the revolution of October 16, 1945. And when the young army officers—who instigated the revolt—called in the AD leaders to form a Revolutionary Junta and take over the civil administration, oil men generally hoped for the best. They were willing to attribute the highly vocal condemnation of the Petroleum Law of 1943 by Romulo Betancourt, AD leader—now chosen President of the Provisional Government—to the extremism of an opposition party whose demands and criticisms would be tempered by the responsibilities of office. An important oil man in Venezuela, addressing his compatriots at the time, called the revolution "a violent manifestation of a current of evolution—in this case, evolution toward democracy," and advised acceptance of, and adjustment to, the trend. Having substantial obligations to labor groups for assistance in the coup, the Revolutionary Junta was as realistically prolabor as was AD historically. The hopes of the oil men seemed justified when, immediately upon assuming power, Betancourt gave assurances to the industry, telling it to operate normally and in close cooperation with the administration. Petroleum, of course, dominated the nation's economy, and the new government had a high stake in its continued prosperity.

But the oil men's confidence in the Revolutionary Junta had to survive a fearful test on December 31, 1945, when the government issued a decree levying an extraordinary income tax on all 1945 profits. Applying to everybody, it caught the oil companies in the 20 per cent bracket and made their share 30 million dollars of the 33 million dollars to be raised. As they say in Venezuela, this was *una ley con nombre y apellido* or, freely translated, "a decree with address and telephone number."

Pointing out that the present AD government—which then had been the opposition—had criticized the method of figuring government profit in the Petroleum Law of 1943, Betancourt declared that the 1944 and 1945 income figures showed the companies to be making far more profit than the government. Therefore, he stated, the government had designed the income-tax levy to produce a real 50-50 government-industry profit sharing. Perez Alfonso, now Minister of Development, carefully explained that the party's objection to the 1943 law had not been on the grounds that it was not a good law, but only that it was not good enough in respect to participation in profits. The 1945 tax, he claimed, provided only a necessary adjustment of values, and the government would prefer to see such a provision basically incorporated in the petroleum law. Though the oil companies did not campaign publicly against the tax decree, purely upon "moral" grounds they protested verbally to the government.[2]

At the time of the October revolution the labor syndicates were preparing an extensive list of demands on the oil companies. In November, 1945, Dr. Raul Leoni, the new Minister of Labor, formally presented to company representatives a proposal to extend the Bs 2-per-day wage increase for six months, with the understanding that the syndicates would drop all pending demands, including those concerned with wages, and would raise no new issues during the period of extension. This, he explained, was an effort to effect a period of

[2] *World Petroleum*, July, 1946, p. 36.

labor stability until the new government could establish itself. On December 8 both industry and labor representatives signed such an agreement to run until April 15, 1946, when the Revolutionary Junta promised a general election. Elections were not held in April, however, and the labor "truce" was extended to May 15. But the violently antigovernment Communists, in the meantime, had become bolder. Much of their noncollaborationist agitation after the October revolution was directed at stirring up labor trouble and strikes.

In January, 1946, the Junta issued a decree prohibiting strikes and lockouts and establishing a method of compulsory arbitration. Nevertheless, abortive or threatened strikes followed in the telephone, cotton-mill, clothing and transportation (bus) industries, as well as along the docks.

Fortuitously, on October 16, 1945—the day of the revolution—a party of about 30 Russians headed by Dr. Foma A. Trebin, Soviet Ambassador, arrived at Caracas. Never before had the Soviet Union had a diplomatic or consular representative in Venezuela, but six months previously, Russia had queried the government about exchanging ambassadors, and Venezuela had felt that it could not refuse, and the exchange was effected. During the war the center of Soviet propaganda activity in Latin America had shifted from Mexico City to Bogotá, Colombia, where Russia maintained a large diplomatic corps and from whence it sent agents into Venezuela and other countries to talk up the advantages of establishing diplomatic relations and to make the physical arrangements for new envoys. In Venezuela the agents stressed the Soviet's friendship and its genuine concern over the "imperialistic exploitation of oil." Dependence on United States' capital and petroleum techniques soon could be forgotten, they claimed, for Russia—with its oil commissariat—would show the Venezuelans how to nationalize their oil and take over the teaching of the needed technicians. When asked pointed questions as to where the necessary machinery would come from, the agents said that Russia could supply all Venezuela required from left-over American lend-lease materials.

By a curious coincidence, Dr. Trebin, the new Russian ambassador, turned out to be an oil expert—a former professor of petroleum geology at the University of Moscow, who also had held a high official position in the Soviet petroleum commissariat. Incidentally, the number of

Russians connected with the Caracas embassy at the time far exceeded that of any other embassy, including the one of the United States.

Venezuelans—much less foreign oil men—took little stock in Soviet promises of direct help to the oil industry, but they did not underestimate the effectiveness of Russia's direct methods of propaganda, for Venezuelan Communists, though numerically small, became increasingly vocal. They controlled or had access to at least three Caracas newspapers—two dailies and a weekly. Their leaders were Moscow-trained, fanatical and able. At the Inter-American Labor Congress held March 30, 1946, speakers stated that labor must fight for eventual government expropriation of the Venezuelan oil industry—that the time for expropriation "is not now although the start must be made right now."

Manuel Seone, vice-president of the Peruvian Senate and an Aprista Party (Socialist) leader—APRA was outlawed from Peru in 1948—stated in 1946 that Soviet Russia was inciting workers in Latin America to strike and thereby to delay the production of materials which would be needed in the United States in the event of another war. As delegate to the United Nations Social Welfare Committee, Seone described the series of recent strikes in Latin America as part of a "vast plot connected with Russia's desire for revolutionary domination." The Soviet, he said, sought to block off from the United States such Latin-American products as oil, copper, sugar and various industrial minerals. Pointing to the "greatly disproportionate numbers" of Soviet diplomatic personnel arriving in practically every Latin-American country, he stated that "the deduction is clear: Russia, having attained the initial aims of its revolution, is embarking now on a plan of imperialistic domination."

From the standpoint of the oil companies, the big question now was not so much what might be expected from the known leftist policies of the AD—which had come into power and had assumed the responsibilities of power—as to wonder how successfully the provisional government would be able to combat the extreme left. Would the new government be strong enough to put down, and keep down, the machinations of the ardent Communist minority?

Chapter 9

50-50 PROFIT SHARING IN THE LAW

We have seen that the concept of a 50-50 profit sharing in oil was forged in Venezuela against a background of (1) voluntary effort on the part of the oil companies to build a healthy and competent Venezuelan labor force—which is to say a national oil industry employing nationals; (2) social change; (3) political leverage; and (4) radical and Communist labor pressures. Only to the extent that one understands the background can one obtain a realistic picture of what is meant by the nation's 50-50 law—the law which has played, and in the future will play, a significant role in promoting oil progress in other underdeveloped countries. That background is complex.

We were in Caracas on May Day, 1946. Fearing Communist demonstrations, the government previously had prohibited all parades and gatherings. But, later, the Revolutionary Junta had retracted after a number of syndicates controlled by UP and Partido Comunista Venezuelano Unitario (PCVU) called for a general strike on May 1 as a protest against the government order. To take the edge off the strike the Junta had decreed the day a national holiday. Now it proceeded to join in the festivities. Headed by President Betancourt, for over an hour Junta officials watched battalion after battalion of labor syndicates march past the Plaza Bolivar with the paraders carrying placards calling for full satisfaction in all the demands that the new National Federation of Oil Syndicates recently had presented to the oil companies. At other parades and at many mass meetings held in the city speakers strongly attacked the government. In effect, not only did labor demonstrate on May 1, but it went on a one-day general strike at time and a half pay. Most offices were empty. Only five employees reported for work at the Avila Hotel. At Maracaibo the

89

bus drivers struck, and the Communist-controlled antigovernment Professional Syndicate of Bus Workers ordered a bus strike in Caracas for the following day. Would the government permit it? A test of strength on the issue might bring riot and bloodshed—even the government's downfall.

Twelve hours before the deadline, the Junta issued a decree forbidding the threatened strike, granting the Bs 2-per-day wage increase demanded, making arbitration compulsory on both sides and setting up a three-man mediation panel representing workers, companies and the government. The government backed up the decree with army reinforcements for police escorts for nonstriking bus drivers. No strike occurred. For several days armed soldiers rode each bus and patrolled every terminal. Service continued uninterrupted, and the expected bloodshed did not develop. Substantially, both the Caracas and the Maracaibo bus strikers won their demands, but the government had been sufficiently firm to weather the May Day crises.

A few days later, at Guanta, an eastern Venezuelan port, and still later at nearby Puerto la Cruz, a private oil-company water terminal, we awaited the results of a threatened strike, called by the Communist-controlled stevedores' union, which would affect all Venezuelan ports. Again the national guard moved in. Again a government decree prohibited the strike, granted wage increases and set up an arbitration board to consider other demands. Again the strike did not materialize.

Yet the labor situation remained critical everywhere, and in the oil camps it was of powder-keg variety. The showdown in the conflict between Communist labor and the new Revolutionary Junta was expected to occur in the oil industry in connection with certain postponed labor demands, soon coming up for discussion.

On May 15, 1946, the first general industry-labor contract negotiations opened in Caracas. Minister of Labor Raul Leoni presided at the meetings; Dr. Angel Brice, head of Creole's law department, acted as chairman of the industry group; and Luis Tovar, president of the newly formed and soon to be legalized National Federation of Petroleum Syndicates, headed the labor representatives. Discussion revolved around a set of demands, or *pliego de peticiones,* made by the federation. Since the existing 1938 law was one of the most liberal labor laws written until that time, further labor demands had to be extremely radical to be tarred with the Communist brush, but the *pliego* was characterized as clearly so by the oil people. Although Communist-controlled oil unions had not yet joined the federation, individually they backed the *pliego*, as did the Political Board of the Central Committee of the Venezuelan Communist Party.

Some demands in the *pliego* were considered reasonable, but the character and extent of others further would involve the companies in the paternalistic functions of government and family head. These, the companies contended, patently were impossible to fulfill. The oil men especially feared a clause providing that upon syndicate request the companies would be obliged to remove any official whose actions, in the syndicates' opinion, "did not guarantee the harmony which ought to exist between labor and management." Such a provision, in the judgment of the oil men, would be a surrender of management prerogatives to labor and, once the precedent had been set, probably would be only the first of many to come.

From the very nature of the petition, it was possible to conclude that the demands deliberately had been designed to bring on strife. Furthermore, the petition raised the ghost of Mexico where labor demands one on top of another not only had made economical operation impossible but had culminated, in 1938, in the expropriation of most of the foreign oil properties. Many observers saw the fine Mexican hand of Lombardo Toledano in the *pliego*, which followed the general line of the resolutions adopted at the CTLA convention at Cali, Colombia, where he had presided in December, 1944. Indeed the petition's resemblance to the Mexican labor demands of the 1930's could be pointed to not only as to intent but also as to actual phraseology. Some of the clauses followed the earlier demands so precisely that they even were worded in Mexican rather than in Venezuelan Spanish. Since Toledano's Moscow connections were no secret—the following year after returning from a visit to Moscow, his application for a United States visa was to be turned down—the oil companies entered negotiations with considerable anxiety. Chaotic strike conditions in the United States strengthened the Venezuelan syndicates' attitude and did not help the companies, nor did the knowledge that the prolabor AD government earnestly sought the workers' vote in the forthcoming elections when a Constituent Assembly and subsequently a President would be chosen by popular vote. Against such a backdrop little likelihood appeared that the government would, or could, exert a restraining influence on the oil workers.

In Venezuela, during this period, old-time oil men, who had seen Venezuelan families progress in their new way of life in the oil camps, often were poignantly—sometimes bitterly—disappointed to find that some workers were easy prey for radical and Communist agitators. "We've been father, mother, counselor, doctor, educator—everything to them," they would say. "We bring their children into the world, care for them and this is how they pay us back!" The tide of Communist propaganda swept the camps which were the battle lines. Probably the cause of the old-timers' frequent cries of anguished disillusionment lay more in the bewildering propaganda of national and world politics flooding in on the nationals than in any determined disloyalty. After centuries of suppression the Venezuelans were getting their first taste of education and freedom.

During the contract negotiations, nevertheless, the government did assume a definite position as mediator and brought such pressure to bear on both the companies and labor that they reached a compromise before the strike deadline. The agreement was signed in the office of Labor Minister Raul Leoni, and before the Chamber of Commerce President Betancourt dramatically announced the accord as the opening note of a long-scheduled speech—broadcast throughout Venezuela and Colombia—on Venezuelan economic problems. "By the wisdom and good will of the contracting parties, it has not been necessary to enter into one of those strikes which are disrupting the economies of the great industrial countries," he declared.

Fortunately, companies, labor and government never had permitted the negotiations to reach a deadlock and by adroit maneuvering had been able to find a sufficiently large area of agreement to avert a tie-up and to serve as a basis for a collective contract which would continue in effect to the end of 1947. Back in the United States the trade press hailed the attainment of this result as a remarkable accomplishment "in view of the peculiar national and international factors which complicate the Venezuelan situation . . . [involving] so much potential conflict and so many abnormal situations."

Actually, labor gained many of its demands, but the companies held the fort against encroachment on management.

The principal gains granted to the workers were permanent inclusion in their base pay of the Bs 2 (60 cents) daily wage increase given the previous year to meet the increased cost of living, daily wage increase of Bs 2 for all workers (their demand had been Bs 4, $1.20), salary increases of 3 to 15 per cent for employees, 56-hour pay for a 48-hour week, full pay for traveling time to and from work exceeding 15 minutes, sick pay, 15-day vacations with pay for all workers, workers for contractors or subcontractors of the companies to receive same pay and benefits as oil workers. Numerous other benefits were granted covering betterment of living conditions, savings funds, scholarships, industrial schools, life insurance, company commissaries and hospitals.

Estimates of the additional annual cost of the agreement to the companies varied from 12 million to 33 million dollars. The companies figured that the settlement represented a 35 to 50 per cent increase in wages for Venezuela's 25,000 oil laborers.

After the first collective labor agreement had been made and when the 50-50 profit relationship with government was becoming impressively evidenced, Ruth Shelden wrote in *World Petroleum:* "The international oil spotlight is focused sharply on Venezuela where precedent-setting events are taking place with repercussions that may be felt politically and industrially throughout the world. . . . The internal changes and the shifting of emphasis of the government approach to Venezuelan oil problems are of world interest in their possible influence on the oil thinking of other countries." [1]

These were prophetic words.

This first collective contract was an epochal event. It gave the new government a breathing spell—a chance, with labor peace, to stabilize itself for more than a year, though the immediate satisfaction over the signing was marred by a declaration of Luis Tovar, president of the oil workers' federation, "We have gained many million bolivares but the fight isn't over. We must obtain all the demands in our petition and take the petition as a battle program."

How valuable the respite, was attested by the success of AD when it went before the people in the general elections. In December, 1947, the elections, promised by the Junta two years before, finally took place—the first free elections in Venezuela's history. Rómulo Gallegos, noted author, teacher and philosopher, AD candidate, won hands down

[1] *World Petroleum,* July, 1946.

—872,000 to 262,000 for the Copei opposition, with several minor parties, including the Communists, polling a combined total of only about 50,000 votes. The free elections were hailed as a timely demonstration before the world of democratic institutions at work in Latin America. The results bespoke popular endorsement of AD's program for sweeping political, social and economic reforms.

Almost immediately the government tackled the matter of taking the final step in getting the 50-50 profit principle on the statute books. In January, 1948, at a conference attended by representatives of all the principal petroleum companies operating in Venezuela, Perez Alfonso, Minister of Development, and Dr. Jose Martorano B., chief of the Venezuelan Petroleum Bureau, served notice that in the future the government would insist on taking 50 per cent of declared petroleum profits and would make special assessments of such portions of this percentage as were not already being collected in taxes. In March, Martorano explained that—as the AD had foreseen—the Petroleum Law of 1943 did not accomplish an equal participation of the government and the companies in the profits of the oil industry—the principle which had been the basic reason for the reforms instituted by the 1943 law. Hence the Revolutionary Government had assessed the additional income tax at the end of 1945 and had passed another income-tax law the following year. Even these measures, however, did not adjust themselves to the "reality of the situation" and further revision of the income tax did not seem advisable. Beginning with June, 1947, therefore, the government had initiated a series of conferences with the two oil companies—known to be Creole and Shell— "whose share of the profits exceeded the 50-50 participation sought by the government, so that they would agree voluntarily to pay the balance required to equalize the nation's share in those profits." [2] To this proposition the companies agreed, and that same year the government worked out a special tax formula with all companies.

To clarify this, the final step in the evolutionary progression of the 50-50 law, perhaps a brief backtracking would be helpful. In Venezuela the 50-50 formula was *not* written into the 1943 Petroleum Law. But it was informally and privately advanced as a basis for that legislation's proposed adjustment of royalties and taxes—as a sort of "floor"— by Max Thornburg, A. A. Curtice and Herbert Hoover, Jr., the

[2] *The Oil and Gas Journal*, March 25, 1948, p. 96.

Venezuelan government's petroleum consultants, in negotiations with oil companies' representatives. However, at least a 50-50 split publicly was announced as the government's objective. In other words, the government, being under considerable pressure from the Acción Democrática, let it be indicated that a 50-50 split *was* a basic element of the law. Furthermore, in the Venezuelan Senate it was announced that, if the petroleum law did *not* work out so that the government would receive 50 per cent of the profit, there was always the income-tax law to invoke. The historic date of birth of 50-50 profit sharing written into the law must be, therefore, not 1943 but 1948 when the income-tax law was amended to make equal division mandatory.

On November 12, 1948, Venezuela amended its income-tax law to provide for an additional tax on oil companies—and others holding concessions for the development of national resources—when their net profits exceed the taxes already paid, provided that the companies have earned more than 15 per cent on their invested capital. The additional tax equals half the amount by which the taxpayers' net income exceeds the taxes paid. Drawn in a manner which affords some protection to the industry in times of low earnings, it also gives relief to those companies which have recently undertaken operations in Venezuela and have not yet recovered their invested capital. The whole plan was the product of close collaboration between the Venezuelan government and the oil industry.

The pertinent sections are contained in Chapter XI, Articles 31, 32, 33, 34 and 35 of the Venezuelan income-tax law of 1948 and regulations of the same law decreed in 1949. They read as follows:

Article 31.—In the cases of net income of taxpayers obtaining earnings derived from the [extractive] mining or hydrocarbon industry, including royalties and other participations of the same origin, if after the cedular and complementary tax have been deducted the remaining income exceeds the aggregate of the taxes caused by reason of the activities of the industry during the taxable year, such excess shall be subject to an additional tax of 50 per cent.

Paragraph One.—There will be exempt from this tax those taxpayers whose net income, after deducting the cedular and complementary tax, does not exceed 10 per cent of their patrimony.

Paragraph Two.—When the net income is greater than 10 per cent and does not exceed 15 per cent of the patrimony, this tax will apply only upon the half of the excess income over and above the aggregate of the taxes caused during the taxable year by reason of the activities of the industry.

To determine the patrimony, the average of its amount will be taken at the beginning and at the end of the taxable year.

The assets and liabilities of the concern held abroad will be included, when these are related with its operations in Venezuela.

Paragraph Three.—The National Executive is empowered to exonerate from payment of the additional tax in whole or in part, for a determined period of time, concerns having as their principal object the exploitation of the mining industry but whose business may not yet be fully developed, when in its judgment such a measure may result convenient for the interest of the national economy.

Article 32.—For the effects of the tax established in the preceding article, by net income shall be understood that which may appear in the balance sheet prepared according to the books and records of the concern, including non-taxable earnings and the normal and necessary undeductible disbursements, for the purpose of the cedular and complementary taxes, provided that these be related with and be applicable to operations in Venezuela. The deduction of reserves for normal and necessary future expenses will be permitted, but those should be included among the earnings when such be destined for other purposes.

Dividends received from Companies which may have paid the additional tax shall not be included in the net income; neither shall there be deducted from net income those income taxes which the taxpayer has to pay in other countries.

Article 33.—In the amount of the taxes which must be subtracted from the net income in order to obtain the taxable excess, there shall be included all those taxes caused during the fiscal period even though the same may have been capitalized, with the exception of exploration taxes and the initial exploitation tax.

Article 34.—When two or more taxpayers may be controlled by the same interests and one of them be subject to the additional tax, they shall be considered as a single taxpayer for the purposes of this tax.

The National Executive may exclude any one of such taxpayers, when such action may be considered sufficiently justified. A similar separation may be made with respect to earnings originating from uncontrolled concerns.

Those taxpayers considered as a single entity for payment of the additional tax must communicate to the Minister of the Treasury, prior to making the respective income declaration, the name of the entity against which must be liquidated the tax corresponding to the group.

Article 35.—When the beneficiaries of royalties and other participations are natural persons, there shall only be taken into account the net income originating from said royalties and participations and the proportional part of the cedular and complementary taxes which the taxpayer must pay. If said income does not exceed 10 per cent of the portion of the patrimony which produces it, calculated upon the basis of the unamortized cost of the investment, it shall be exempt from the additional tax. Should it be greater than 10 per cent, but does not exceed 15 per cent, there shall be subject to the additional tax only the half of the excess of the income over and above the proportional part of the cedular and complementary taxes.

The so-called "50-50 formula" assures that the government's share of the profits never will be less than that of the companies.

Since the passage of the 50-50 law in 1948, much water has gone over the political and labor dam in Venezuela. When, in 1948, the second collective-bargaining contract was under negotiation, a stronger, more assured government acted as umpire. Even so the situation in the oil camps became tense. Despite the efforts of the agitators, however, no serious conflicts resulted. As finally signed, the contract—to run three years—again granted oil workers pay raises and other benefits, but once more the syndicates were held at bay in their demands for certain management prerogatives. Estimates indicate that the 1946 and 1948 contracts combined gave employees wage and benefit gains of 86 per cent.[3]

On November 24, 1948, eleven months after Venezuela's epochal free election, and 5 years after the AD party had been advanced to power, the regime came to an abrupt end after a bloodless coup carried out by the same group of army officers which had brought it to power. Disapproving of the policies and of the increasing control exercised by AD, these officers formed a Military Junta, and quickly dissolved Congress. Betancourt, the former provisional President of the Junta, fled the country. After a brief arrest, President Gallegos followed him into exile. Other AD leaders and members either fled or were jailed.

In defense of the coup the new Junta stated that Gallegos had lost control of a situation which threatened to develop into a general strike or a civil war between the alleged Acción Democrática "armed militia" and the Army and also that Communists had infiltrated AD. The Junta abrogated the AD-sponsored 1947 constitution, with its provisions for universal suffrage.

As had been the case when the AD had been installed as the civil government in 1945, the Military Junta renewed assurances to the oil

[3] Creole Petroleum Corporation, *Fortune*, February, 1949, p. 178.

industry. Though, at the time of the coup, several abortive local strikes were current, and a tense situation prevailed in the oil camps, no general strike materialized. In March, 1949, however, scattered protest political strikes by militant oil workers were broken only by the Junta.

In February, 1951, at the expiration of the three-year contract the oil companies were unable to reach an agreement with unionized workers, and the matter was consequently settled by government decree. Later in the year, however, in concluding two contracts directly with marine personnel, the industry preserved the principle of direct bargaining with workers' representatives. As a result, no work stoppages occurred. In August, 1953, following expiration of the government's decree, a new collective contract was signed; also in September new marine workers' contracts were signed. All contracts gave substantial increases—the increased cost to Creole alone was estimated at $10,800,-000 per year. All contracts were for a period of three years.

On the basis of the collective contract now in force, the estimated average direct payments by Creole to wage employees in 1954 was $14.50 a day, compared with $6.09 in 1945, an increase of 138 per cent. Benefits and welfare plans represented $4.03 a day against $1.98, and supplementary contributions were $1.64 a day against $0.03. This meant that in 1954 the company was paying the average oil worker in wages and benefits at a daily rate of $20.17 compared with $8.10 in 1945.[4]

For two generations an oil industry has thrived in Venezuela. As it has grown, the labor force has grown. Under highly advanced social benefits—initiated by the foreign oil companies and written into law—oil workers have become the envy of the nation's other industrial workers. No longer do Venezuelans hesitate about living in oil-company camps. The physical and cultural value of the housing, schooling and medical care found in camp living is generally appreciated. Companies fell behind in providing housing because of shortage of materials. In such cases, housing allowance is paid, and is still preferred by many workers over camp living.

Moreover, their towns today gradually begin to reflect the benefits of distributed oil revenues and wages. No longer are the companies

[4] Appendix I, Table 5, Comparison Wages and Benefits Paid Venezuelan Oil Workers, 1945–1953.

called upon to perform the functions of local government in supplying utilities and sanitation to petroleum-area villages. Symptomatically, no longer is the government-built model village of Ciudad Ojeda on Lake Maracaibo a ghost town. Much larger than it was when immediately after the war it lay silent in a curious blend of architectural beauty and unearthly vacuity, Ciudad Ojeda today is a clean, populated city. Voluntarily, people moved into it from the slums of Lagunillas! The Venezuelan people are stirring themselves to better their daily living conditions.

With so much in Venezuela dependent on petroleum, inevitably oil is a political issue which, in one way or another, has figured in the nation's political upheavals. But the oil companies steer away from politics as far as possible. It is noteworthy that except for one newspaper quote—later denied—not a single exiled Acción Democrática leader blamed the oil companies when the party was removed from power in the 1948 coup. This alone is a measure of the length of the road traveled since the days of New York and Bermudez Asphalt. The fact is all the more remarkable when one recalls that, before having been lifted to power by the Army Junta in the revolution of October, 1945, these same leftist leaders charged the companies with "robbery" in profits and with shipping out oil in false bottoms to avoid paying duties. The invectives which they hurled against the petroleum companies, and their demands for restitution, all were highly reminiscent of the agitation in Mexico during the twenties and thirties.

During the three years that AD was in power, the government's oil revenues almost tripled. It was a period of tremendous consumption of oil products throughout the world, and the demand was reflected in Venezuela. Venezuelan companies doubled their labor force from 30,000 to 60,000, poured 600 million dollars into the country for capital expenditures and almost quadrupled their operating expenses.

After a transitional period during which the Army Junta ruled, on November 30, 1952, elections to choose members of the constituent assembly were held as a step toward returning the country to a constitutional form of government. Following a disputed count, the Junta-sponsored Independent Electoral Front (FEI) was declared victorious, and, on December 2, young Colonel Pérez Jiménez was selected provisional President and the Junta government dissolved. Subsequently, in 1953, Pérez Jiménez was elected President for a five-year term.

The present Pérez Jiménez government is said to be convinced that, were its outlawed political opposition, the AD, to return to power, it would destroy the oil industry through nationalization, though during its brief tenure it never made a move to do so, nor does anything in the record indicate that the party's exiled leaders advocate nationalization now. In this connection, however, Sydney Gruson, in a special despatch to *The New York Times* on the Venezuelan situation dated December 14, 1953, wrote from Mexico City:

"However, [Venezuelan] government spokesmen charge that the Communists have so thoroughly infiltrated Acción Democrática since 1948 that they would call the tune in the oil fields if Acción Democrática were to return to power. Although American observers in Venezuela do not agree with the government on the extent of Communist penetration of Acción Democrática, they believe that any government succeeding the present administration could justify itself only by 'going far left.' Conceivably, they believe, this could mean agitation for nationalization on the pattern established by Mexico in 1938."

At the present, however, oil men express themselves as not being unduly worried in regard to nationalization—or "creeping expropriation"—in Venezuela. They still can point to Venezuela as the model foreign operation—the nation where the 50-50 profit-sharing principle evolved, the country which is living proof of the mutual advantages of petroleum development to both nation and private enterprise.

Chapter 10

THE PRACTICE OF 50-50 IN VENEZUELA

What Doheny never quite learned in Mexico, Standard of Jersey did. At once the evidence and the result is Jersey's Creole. Doheny believed in rugged development practices. All Creole's operations are based on the progressive premise that the oil in the soil of Venezuela belongs to Venezuela and becomes valuable to that nation only as it is found, brought out of the ground and exchanged for money to give its people better food, housing, health and greater security—more reasons, in short, to enjoy working and living. And its credo is, "What is good for the country is good for the company." Jersey did not want a repetition of Mexico in Venezuela. A decade ago, speaking of internal improvements in connection with Venezuelan operations at an annual Standard of Jersey stockholders' meeting, Eugene Holman reasoned that in foreign operations plans must be made for the long rather than the short pull. Holman, then Jersey's new president—in 1954 he became chairman of the board—had been president of the original Creole after Jersey took it over from "Josh" Cosden.

"The inauguration of a new industry in any country is of benefit not only to the nationals of the country but to the government through increased revenue and to the foreign concern which is able to make a return on its capital investment which creates dividends for the shareholder," said Holman, "and it is sound business to aid in improving the health of the nationals of the country who because of undernourishment and tropical disease are often found incapable of doing more than the equivalent of a half-day's work. It also seems to be good business to train them for the many highly specialized jobs required by the petroleum industry.

101

"I personally feel that industry has certain obligations in the promoting of economic, social, and cultural welfare of various countries," the executive went on. "In the first place, transportation is a very important thing for Venezuela and we recognize basically that unless we have stable conditions in Venezuela, unless Venezuela as a country prospers, your company won't prosper, and we think that good transportation is one of the fundamental things necessary for any country in order to improve its national setup.

"The more good roads you have, the more asphalt you sell; the more automobiles you have, the more gasoline and lubricating oil you sell. So purely from an economic standpoint, we think that it is worthwhile.

"But perhaps a thing at the present time that influences us most strongly in advocating such a program is this, that the cost of living in Venezuela is very high, and it has been brought about, we think, largely because of the fact that they don't have satisfactory transportation to market the products that can be grown in the country.

"So we think a good transportation system all over the country would in turn lower the cost of living and would save the company a substantial amount of money in that respect.

"Public works that we have financed have been largely roads and hospitals. The same argument I used in selling asphalt applies in connection with public works. . . . We are required by law, of course, to build a certain number of hospitals. Even if we weren't, we would proceed with the program which we are following.

"I think that the various people who have been in Venezuela can show you the advantage from a purely dollars and cents standpoint of developing your workmen. . . . We know from the statistics we have compiled that a man today can do considerably more work than he could formerly, and we think that is largely due to the fact that we have helped take care of him physically.

"So we think our statistics prove pretty conclusively that hospitals are a good investment, even though we spend a substantial amount of money in hospitals."

When these words were spoken in open meeting on June 6, 1945, they still constituted strong medicine for American stockholders, and certainly they were a far cry from the romantic days of the New York and Bermudez Company.

Until a few years ago, when Middle Eastern Aramco snatched the title, Creole was the world's largest single oil-producing company and Jersey's most profitable foreign investment. Not always has Creole been popular with other companies in Venezuela, most of which have had to be satisfied with the "crumbs" left by Creole, Shell and Gulf. Accounting for an average of 45 per cent of Venezuela's production, Creole at once was on the hot seat with the government because of its great income and with the less fortunately placed oil companies which were less able to "yield" to labor and government demands. When physical and operational costs rise, naturally a less successful company still in its wildcat and development stage is far more affected than a going concern. The same is true, of course, when labor and social costs rise. As an integral part of the Venezuelan picture, the dilemma thus created cannot be ignored.

During the early forties, Creole was the first company to recognize the syndicates. At the time of the first collective contract negotiations, other companies were critical of Creole's tendency to grant the demands made upon the industry for wage increases and benefits. But today all agree that Creole stood firm in the negotiations when questions of yielding management's prerogatives arose.

One of the secrets of success in Venezuela is that Venezuelans themselves are getting a chance to run the oil industry. The petroleum law stipulates that 75 per cent of all employees and workers must be nationals. At the end of 1952—the latest available year—of the 46,000 people working in the entire Venezuelan oil industry, 91 per cent were Venezuelan. At the end of the following year, 94 per cent of Creole's 14,568 employees were nationals.

The statistics, however, tell but a part of the story. Nationals have largely replaced North Americans not only in numbers but also to a great extent in skilled and supervisory jobs. Creole was closely followed by Royal Dutch–Shell, its nearest rival in Venezuelan petroleum development, in turning over drilling and clerical jobs to nationals. By the mid-thirties Creole was operating a definite job-training program in every oil-field and office trade, including typing, stenography and accounting. By 1944 it could announce that all its drillers in proved areas were Venezuelans. Many of its top-rank drillers, its *caporales,* or foremen, as well as supervisors also are nationals. For years the company has provided scholarships for study in North American universities in such subjects as civil, petroleum and mechanical engineering, geology, chemistry and medicine. As a result it employs scores of Venezuelan geologists, petroleum engineers and other high-grade technicians. Two Venezuelans, Dr. Siro Vasquez, a graduate of Tulsa University, and Dr. Guillermo Zuloaga, a graduate of M.I.T., are members of Creole's board of directors. By law all Creole's 68 physicians are Venezuelans. Students who have received company scholarships continue to be an excellent source of new personnel. In 1954 this program called for 238 scholarships, 53 of which were for studies in the United States. Intensive efforts constantly are made to train and upgrade present company personnel on all levels.

Occurring in Venezuela, therefore, is a form of nationalization quite different from the customary meaning of the word—for Venezuela's nationalization is based on a policy of inclusion rather than exclusion. Countries tempted to nationalize their natural resources, such as petroleum, think in terms of excluding the foreign companies which have developed those resources. Sometimes, the attempt is made without considering the fact that the nation's own workers have not attained the know-how necessary to run a technical and complex industry. Other factors of vital importance also are overlooked. Oil development requires—as we have seen—not only know-how but also great sums of risk capital. Furthermore, in such prolific oil-producing countries as Venezuela and certain nations of the Middle East, petroleum development essentially is a part of a world industry and as such is subject to factors of availability of transportation and of product marketability under world competitive conditions.

In Venezuela we see foreign companies educating nationals in all the arts of the trade, including the technical and managerial, so that they can take over. But "taking over" in this sense does not mean that some day the nationals will throw the companies out of the country. Rather, the inclusion works both ways. The foreign companies—which are making their employment all-inclusive as regards nationals and which are equipped with outside and often world-wide facilities—would remain, but, at the same time, their activities in the nation would be run by nationals to the fullest possible extent.

Building up a truly national industry provides ever-increasing employment of home labor and strikes a popular response which appeals to the Venezuelans' personal and national pride. In these respects the progress of the oil industry in Venezuela is a pronounced success. Thus, Holman's views have proved sound. It has been good business to train nationals for the many highly specialized jobs required by the petroleum industry—more than that, it has proved good politics, a bulwark against expropriation.

Holman felt that it was sound business to aid in improving the health of nationals, many of whom often were incapable of doing more than the equivalent of a half-day's work because of undernourishment and tropical disease. For the benefit of their employees and families in permanent camps, Creole, Shell, Mene Grande and other companies maintain hospitals and clinics which also treat persons living in neighboring villages. In 1952 Creole alone reported having, in 14 locations throughout Venezuela, four hospitals, 17 dispensaries, 10 pharmacies and 15 laboratories—employing 68 doctors, 200 nurses, 24 pharmacists, 24 laboratory technicians and 197 miscellaneous medical workers. Hospital beds totaled 298, and admissions numbered 4,734 inpatients and 129,774 outpatients. Over the years, results have been so satisfactory that Venezuelans today can hold their own in turning out a reasonable day's work.

Providing housing and sanitary conditions in camps has contributed largely to improved health and well-being. The oil industry has built over 30,000 homes for workers and their families, and the gross investment is constantly mounting—from 180 million dollars by all companies in 1950 to 204 million dollars in 1952. Houses are modern and sanitary, with water, light, gas and sewer systems. Only a nominal rental charge is made. And physical, spiritual and mental well-being of workmen and their families is cultivated by such facilities as movie theaters, sports, churches and social clubs.

The foreign oil companies have brought real benefits to the Venezuelans—benefits easy to trace and record. Because working in the tropics necessitated caring for the health of North Americans and nationals alike, the oil camps pioneered in sanitation, preventive medicine and public-health work in Venezuela. Through the use of DDT in its camps, Creole, for example, reduced the number of hospitalized cases of malaria in one area alone from 400 to 77 in less than one year. Now the oil companies are cooperating with the government in the regular spraying of large areas adjacent to their camps.

Holman laid particular stress on the economic value of roads. For their own operations the oil companies have built over 1,240 miles of all-weather roads in Venezuela, and they are open to public traffic at all times. In recent years the government has undertaken the construction of a vast highway system. In 1953 highways and roads of all classes totaled approximately 5,500 miles, 4,738 miles of which were national highways under supervision of the Ministry of Public Works.

After Gómez, López Contreras put education into the law as a requirement. For years, before and after that, the companies undertook the job of educating their workers and families, but, under a law passed in 1948, the Ministry of Education now has complete control of company school curriculums as well as of the selection of teachers. In the oil camps the companies, however, still must build and maintain the schools and pay the teachers. The latest information on educational facilities provided by the oil industry as a whole shows that in 1950 the companies employed 496 teachers instructing a total of 12,622 pupils. In 1952 Creole's contribution to education included the provision and maintenance of 22 primary and two secondary schools with an average enrollment of 8,500 pupils taught by 265 teachers. As a result of evening classes for the workers and their wives, illiteracy among oil workers has been reduced greatly—in the case of Creole, the rate dropped from 82 to 12 per cent in less than 10 years.

While the emphasis is on employment and the training of nationals, this does not mean that the North American workers, dwindling both in numbers and in ratio, are less important than they were. In a way, the opposite is true today, for not only must they be technically qualified for their jobs, but also they must possess definite supervisory, teaching and mixing—or public-relations—qualifications, which are very much part of their jobs. North American employees are hired to supervise operations, to do specialized work for which qualified nationals are not available or to train and develop nationals in accordance with the over-all nationalization program.

Creole, for example, insists upon the careful indoctrination of overseas personnel working for Creole in Venezuela. To promote the social and economic development of Venezuela, just after World War II Creole set up a program to equip new employees with the fundamentals of the Spanish language; a background of the company's history, organization, policies and operations; a knowledge of the country's social customs, problems, history and legislation; and schooling in the necessary supervisory and teaching techniques. Thus trained, Creole employees have a reasonable chance of success when actually placed on the job.

Management of all companies today is handpicking the people whom it sends to foreign countries. Gone forever are the days when a boss who could get a hole down quickly through sheer toughness was considered desirable. Now, the man who gets the hole down—or any job done—is one who leads instead of one who drives. In the early 1920's, when the United States companies first went into Venezuela, an oil community simply sprang up built of the physical and human elements at hand. Now a previously planned, completely integrated company community is set up. Under the legal requisites and social challenge of Venezuelan oil operations, the young art of industrial relations is getting perhaps its most challenging try-outs. In Venezuela, the operating head of a company's divisional operations told us that his job, which fundamentally was to produce oil, actually was 85 per cent industrial relations—keeping both the nationals and the North Americans happy.

In the camps, one sees the efforts made in this direction, but one sees the problem, too. Technicians, skilled and white-collar workers, both Venezuelan and North American, live in staff houses and enjoy equal privileges as to club and recreational facilities. They are differentiated from the laborers who live in the labor camps, have their own recreational facilities and are purely Venezuelan. Because the language barrier is being broken down, the social problem, which once constituted perhaps the foreign companies' greatest vulnerability, is being overcome.

In 1952 Creole announced a new long-range plan which evidently the company believed would solve the camp problems resulting primarily from the paternalistic role thrust upon the oil companies. The company's objective in regard to worker housing, it was stated, was the development of modern communities in the company's operational areas rather than of camps limited to its own employees. In such communities, Creole hoped, the workers would become integrated in the activities of small municipality life—buying or renting homes, patronizing free-enterprise business establishments and services and utilizing the benefits of the town's schools and churches. As a starter in 1951 at Judibana, near the company's new Amuay refinery on the Paraguana Peninsula, the company built approximately 225 homes and offered them for sale to its employees on liberal terms. Early in 1953 the company reported that the project was progressing satisfactorily and was of much interest to the Venezuelan government. It stated that the construction and expansion of other camps at permanent locations were being planned so as to permit the future application of community development if the idea proved useful. Studies on housing and community development continued during 1953, and Venezuelan architects were developing new designs "to ensure that housing will be attractive, require minimum capital outlays, and fit into long-range plans of the company." Meantime, however, little progress has been made on government adoption of the Judibana community-development plan, which is still under review.

With government encouragement, possibly the days of the oil camp in Venezuela are numbered. If so, it would be another manifestation of evolutionary processes accompanying petroleum development which are in the nature of expanding its benefits.

Chapter 11

COOPERATION VS. NATIONALIZATION
IN THE MIDDLE EAST

As we have seen since 1948, when Venezuela's 50-50 regime began, much has happened both to confirm the early view that the "50-50 gospel" would spread and to fulfill the promise of harmony inherent in its principles. The adoption of the concept in the Middle East has had particularly profound repercussions.

Sometimes 50-50 sharing misleadingly is referred to as a government-industry "partnership." A partnership implies equal or joint voice in the operations. The 50-50 deal gives the government 50 per cent of the profits but no voice in the operation or management.

In 1943 the oil companies in Venezuela—including Creole—resisted the adjustment to, or the announcement of, a 50-50 split largely because they recognized its precedent-breaking significance. They feared that the new concept might disturb contracts or concessions existing elsewhere. Mainly, however, they shied away because of the simplicity of the 50-50 formula and thought it might be provocative of a 60-40 or 75-25 formula—with the oil companies on the short end. Avid, opportunistic or uninformed governments easily could pervert the principle—within limitations, admittedly sound—into an unsound practice. For such reasons, then—though they agreed to the principle in 1943—the major companies succeeded in keeping out of the petroleum law of that year the enunciation of 50-50. Not until 1948 was it written into Venezuelan law—the income-tax law.

As anticipated by the oil people, the expression in Venezuelan law of a government-industry 50-50 divison of oil profits was not overlooked by the governments of other major oil-producing countries nor, indeed, by those of small or potential producing nations. Since

109

it was implemented by Venezuela's 1948 income-tax law, the 50-50 principle has been adopted in the Middle Eastern states of Saudi Arabia (December, 1950), Kuwait (December, 1951), Iraq (February, 1952) and Turkey (March, 1954). Bahrain and Qatar also have made 50-50 agreements. Back in South America, Peru also adopted one in May, 1952.

Some oil men contend that the 50-50 split today, in actual fact, is probably closer to 60-40 in favor of the governments of Venezuela, Saudi Arabia, Iraq and Kuwait, the prolific producing countries. They base this conclusion on the fact that, prior to the establishment of the share-and-share-alike principle, the companies had carried the total cost load of exploration, development and related activities. At the time that they began to share on a 50-50 basis, the governments did not take into consideration either (1) that the companies had not recovered their investment to a point where an equal sharing of profits might seem equitable or (2) the time lag on investments and commitments extending into the future. These oil men think that a calculation on the basis of the governments' assuming a reasonable share of such costs and of continuing time-lag commitments would make today's 50-50 nearer 60-40.

The company assumes and actually makes the investments necessary to carry on the operation. Theoretically, it gets one-half of this depreciation back over a period of approximately 10 years, but during that period it receives no interest on its investment. Also, the company will not get its money back on any investments made toward the end of the concession unless amortization of this money is made on a basis where it will be completely amortized by the end of the concession. While an exact calculation of these factors is impossible, it is obvious that the companies in the properties now on a 50-50 basis will not recover 50 per cent of the profits over the life of the concession but more likely only 35 to 45 per cent of the total profits.

Moreover, these oilmen point out that sharing in profits on a 50-50 basis is practicable only in countries with prolific production. They base their opinion on the view that companies first must recover their investment and achieve a profit position before they can afford to pay any dividends, that dividends disbursed must be commensurate with the success of the operation and that a 50-50 split with the government becomes feasible only after production and flow to markets in great quantity have been attained. Otherwise companies adhering to sound business practices would hesitate to enter into development in a country or, if operating in a country, would be forced to withdraw.

In fact, Venezuela which started it all, has recognized this concept in relation to smaller companies, and so has Turkey, the latest to incorporate the 50-50 principle. They have set profit minimums below which they do not levy a 50 per cent tax—in their own interest and in the interest of the encouragement of oil investment.

Some oil men believe that, if the British had been more alert to the 50-50 profit-sharing trend, Iran might have been saved its costly experience with nationalization. Yet, as we shall see, there is another side to that story.

We have seen in Chapter 5 that, because of a declining income from pilgrimages and because of the war's depressing effect on oil royalties, Ibn Saud pressed Aramco for more revenue from oil. When on December 30, 1950, representatives of the king and of the company signed the Arabian government–Aramco 50-50 agreement at Jidda, Aramco had been under considerable pressure for two years regarding the government's income. Incidentally, in the Middle East though the 50-50 arrangements commonly are referred to as "agreements," this is not entirely accurate. Actually the income-tax provisions are imposed by law or decree.

In fact, at the time of the Jidda arrangement, all Middle Eastern governments were pressing their oil concessionaires for greater returns. The Anglo-Iranian Oil Company's relations with the Iranian government, for example, were in accordance with a concession agreement confirmed by the Majlis (Lower House) in 1933. The financial clauses of the agreement provided for an annual tonnage royalty on oil sold or exported and an annual payment per ton in consideration of exemption from Iranian taxation, both payments being adjusted for variations in the price of gold in London. Provision also was made for a payment equal to 20 per cent of any distribution to the ordinary stockholders in excess of £671,250 in any one year, whether the distribution was by way of a dividend or from general reserve. Furthermore, upon expiration of the concession, the government would receive a payment equal to 20 per cent of the difference between the general reserve at the time and as of December 31, 1932.

Under usual circumstances a larger ordinary dividend would have been justified in 1947, but in conformity with the British government's wish to limit the dividends of United Kingdom companies, the annual dividend had been maintained at 30 per cent. Large sums, therefore, had been placed to the company's general reserve, with the result that for the time being the Iranian government did not receive as large payments as otherwise would have been the case. On June 1, 1948, the company indicated to the government that, if it considered that hardship would result from this limitation of dividends, the company willingly would discuss any proposals to remedy the situation.

Discussions began in Teheran in September, 1948, and continued at intervals until July 17, 1949, when the Supplemental Agreement of 1949 was signed, substantially altering the financial clauses in Iran's favor. Under its terms there would have been a payment in respect of the amount standing at general reserve at December 31, 1947, which would have amounted to £5,090,000. The payments for the years 1948 and 1949 on the basis of the 1933 agreement amounted to £9,-172,000 and £13,489,000, respectively, while the estimated figure for 1950 would have been about £16,000,000. With the Supplemental Agreement ratified, the corresponding payments would have been £18,667,000, £22,890,000 and about £30,000,000.

Under Iranian law, however, the Supplemental Agreement required parliamentary ratification and was duly submitted to the Majlis. Headed by Dr. Mossadegh, a small but vigorous opposition group known as the National Front monopolized such debate as took place, and the 1949 session was dissolved before a vote could be taken.

During this time the terms of Anglo-Iranian's offer were generally known throughout the Middle East. They were by far the best terms offered to the government of any oil-producing country in the area up until that time. Largely because AIOC had plowed back much of its profits into developing the oil industry of Iran, the country had become a major world oil producer, and its 70,000 national oil workers were the best paid and best housed working group in the nation. Even without the additional payments proposed under the Supplemental Agreement, the total sums disbursed by the company in 1949—in respect to capital and revenue operations and including sums received by the government for customs, excise and other taxes—amounted to £65,700,000. If royalty payments at £13,500,000 for 1949—which would have amounted to £22,900,000 had the Supplemental Agreement been ratified—were added, the aggregate would almost have equaled the entire annual revenue of the Iranian government.

The prospect of higher royalty payments in Iran constituted a pressure on Aramco to make an adjustment with the Arabian government, and an increase in royalties was negotiated in Iraq around this time. Too, the pressure of Venezuela's 50-50 law of 1948 made itself felt halfway around the world, for all four of Aramco's owning companies —Standard of California, Texas, Standard of Jersey and Socony-Vacuum—had Venezuelan subsidiaries which had accepted the plan of government participation equal to their profits.

While recognizing the government's case for higher revenue, Aramco felt constrained toward delay because its postwar expansion program, though nearing completion, entailed heavy expenditures. But in October, 1950—two months before the Jidda agreement—the Saudi Arabian government forced the issue by decreeing the country's first income tax providing for a 20 per cent levy on corporation profits and a 5 per cent tax on individual incomes. Aramco, the largest enterprise in the country and already the source of nearly all the government's income, protested vigorously. Conceding the taxing power of a sovereign government, the company cited a clause of its original contract which specified that it was exempt from taxes within the country. Along with the tax the government made a number of demands on the company, all of which were completely unacceptable, and negotiations to resolve differences immediately began. The result was the 50-50 agreement of December 30, 1950—the first of its kind in the Middle East.

The Saudi Arabian–Aramco agreement allowed the government total participation in the operation up to one-half of the company's net operating revenue, but the government's share was inclusive of royalty which Aramco was required to pay regardless of its earnings. At the then anticipated level of production—over 600,000 barrels a day—the agreement increased the government's revenue from Aramco by approximately 30 million dollars, or, more specifically, from between 60 million and 64 million dollars—estimated for 1950 and retroactively covered—to between 90 million and 94 million dollars. The 1951 payments, it was thought, probably would exceed 100 million dollars.

From Aramco's standpoint, however, the arrangement set a ceiling on all payments to the government. Royalty, miscellaneous levies and income taxes never could exceed one-half of the net operating revenue. Equally important, the agreement placed all monetary transactions between company and government on the basis of official, internationally accepted exchange rates, thus eliminating the premium gold-sovereign rate at which the company previously had been paying royalty. Generally the terms of the pact follow much the same pattern as in Venezuela where the government adjusts its income tax to obtain a total income, including royalty, that is equal to company profits.

Adoption of the share-and-share-alike principle in the Middle East had particular significance at the time. Under exclusive American operation, Saudi Arabia was on the verge of wresting first place as an oil producer from Iran. In the explosive Middle East, the oil spotlight was on Iran and the stalled Supplemental Agreement. The Aramco settlement, it was predicted, might result in further concessions by other companies operating in the Middle East.[1]

With the benefit of second sight, it is easy to claim—as some people have—that nationalization in Iran occurred because the British offered too little, too late. But the statement is not in accordance with the facts, for, as previously pointed out, AIOC's 1949 proposal had been the best to date to any government in the area. Conversely, it might well be asked whether or not the Americans in Saudi Arabia were influenced by the deteriorating situation—including the threat of nationalization—in Iran. For the record, it might be noted that after the failure to ratify the Supplemental Agreement in 1949 Iran's elections to the next Majlis were delayed materially. Not until June, 1950, did the government propose to the Majlis that the Supplemental Agreement Bill should be examined, previous to debate, by a parliamentary commission. The Majlis adopted the suggested procedure, and under the chairmanship of Mossadegh and containing several National Front representatives, the commission held meetings from June until December, 1950. On December 12 the commission reported against the Supplemental Agreement Bill on the grounds that it did not satisfactorily safeguard Iranian rights and interests. The government withdrew the bill on December 26, and on December 31 Saudi Arabia and the Arabian American Oil Company concluded their 50-50 agreement.

[1] *The Oil and Gas Journal,* January 11, 1951, p. 60.

The incident, of course, attracted wide attention in Iran, and about the end of January, 1951, AIOC expressed its willingness to discuss a new agreement on the basis of an equal sharing of the profits from its operations in Iran, or for that matter any other reasonable proposal.

It is interesting to recall, incidentally, that royalties based on trading profits had been provided for in the company's original Iranian concession granted to D'Arcy in 1901. Experience during the depression years, however, had proved conclusively to the Iranian government of that period that the system contained considerable disadvantages, owing to wide fluctuations in annual payments because of changing market prices, and because of difficulties in arriving at mutually acceptable assessments of net profits. It did not necessarily follow, therefore, that any new agreement based on this system would be the most advantageous for Iran.

The Iranian situation underwent a radical change on February 19, 1951, when Mossadegh, then chairman of the Oil Commission, proposed to that group the nationalization of the oil industry. Thereafter events moved rapidly to their fateful climax—the nationalization law of May 2, the stoppage of the industry, the closing of the world's largest refinery at Abadan, the expelling of the last of the British oil staff from the country on September 28, all occurring as Mossadegh fanned the flames of xenophobia to excesses of riot and bloodshed.

From the foregoing chronology the reasonable conclusion emerges that the Arabian government–Aramco agreement did not precipitate the crisis in Iran, nor did the tension in Iran hasten the adoption of the 50-50 principle in Saudi Arabia. The decision of the four American companies owning Aramco to offer a share-and-share-alike arrangement was based on the view that the 50-50 principle has certain definite foundations which are fundamental to foreign oil development. As applying to the nation, it means that, in return for its share, the government (1) will open its natural resources to development, (2) will provide physical protection to operators and their workers, and (3) will guarantee the normal protection of its laws. On the part of the companies, it means that, in return for their share, they will provide (1) the initial risk capital, (2) the know-how, and (3) access to markets.

Incidentally, the lack of the last-named was the costly price paid by Iran for Mossadegh's adventure in expelling Anglo-Iranian. Iran still possessed the oil reserves, the great refinery and, to an extent, the technicians, though a small number of key foreigners were essential to full-scale and efficient operation of both oil fields and refinery. But without access to markets, Iran had no oil industry, the government had no oil revenue, the oil workers had no jobs—though they were kept on the payroll; that is, were actually paid while not working—and the people as a whole had no indirect income or collateral benefits from a prosperous major industry.

As anticipated, adoption of the 50-50 principle quickly spread to Iraq and Kuwait, two other Middle Eastern countries having large production and proved reserves.

In Iraq, after friendly negotiations extending over a period of 4 months, a new agreement involving 50-50 profit sharing was reached in August, 1951—though it was not signed until February, 1952—between the Iraqi government and the Iraq Petroleum Company and its associated companies, Mosul Petroleum Company and Basrah Petroleum Company. At the time, the first-named company was producing about 150,000 barrels daily while the two other companies were nearing the completion of pipeline facilities which would bring them to the production stage. Together the concessions of the three companies cover virtually the whole of Iraq, and the agreement was the more satisfactory because previous relations between government and company had not been wholly friendly. In English courts, for instance, the Iraqi government had filed suit against IPC in connection with the interpretation of the gold basis of royalty payments. Various other claims had piled up, and complaints in government circles were growing that Iraq oil development—which constituted the nation's greatest revenue source—had not enjoyed the expansion of other Middle Eastern countries, such as Iran and Saudi Arabia, and was in fact being discriminated against. Moreover, during the Arabian-Israeli conflict Iraq had cut its pipeline outlet to Israeli Mediterranean ports and consistently had refused to reopen it, thereby sacrificing large oil revenues. Only the opening of new pipelines, then nearing completion, and higher royalty payments would satisfy the government.

The situation also was potentially explosive politically and similar to that which had ignited in Iran, since the Iraqi government was under pressure from extremists crying for "nationalization" and the expulsion of foreigners. With AIOC and Royal Dutch–Shell each holding 23¾ per cent of IPC shares, the British too were involved in Iraq, a parallelism with Iran not overlooked by an anxiously watching Free World while the negotiations were taking place. Their happy conclusion provided intense satisfaction in oil circles.

Under the agreement the companies committed themselves to produce stated minimum quantities of crude oil, subject only to *force majeure* or circumstances beyond their control. Beginning in 1955 Iraq Petroleum and Mosul Petroleum together would produce a minimum of 22 million tons (165 million barrels) of crude oil a year, and starting in 1956 Basrah Petroleum would produce an additional minimum of 8 million tons (60 million barrels) yearly. The new minimum quantities corresponded to the pipeline capacity then existing or under construction and having seaboard terminals in Lebanon and Syria. Still unrelenting in the matter of opening the long-closed pipeline from Kirkuk to Haifa or the nearly completed parallel 16-inch line which would have had a combined carrying capacity of some 8 million tons (60 million barrels) a year, the Iraqi government could better afford to maintain its stand because of new pipeline outlets and the higher income which promised to remove any anxiety over the loss of income which had accompanied the Israeli ban. Indeed, in a few years' time the combination of higher royalties, together with greater stipulated exports or sales, would yield oil revenues double the country's 1951 annual budget. The government calculated that its annual income from oil would rise from 15 million pounds in 1951 to nearly 60 million pounds in 1955.

Because of varying characteristics and conditions, necessarily the operation of the 50-50 differs somewhat in method and detail from nation to nation. In Iraq the arrangement is particularly complex by reason of Iraq Petroleum's being an international company owned by companies of British, Dutch, French and American incorporation. Each component of the ownership, of course, is subject to widely varying taxes in its respective country which makes arrival at a basis of government-industry 50-50 participation an exceedingly complicated procedure, involving the drawing up of individual concession conventions and the organization of separate income-paying national companies by the subsidiaries of the owning groups. Many of these problems remained to be resolved in 1954.

Clearly stating that before any deduction for foreign taxes the government would receive 50 per cent of the oil companies' profits upon their operations in Iraq, the agreement made IPC liable for payment, pending the working out of all details. Full provision was made against the contingency that the scale or rate of profits might be below that which could reasonably be anticipated. In all circumstances except *force majeure*, the government was assured that its total income from the oil companies' operations would not be less than 25 per cent of the seaboard value of all crude oil exported by Iraq Petroleum and Mosul Petroleum plus 33⅓ per cent of the seaboard value of crude exported by Basrah Petroleum. It also was stipulated that the government was entitled to receive in kind 12½ per cent of all oil available for export, which it would have the option of selling in the open market or of requesting the companies to buy back at posted seaboard prices.

To ascertain the profits to be shared between the government and the companies, formulas were developed for calculating production and transportation costs within Iraq as well as for evaluating Iraqi crude in line with world prices. In the event that a neighboring country should obtain a higher rate of income per ton than that received under the new agreement by Iraq, stipulation was made that the Iraqi government might ask the oil companies to raise their payments correspondingly. If circumstances of *force majeure* imposed a suspension of oil production in the country, the oil companies, unconditionally, would pay the government a minimum annual revenue of 5 million dinars (1 dinar equals £1) for two years.

Two Iraqi directors were added to the boards of the oil companies. Iraqi nationals were to participate in the development of the country's oil resources, and the companies consented to a government proposal that foreign employees would be engaged only when the Iraqi government had concurred that no national was available to fill the posts competently. Realizing that difficulties might arise from this practice, the oil people thought that they would largely be overcome by the fact that the government now had a direct financial interest in ensuring efficient local operation of the companies. Moreover, constructive steps to train suitable Iraqi personnel were to be taken. At their own expense the oil companies continuously would maintain at United Kingdom universities 50 Iraqis who would study subjects relating to oil production. In Iraq, against their expense, the companies also undertook to maintain a technical school accommodating 240 students who normally would undergo 4 years' technical training. The training of Iraqi personnel was a continuation of policies already followed.

Finally, immediately upon ratification of the new agreement by the Iraqi Parliament, the slate was to be wiped clean of past differences and claims with a single lump-sum payment by the oil companies of 5 million pounds over and above the 50-50 arrangements. And the government dropped the case it had instituted in the English courts against Iraq Petroleum relative to the interpretation of the gold basis of royalty payments.

So happy and timely a settlement in Iraq against the flaming backdrop of National Front xenophobia in neighboring Iran served to relieve tension in the former nation. Moreover, the implications and promises in the concept of partnership now received dramatic attention.

"These new agreements are leading to a new stage in the development of international relationships determining access to such a vital raw material as oil," wrote the Petroleum Press Service, London.[2] "The sense of fruitful partnership to which they give practical effect is a powerful factor making not only for harmony between the concessionary government and the concessionaire, but for bringing to the peoples of the oil producing countries concerned a fuller share of the resources of their soil. A large part of the oil revenues to be received by Iraq will be devoted to irrigation and other development projects.

"It is highly satisfactory that at the present time an agreement, as clearly beneficial to Iraq as it is enlightened on the part of the oil companies concerned, has been reached with a country whose oil resources are among the most extensive in the Middle East and which, like Saudi Arabia, can make oil available both on the Mediterranean and at the Persian Gulf. But Iraq also has a leading role to play in promoting stability and peaceful progress in the disturbed Middle East of today and on this ground alone the new agreement and the economic strength which it provides are to be warmly welcomed. Unafflicted by the extreme nationalism and xenophobia that characterizes the present National Front government in Persia (Iran), the Iraqi

[2] September, 1951, p. 286.

government has shown a clear appreciation of the fact that its higher interests lie in a reasonable and fruitful partnership with the leading oil companies of the world. On this firm foundation Iraq, with her relatively small population of about five millions, may now boldly face the task of bringing about the social reforms and economic developments which will lead her to the high road of full prosperity."

The event immediately influenced other Middle Eastern nations. The Iraqi government-industry arrangement was a before-taxes 50-50 participation plan. In June, 1952, Aramco agreed to revise its agreement with the Saudi Arabian government to provide for a split of profits before the payment of United States taxes. Aramco also consented to the appointment of two Saudi Arabians to the company's board, following a pattern of closer identification between overseas oil companies and the countries where operations are being carried on. In that connection and at the request of the Saudi Arabian government Aramco transferred headquarters and top management from New York to Dhahran.[3]

Kuwait, too, reacted to the influence of the new pattern. On December 1, 1951, Sheik Abdullah of Kuwait and the Kuwait Oil Company, in which Anglo-Iranian and Gulf Oil are equal partners and which operates a concession covering all the tiny sheikdom, agreed to an equal division of oil profits. This was at the time that Kuwait was looked upon as a source to make up the deficit resulting from Iran's disappearance from world oil markets, and the oil production of the little country was beginning to attain huge proportions. Already Kuwait had surpassed Iran's peak output and was exceeded in the Middle East only by Saudi Arabia.

In the 1951 agreement the royalty rate of 3 Indian rupees—4 annas or 4s. 8.75d.—per ton remained unchanged. It was agreed, however, that the Sheik would levy an income tax—hitherto unknown in Kuwait—applicable to the Kuwait Oil Company at such a rate as to bring his total oil revenue, including royalty, up to 50 per cent of the company's profits before foreign taxes. Moreover, the company was to make a substantial financial contribution to the cost of the higher education of Kuwaiti students at schools and universities outside Kuwait. Should a more advantageous basis than 50-50 be granted to other major oil-producing Arab states, the arrangement would be reviewed.

[3] *The Oil and Gas Journal*, June 30, 1952, p. 49.

Under the new agreement the concession granted to Kuwait Oil Company in 1934 was extended for 17 years—that is, the original term of 75 years commenced afresh December 1, 1951, and, as had been the case in the Iraq agreement, all current questions in dispute between government and company were washed away. As trustee for his people the Sheik of Kuwait would receive an income in the region of 60 million pounds a year at the then current level of production which was approaching 40 million tons (300 million barrels) annually.

Kuwait's royalties had been fixed at a rather low level originally because the concession had been negotiated in 1934 when the oil industry had been surfeited with petroleum and was just beginning to emerge from a serious crisis of overproduction, low prices and reduced demand. At that time, too, there was no inkling that the oil potentialities of the territory were so immense. Sheik Ahmad as Subah, the original grantor of the concession, asked for increased royalties after the war. Following his death in January, 1950, Sheik Abdullah, his successor, renewed the request for a revision of the royalty rate. Meanwhile, however, production had increased so greatly that much larger oil revenues were available—more, in fact, than could be absorbed locally, despite marked rises in state expenditures. Nevertheless, when the request was again renewed in 1951, the 50-50 agreement came swiftly.

Thus, in the Middle Eastern conflict—so to speak—between cooperation and nationalization, the score heavily favors cooperation. As a matter of fact, *denationalization* of oil actually became a reality in Turkey on March 7, 1954, when the Grand National Assembly passed a new petroleum law containing the 50-50 partnership principle. Toward the close of 1952 the Turkish government recognized that exclusive state operation of its oil industry over a period of approximately 20 years had been unsatisfactory—in the 1949 to 1953 period, for instance, the nation's output averaged no more than 700 barrels annually. Recognizing the need for tremendous capital, the government announced its decision to open the country to foreign exploration and engaged Max W. Ball, former director of the Oil and Gas Division of the United States Department of the Interior, as a consultant to help frame the necessary petroleum legislation.

The new Turkish law is conspicuous in that it establishes the principle of 50-50 sharing in a virtually nonproducing country, stipulating that the formula be applied, however, only after investment had been recovered. Saudi Arabia, Iraq and Kuwait possessed going petroleum industries and great known oil reserves—as did Venezuela—when 50-50 participation was written into the nations' laws and the companies' concessions. Profits were being made. The only other country which had passed a 50-50 law with any resemblance to the Turkish action was Peru. That country passed a new oil law in May, 1952, which provided for a basic 50-50 profit-sharing approach to oil development and set forth incentives by way of higher depletion allowances in regions where the risk or where exceptionally large capital investment would be necessary before substantial returns could be expected. Peru, of course, had been an oil producer for many years from reserves along the coast. The new legislation, however, was directed particularly toward attracting foreign capital to engage in expensive search and development in the vast isolated area of the Peruvian Mountains which—situated between the Andes and the Brazilian Shield—contain oil seeps.[4] (See Chapter 21, Resurgence of Foreign Oil Investment.)

With little question the 50-50 principle has become an established world formula in relation to underdeveloped countries.

[4] *The Oil Forum*, June, 1952, p. 209; *World Oil*, May, 1953, p. 288.

PART THREE

"SOWING THE PETROLEUM"

Chapter 12

"SEMBRAR EL PETRÓLEO" IN VENEZUELA

Some old-time Venezuelan oil men say that, if the oil companies had known what they do now about human and industrial relations, they would still be in Mexico. Others claim that nothing could have stopped expropriation. For American oil men engaged in foreign operations, Mexico was the baptism by fire. One old-timer says, "Don't blame Doheny. It was a different world then. Doheny was of the rigid, tough school of the sourdough. He had lived in mining and oil camps the first 30 years of his adult life. Compared with them, the quarters and the health and recreational facilities he provided for expatriates at Ebano were palatial and attractive. He was proud of Ebano but probably thought it all effete. What he gave the Mexicans in the labor camps was nothing worse and usually far better than anything he himself had been used to in United States mining camps. He paid the highest wages of any industry in Mexico. He spent a lot of time in Mexico and mixed with the low as well as the high. He built hospitals and tried to establish an educational foundation. And don't forget Doheny is the man who invented the phrase, 'Sow the Petroleum'—the practice of plowing back oil profits into public works and projects designed to stimulate agriculture and diversification in industry."

But if we should give the impression that the oil companies are responsible for all that has been done in sowing the oil in Venezuela, we would be painting an inaccurate picture. As an oil man working in that country and familiar with the progress made, particularly since World War II, says, "We primed the pump, all right, but the pumping is being done by the Venezuelan people and the government." Oil companies do not claim credit for other than introducing or spearheading certain of the economic and social gains made in the country.

They declare that they simply were the vehicle for making oil a profitable industry and for implementing liberal social legislation passed by the government, that the government must be given credit—not they—for sowing the petroleum. Particularly would this be true since the war. They point out that, after all, oil prosperity has come to Venezuela only in recent years; that largely pioneering conditions prevailed up to World War II; that the war was a "disturbed" period; that only since the war, with the great expansion of world demand and the Venezuelan industry, did the great oil revenues begin to pour in. Nationally and locally, the government has assumed responsibilities that previously seemed to be lacking, notably in new boom towns that followed the well drillers. Company paternalism is no longer necessary; nor is it wanted. Social benefits have spread far beyond the oil regions—that is, to other than the oil workers and their families and the tradesmen and others who profit by their spending. The administration and leadership in education, health control and road building is definitely a government leadership, just as it is in utility and farm projects.

Oil is sowed today to an extent Doheny never dreamed of, in Venezuela, in Saudi Arabia, in other prolific producing countries. As to Venezuela, that country in 1954 was a boom land developed on oil profits. The evident prosperity of the economy represented by the oil fields, the modernity of Caracas, the superbly engineered highways through the mountains all attest to the arrival of the twentieth century in this sweeping country. Yet it is a modernity superimposed with devastating brusqueness, within the last 40 years, upon an older culture and an almost primitive economy.

With an area of 352,143 square miles—about the size of Texas and Utah combined—Venezuela is the sixth largest country of South America. Though it lies completely within the tropics, its climate varies according to the altitude, from the steaming heat of the southern jungles to the chill winds of the snow-capped Andes. In Caracas, more than 3,000 feet above sea level, the temperature averages a springlike 67.3° Fahrenheit.

Venezuela has four main geographic areas, but four-fifths of its people live in two of them—the invigoratingly temperate Andean Cordillera, or mountain ranges, with their adjacent coastal regions, and the predominantly tropical Maracaibo Basin. Most of the remaining fifth of the population is found in the sparsely settled *llanos*, or broad plains, stretching 600 miles from the Andes on the west and north to the

Orinoco River. Though they comprise almost half of the country, the Guiana highlands, south of the Orinoco, largely are uninhabited.

With a population of only 5 million, Venezuela is one of the least densely populated countries of South America—about eight times the size of Cuba, it has fewer people. Space abounds for expansion and for immigration into rural areas, and despite an increasing concentration of people around Caracas and the oil fields, the population remains overwhelmingly agricultural.

A high birth rate and a decrease in the death rate, including infant mortalities—because of improved governmental measures in the fields of health and sanitation—have combined to make Venezuela one of the fastest growing countries in South America. Since 1941 the population has increased 29 per cent. In the Federal District, comprising Caracas and its environs, the increase for the same period was 84 per cent, and though few in number, the principal cities, roughly doubling in a 10-year period, have grown much more rapidly than the country as a whole. And Venezuelans are a youthful people. In 1941 half the people were under twenty years of age and three-tenths of them were in the twenty to thirty-nine year group. Less than 5 per cent were sixty years of age or over.

Exclusively to equate the Venezuelan economy with oil would be misleading; yet the development of the petroleum resources of the country undoubtedly has been responsible for the most significant changes that have occurred since the turn of the century, and the impact of those changes on the nation and on the people gives the key to Venezuela today—and perhaps tomorrow. Foreign capital, more than half of it from the United States, financed this development, and on December 31, 1952, the gross investment in fixed (capital) assets for all companies was estimated at 3 billion dollars. United States' oil companies' production in 1953 accounted for 67 per cent of the total crude-petroleum output.

The government share of half the oil profits provides it with 98 per cent of its foreign exchange. Because of its oil, Venezuela ranks third in Latin America in total value of foreign trade and has a stable currency and a favorable trade balance. During the last decade, Venezuela's exports in terms of value per capita were second highest in the world, exceeded only by those of New Zealand. Petroleum is responsible for 97 per cent of the value of exports and for the rapid growth of Venezuelan trade.

While agriculture provides the livelihood of about 60 per cent of Venezuela's people, coffee and cacao, the major agricultural products, accounted for only 2 per cent of the total value of exports in 1949. And Venezuela's imports show a strikingly high proportion of capital goods which, of course, are brought in by oil and other industrial companies as well as by the government. In recent years, they have accounted for 50 per cent of the total, with the remainder comprised of consumer goods, raw materials, semimanufactures and—significantly in view of the predominantly agricultural economy—foodstuffs. A consistent annual excess of exports over imports for several decades has permitted Venezuela to expand its national budget continually and yet keep solvent.

Regardless of their political hue, successive administrations in Venezuela have held fast to the principle of sowing the petroleum. How effective in improving the lot of the mass of the people are these efforts? How extensive or substantial are they? What is their future promise? Such questions arise in all underdeveloped countries where oil has become, or promises to become, a major development resulting in an unbalanced economy. The answers to them bear profoundly on the subject of foreign oil and the Free World.

A newly arrived visitor to Venezuela immediately notes the lavish expenditures on public works and on private construction. One touches down at Maiquetia Airport, La Guaira—just a stone's throw from the sea—and is processed quickly through an efficient, modern airport building. At 50 miles an hour one taxies over a magnificent new four-lane (60-million-dollar) superhighway to Caracas, 15 miles distant, with every hundred yards recalling by sheer contrast the tortuous, hair-raising, time-consuming drive of a few years ago on the old two-lane switchback mountainous road.

The booming capital city of Caracas, snugly and beautifully located on a plateau in the Andean foothills, is taking on an ultramodern skyscraper appearance, with new and higher buildings going up as the older ones come down or are added to. Here the most modern architects find fulfillment. Fabulous University City (14 million dollars) with its futuristic trimmings was well publicized in the United States when the Tenth Inter-American Conference met there early in 1954. Nearby stand a brace of streamlined concrete stadia. A few blocks beyond is the busy local edifice of Sears-Roebuck. Other eye-openers are the Hotel Tamanaco (9 million dollars), the Armed Forces Club

(8 million dollars) and the new open-air amphitheater with its special acoustical arrangements. An office-building section in Caracas, similar to Rockefeller Center, is under construction.

All this architectural splendor is a phase of sowing the petroleum. Old-timers state unequivocally that 30 years ago Caracas was a sleepy, purely agricultural town of some Spanish charm. Caracas today is a bustling metropolis, plagued by a shortage of parking space for new American automobiles. Modern apartment buildings rapidly replace unsightly slums. However, rents up to $400 a month are not uncommon for comfortable homes in a desirable part of town. Yet with all the show of boom and opulence, large slum sections remain. For Caracas also has its poor, and their cottages and makeshift shacks cover whole hillsides. But the capital and other larger cities are the "show," the visual evidence of a deep-rooted economic well-being. As an oil man remarked of Caracas' opulent front, "Don't we all 'put it on'? Look at New York, London, Paris, Rio, Buenos Aires!"

The financial world views Venezuela's economy and its "phenomenal prosperity" as nothing short of miraculous. Venezuela is the only Latin-American state to come through the postwar years without foreign-exchange trouble or dislocation of its trade balances. "A nation of only five million people which in this anxious age has no foreign debt, virtually no internal debt, perennially balanced budgets, and a gold reserve of some 120 million pounds sterling (Bs 1.108 million) deserves the attention of every economist!" the *London Economist* recently exclaimed. The boom which has taken place since the end of World War II has few, if any, precedents in modern history. Since 1945, government income and expenditures have increased nearly fourfold, imports have almost tripled and both monetary circulation and international reserves have more than doubled. Proportionately, the Venezuelan public budget is the largest of all Latin-American republics.

When he told Jersey stockholders 10 years ago that the cost of living in that country was very high, Eugene Holman put his finger on one of the weak points in the country's economy that still is apparent today. That the Venezuelan government has thrived fiscally under the country's long and consistent policy of promoting oil development and that Venezuela's credit among nations is unmatched are indisputable and can be directly traced to the country's long and consistent policy of promoting the development of its oil resources.

But that Venezuela's is an unbalanced economy, that Venezuela's economic life is dependent on oil—61 per cent of the government's income is derived directly from the petroleum industry—make for a complicated situation, one which projects the oil industry into the center of the nation's political, economic and social well-being.

The chief solutions advocated to solve the problem of economic unbalance are (1) diversified industrialization, and (2) further agricultural development and (3) as a corollary to both—particularly the latter—increased immigration. Diversification of industry is being stimulated by a policy of encouraging private investment. The most important development is the opening by American companies of a high-grade iron-ore industry. Progress is apparent in such industries as cement, rubber, tires, vegetable oils and textiles. However, Venezuela continues to import most of its needed capital and consumer products.

Its 1953–1954 budget shows how the present government sows the oil. This reveals $229,800,000, or 30 per cent of the $764,600,000 total, allocated for public works—more than all the government's expenditures in any year previous to 1946. Health and social welfare required $52,200,000, education $47,400,000, communications $40,600,000, agriculture and livestock $38,300,000—together comprising 23 per cent of the total as indicated by the following table:

VENEZUELAN GOVERNMENT'S BUDGET BREAKDOWN, FISCAL YEAR 1953–1954

Interior	$119,312,000
Foreign relations	11,164,000
Treasury	79,820,000
Defense	64,709,000
Development	38,845,000
Public works	229,801,000
Education	47,411,000
Health and social welfare	52,180,000
Agriculture and livestock	38,285,000
Labor	7,722,000
Communications	40,590,000
Justice	24,736,000
Mines and hydrocarbons	6,803,000
Adjustments	3,243,000
Total	$764,621,000

Converted at Bs 3.09 per dollar.

Source: *Venezuela Up-to-Date*, August, 1953, p. 1

Repeatedly, successive administrations have inaugurated plans calculated to benefit the people as a whole by aiding farmers, attracting new people to the land, increasing food production, cutting down on imported foodstuffs and bringing about a lowering of the cost of living, with a consequent raising of living standards.

In 1946, while making a tour of eastern Venezuela oil camps, as we drove the 50-odd miles from the Maturin airfield to Caripito over a wide company-made asphalt highway, the humidity seemed to thicken and the malodor of the jungle to grow more pungent. Before reaching the more thickly forested region, we passed some cleared country containing a few shacks with sickly looking adults and children sitting in the doorways, gauntish pigs rooting in the yards and a few poor cattle grazing nearby. Our driver, an old-time oil man, said:

"No, they don't do much with the land down here. I've been around here since 1928 when we first opened up the Quiriquire field. It isn't so much that they don't as they can't. I don't know, though, whether the main reason is the poorness of the soil or the weakness of the flesh. They're all malaria-ridden; they haven't much hardihood or endurance. God knows I've seen them try. It's pitiful to see them. After a while they just give up."

Formerly the *llanos* country in eastern Venezuela was a great cattle country. When the oil people first went into it from the south, by way of the Orinoco River, they could still see a few large herds. No signs of cattle appeared in 1946. The story was that the plains were burned over too often. In his *Road to Survival*, William Vogt says that Latin America's geography is the "harshest and most inescapable factor limiting its human betterment." The farming that exists is done mostly on the hill and mountain slopes where erosion washes away both farms and future farming prospects. The coastal plains, greatly extended during the past 800 years by soil eroded down from the upland, also suffer from excessive heat and rain. In his *Population of Venezuela and Its Natural Resources*, Vogt further states that, "The *llanos* of Venezuela are poor in soil for the most part and receive a very unfavorable rainfall—excessive for part of the year and inadequate for the rest." [1] He calls the people who try to eke their food out of the "hostile land" in these areas the ecological displaced persons and

[1] Pan American Union, Washington, D.C., 1946.

calls the solution of the European DP problem simple by comparison. "In many areas," Vogt says, "malaria has actually been a blessing in disguise, since a large proportion of the malaria belt is not suited to agriculture, and the disease has helped to keep man from destroying it—and from wasting his substance upon it." He scoffs at plans to bolster agriculture by bringing in great numbers of European immigrants and states that from an ecological standpoint even the so-called "underpopulated" Latin-American countries, such as Venezuela, actually are "overpopulated."

The Venezuelan government, while recognizing the seriousness of the problem, takes no such pessimistic view. Without doubt the statement of the old-timer as to the plight of the Venezuelans in the malarial area was true in 1946, but already mosquito control gradually is changing the picture. And now herds of cattle may be seen in the *llanos* country.

The shift of rural population to cities and the growth of the urban middle class are the most striking aspects of Venezuelan society today. To offset the latter, in April, 1954, a 40-million-dollar 3-year government program to increase farm production was announced by Dr. Armando Tomayo Suarez, Minister of Agriculture. One of the goals of the program is to revitalize the Venezuelan cattle industry. Other aims are to restore the State of Guarico to its former importance as the nucleus of the cattle industry and to increase the productive land through irrigation of arid regions and by deforestation of jungle areas.

Numerous agricultural colonies are planned as part of a comprehensive program intended to bring back to the land those farmers who have migrated to the more lucrative oil fields. Government-built dams, canals, storage facilities and highways will make the colonies efficient and accessible, and land will be given to interested and capable farmers. All such features are designed to make farm life more attractive, more scientific, more profitable.

The National Institute of Agriculture in Maracay, one of the agencies working on the program, maintains laboratories and research centers, experimental agricultural schools and a veterinary school. It provides courses in farm demonstration and machinery work and operates extensive experimental farms. The institute coordinates its work with that of the National Agrarian Institute which, already having established 22 cultural colonies, also is in charge of immigration and makes an earnest effort to select those who are content to live on the land. In turn, the Agrarian Institute cooperates with the Banco Agrícola y Pecuario, which is in charge of the granting of credits, the control of markets, the distribution of seeds and plants and the administration of the storage plants and silos built for farmers by the Development Corporation, an organization whose function is to carry out projects planned by the other agencies. In 1954 the corporation was working on a national electrification plan largely designed to aid agricultural development. It also supervised a national rice plan, under which Venezuela hoped to become self-sufficient in that grain. Already it has been successful in a national sugar plan, by which the production of sugar was increased enough to meet domestic needs.

All these agencies work closely with the Ministry of Agriculture, which directs the over-all plan to develop agriculture and increase the production of livestock. Another part of the Ministry's plan is to restore the nation's coffee industry, in which 60,000 Venezuelans are engaged, 98 per cent of them owners of small farms. Progress also is being made in rehabilitating cacao plantations which have been neglected in recent years. Cocoa production in 1953 was triple that of 1950, and the quality had improved.

Thus the government sows the oil on various sectors of the agricultural front.

The oil companies have shown no hesitancy in backing up an optimistic belief in Venezuela's agricultural future. They largely supported Nelson Rockefeller's Venezuela Basic Economy Corporation. VBEC was formed immediately following World World II to produce farm staples through the use of advanced methods and modern equipment with a view toward increasing the standard of living of Venezuelans by lowering the cost of food. To it Creole, Shell and Gulf contributed $8,000,000, $4,250,000 and $3,000,000, respectively. The organization established farms, food distribution and fishing companies, and after a number of years, its functions were modified as the government increasingly concentrated on methods of encouraging farming and fishing. By the end of 1952 the companies had divested themselves of investment in the VBEC, but in and around the oil regions, the companies continue to aid in innumerable local experimental farm projects to encourage production. In an endeavor to improve the cattle industry, for instance, they have imported bulls of the Santa Gertrudis breed.

Sowing the petroleum, in point of fact, vitally affects every aspect of Venezuelan life. New highways, paved streets, schools, airports, port improvements, hospitals and other public-health facilities, aqueducts, rural and urban electrification, sewage systems, recreation facilities, low-cost housing and farm developments, industrial and commercial loans, crop and cattle-raising loans, irrigation, reforestation, modernization of government services, new public buildings—the great construction and reconstruction activity that one sees in all parts of Venezuela is proof positive of a vigorous determination to employ usefully the resources of the government treasury which largely are derived from oil development.

Moreover, the better way of life created for the oil workers—a minority of the population—has developed a provocative contrast. Politically and economically Venezuela still is dominated by a small segment of society, an aristocracy whose standard of living is reflected in large urban estates, country clubs, modern office buildings and luxurious apartment houses, while the majority of the nation's population remains ill-fed, ill-clad, poorly housed, illiterate and disease-weakened. Most rural families live in primitive huts without illumination, privacy or decent sanitary facilities. With antiquated tools, they eke out a meager existence from the soil. Undeniably a great gap still yawns between the poor and the landed aristocracy or the oil-wealthy, but the rise of an industrial working class, the spread of popular education and a growing middle class, all are promising evidence of the results of sowing the petroleum.[2]

The oil industry of Venezuela has at once a selfish and a humanitarian concern in Venezuela's efforts to solve the problem of economic unbalance by sowing the oil, for it finds itself in the middle of the problem of an unbalanced petroleum economy. As the largest and most profitable industry in the country, and one constituted almost entirely of foreign capital, it is an easy target for political attack by agitators who raise the cry of "foreign exploitation" or "imperialism."

As we have seen, however, government recognition of the importance of oil to Venezuela's economy has worked toward the continued expansion of the industry. Successive governments have man-

[2] "Venezuela: Oil Transforms a Nation," *Background*, February, 1953, p. 1.

aged not only to advertise the fact but also to apply—to a degree at least—the *sembrar el petróleo* (sow the petroleum) philosophy, with the result that by and large the Venezuelan people see oil as a godsend in helping to build other industries and jobs and in promoting agriculture. If government promises come true, Venezuela eventually would become free of its lopsided dependence on oil. Though it is a slow process, successive governments assert their interest by trying to speed it up.

Chapter 13

SAUDI ARABIA "SOWS THE OIL"

The government and the Americans of Aramco cooperate in "sowing the petroleum" in Saudi Arabia. Here, too, one sees what appropriately has been called a "private Point Four in action."

When King Ibn Saud opened the doors of Saudi Arabia to American oil men in 1933, not only did he end isolationism for his desert domain but also he was instrumental in planting abroad the largest single American community outside the United States and its possessions. Small as their number is when compared with the nationals—who are employed to the limit in accordance with the Aramco concession agreement—nevertheless 3,717 Americans are on Aramco's payroll in Arabia, proportionately more than in such other producing countries as Venezuela, Colombia and Peru where foreign companies' operations go back at least two generations. In 1952, at the suggestion of the Saudi Arabian government, even Aramco's top officials turned their backs on the company's New York offices for smart but somewhat remote offices at Dhahran, which constitute their headquarters. And every American employee, from Board Chairman F. A. Davies down, is not only a specialist and expert in his field, but a carefully chosen unofficial, nonprofessional representative in the public relations of his company in all dealings with the Arabian people.

"We have recently witnessed [in Iran] the tragedy of one instance in which great economic benefits and years of progress were swept away in a tide of nationalism and emotion," says Roy Lebkicher, Aramco's Director of Training at Dhahran. "Problems which could have been solved in an atmosphere of cooperation and give and take, for a time proved insoluble in an atmosphere of disturbed emotions and inflexibility.

136

"The question of how to avoid a recurrence of such disasters in the field of human relations as well as the field of world economics is one of the greatest problems facing free people today. The problem is one of the same importance to the people of the Middle East as it is to us.

"It should be perfectly clear that the good will of Middle Eastern (or any other) people cannot be bought by 'welfare' projects, paternalism or philanthropy, any more than it can be obtained by coercion.

"If there has been any single conception which has guided the relations between the Saudi Arabs and the Aramco people, that conception has been cooperation. We have had the good fortune to have dealt with a King and Government who, while demanding the fullest supportable measure of participation in the profits of our enterprise, have at the same time shown a desire to help and cooperate in our problems when such help and cooperation have been needed. King Ibn Saud liked to refer to the Aramco people as his 'partners,' brought in by him to help him develop his country."

In Saudi Arabia the dramatic contrast of change as against a timelessness which admits of no change, of forward-striding new methods working hand-in-hand with old ways, strikes one the instant one leaves Aramco's *Flying Camel* at the company's great Dhahran airport. Even the name of Aramco's DC-6B is singularly appropriate, symbolizing, as it does in terms of transportation, the economic and social leap that Saudi Arabia has taken in the short period since the war. For, though Aramco's original concession was dated 1933 and much groundwork was laid before the war, the truly great expansion dates from the end of the second world conflict in 1945. Aramco has two other planes, incidentally—the DC-6B *Flying Gazelle* and the DC-4 *Flying Oryx*, making regularly scheduled flights from New York to Dhahran twice weekly, and, since 1947 when it got into the aviation business on a regular schedule basis, its New York-based planes have made more than 800 Atlantic crossings and flown the equivalent of 267 times around the world. In addition to its transatlantic aircraft, Aramco has based in Dhahran two Convair CU-340's, seven DC-3's, four Twin Beechcraft and two single-engine Navion planes for use in geological exploration expeditions, construction trips, medical emergency service, photographic surveys and pipeline inspection.

In 1933 near Dammam, not far from our point of landing, a group of

Standard of California's geologists, dressed in Arab garb, began the explorations which eventually opened up some of the richest oil-producing fields in the world, fields which were to make Aramco the world's biggest single oil-producing company. Behind them were the limpid waters of the Persian Gulf, before them they saw nothing but an eroded, sun-baked bulge on the earth's surface, a naked hill sloping down into the wilderness of a desert, a collection of shacks marking the Arab pearling village of Alkhabar. Far to the north a thin band of green stretched in welcome contrast along the horizon—the date-growing oasis of Qatif. In the surrounding arid wastes a few Bedouins and their herds scrabbled out a living.

Building an oil industry in Saudi Arabia entailed the creation of new self-contained cities and towns—communities complete with homes, streets, utilities, restaurants, hospitals, schools, stores, recreation facilities and vegetation. All these 8,000 miles from the United States' supply base in a country barren of everything except water—and so little of that!—and such building materials as stone and brick. Virtually everything used by Aramco in its Saudi Arabian operation has to be brought in from the "outside." Foodstuffs, for example, are imported from such distant places as Australia, South Africa and the United States. In light of the logistical problems involved—complicated as they were for a time by postwar shortages of materials—the results are phenomenal.

Today the headquarters city of Dhahran, the refinery and shipping center of Ras Tanura and the rapidly growing Abqaiq producing center, where Aramco has established its main camps, are in each case communities complete with such utilities and services as electric power, water, sewage, air conditioning, telephone services, hospital facilities, dining halls, schools for the children, movie theaters, playgrounds and other recreational facilities, social centers, stores, post offices, banks and paved streets.

Aramco's producing operations in eastern Saudi Arabia extend from the Haradh field in the south to the Safaniya overwater operation 350 miles to the north and embracing the Ghawar and Abqaiq fields. These four major producing fields also call for numbers of temporary camps, for throughout the entire area and far beyond, field parties continuously search for geological features which might prove productive.

As of December 31, 1953, Aramco's employees comprised 13,555, or 60.7 per cent, Saudis; 3,717, or 16.6 per cent, Americans; 3,367, or 15.1 per cent, Pakistani, Indian and Palestinian; 734, or 3.3 per cent, Italian and Dutch; and 872, or 4.3 per cent, other nationalities. An additional 10,000 Saudi Arabs are engaged by more than 100 local contracting firms who work principally for Aramco. As the number of Aramco's employees grew under the impetus of sensationally expanded operations, the problem of housing a rapidly growing labor force, both foreign and national, assumed staggering proportions. But both company and government early recognized that problems of labor and housing went hand in hand and that to provide the latter was prerequisite to successful operations and cordial relations. Aramco's housing problem was double-barreled: (1) to make available livable accommodations which would attract American oil technicians and skilled workers to a country where in summer temperatures of over 120 degrees in the shade sometimes are recorded, and (2) to meet the housing requirements for the nationals stipulated in its concession agreement.

The housing objective ranged from private rooms in dormitories for permanently employed American bachelors to small apartments for the more senior employees, an aim impossible to accomplish immediately. Until recently, the majority of employees were crowded two or three to a small room—a situation tolerated only as a temporary expedient but one that unfortunately made for high labor turnover.

As Aramco created work possibilities for increasing thousands of the local inhabitants, it encountered many major civic and social problems. Workers were drawn from the Bedu tribes and from cities and villages throughout Saudi Arabia, and they lived in bachelor quarters but were given time to be with their families, for, though Saudi employees showed great enthusiasm for their new jobs, they are family men to whom a bachelor existence was unsatisfactory. The company, therefore, emphasized the construction of dwellings and ancillary buildings.

By legislation the Saudi Arab government prescribed a minimum requirement for housing national employees—each two employees were to be provided with a room of suitable permanent construction not less than 12 by 15 feet in dimensions. As reasonable as was the requirement, it meant the launching of a housing program of major proportions and of infinite complication since at the very start, in 1947, workers eligible for dwellings were 86 per cent ahead of facilities.

Aramco has three types of camps—general, intermediate and senior staff. The group an employee is placed in is determined entirely by the job he holds. Nationality has nothing to do with the groupings. On December 31, 1953, company housing provided accommodations for 14,568 employees in general camps located at Dhahran, Ras Tanura and Abqaiq. With the addition of 59 new dormitories all general employees living in those districts had moved into concrete, brick, or stone dwellings before the end of the year, and none remained in tents. The cost of the masonry dormitories was over 6 million dollars. To provide comparable living quarters for general employees assigned to temporary camps in areas such as Haradh and Uthmaniyah, construction was started in November, 1953, on 48 fireproof, portable buildings, accommodating 12 persons each. This new type of building, materials for which were bought in Italy and Sweden, has walls made of a combination of cement and asbestos, steel floors, galbestos roofs, and six rooms, each with its own entrance. Bath houses and kitchens are in separate buildings. The progress made, in providing brick, stone and concrete housing in general camps, is shown by the fact that as long ago as 1947 over 14,000 employees were eligible for accommodations in general camps, with accommodations available for only about 2,000, or 14 per cent; by 1952 when 17,000 were eligible, accommodations had reached over 13,000, or 77 per cent.

The opening of intermediate camps at Dhahran, Ras Tanura and Abqaiq during 1952 marked the completion of a major phase of Aramco's herculean housing program. Costing more than 10 million dollars, these camps provided 2,675 intermediate employees with comfortable and attractive dwellings. The 12 rooms in each of the housing units are electrically lighted, with outlets for appliances. Each unit includes a kitchen with a gas stove, electric refrigerator and drinking fountain and dining room, laundry and bathroom. Employees may have air-cooling units installed in their rooms on a low-cost rental basis, and all barbershops, canteens, recreation centers, offices and other general buildings are air-cooled. Modern air-cooled cafeterias provided with stainless-steel equipment serve a variety of foods at reasonable prices.

Recreational facilities are provided in all camps, including swimming pools just completed in most general and intermediate installations.

No important Middle Eastern country clings more tenaciously to its ancient ways than Saudi Arabia; yet one sees the impact of oil everywhere one goes in the few inhabited regions of this great desert country. In the transformation the late Ibn Saud played a conscious role and today King Saud, his son, continues the policy of "sowing the petroleum" which his father started in the nation. Change is inherent in Aramco's operations because of the necessity to provide better housing, to teach illiterate people to read their own language, to train them in manual skills, to care for their health and the health of their families, to provide roads and modern transportation—indeed to drill for water as well as for oil and thereby to make the desert productive for industry and for agriculture. Inevitably change has taken root and is spreading. In the resulting projects, though they may be unrelated to oil directly, often Aramco is a participant called in by the government as adviser or agent.

The relationship of partner and friend has a firm foundation. Ibn Saud's government operated on a financial pittance until oil was discovered on the Persian Gulf coast and the royalties began rolling in. Even so, some years elapsed before the income reached sizable proportions. World War II brought new difficulties which obliged the government to borrow from Aramco against future royalties and to enlist economic assistance from Britain and the United States. Within the last few years—and especially since the concession revision late in 1950 —Saudi Arabia's oil income has grown into impressive figures. Exact statistics on Saudi Arabia's income from oil are not publicized, but estimates, which probably are fairly close, show that in 1950 the government netted about 80 million dollars from Aramco, including royalties, taxes and other charges; in 1951 near 110 million dollars; in 1952 about 160 million dollars; in 1953 in the neighborhood of 200 million dollars, and in 1954 somewhat better than 200 million dollars. Considering that the government does not take in more than 25 million to 30 million dollars annually from all other sources, such as customs, internal taxes and pilgrim traffic, it can be seen what the oil bonanza has meant to the King who receives all revenue and has full power over its disposition to the Royal Household, to various ministries, to the Army, to public works, to providing comforts to Palestinian refugees, to lending money to other Arab states and the like.

The Saudi Arab budget estimates for the year ending March, 1953, as reported by Petroleum Press Service, May, 1953, follow:

	Million Riyals
Estimated Income:	
Oil revenues from Aramco...................	570
Customs duties...........................	70
Gold mining..............................	0.6
Other sources—about.....................	59

±700 (£72.5 million)

Expenditures:	
Armed forces, maintenance and construction work..................................	135
Police...................................	19
Tribes and irregulars......................	50
Town and royal settlement, Riyadh..........	150
Riyadh Administration.....................	66
Royal family.............................	36
Mosques and pilgrims.....................	28
Water improvements......................	23
Ministry of Health.......................	29
Education................................	13
Agriculture...............................	4
Hedjaz railway...........................	55
Air Force................................	10
Debt reduction...........................	100
Various other items......................	8

±726 (£75.2 million)

Year's shortage .... 26 (£2.69 million)

Before Ibn Saud completed the consolidation of the Saudi Arabian nation, only a quarter of a century ago, a few schools functioned in the territory comprising the new-old nation, and those were in the western province of Hedjaz where the holy cities Mecca and Medina are located. In all the eastern section where the oil was found, no public schools existed. Aramco undertook the education of employees and their children and continued in this endeavor until the government took over a few years ago. When recruited by Aramco, 88 per cent of the Saudi employees were illiterate. To train men for skilled or semi-skilled jobs, Aramco successfully undertook the task of teaching the Saudis their own language as well as the rudiments of handling modern tools and machines.

The taking up of industrial jobs and settled lives regulated by the

clock demanded much adjustment on the part of the nomadic Arabs—
and still does. Labor turnover is large. But visitors never forget the
company's annual ceremonies when service awards are made, for they
bring home the reality of the existence and permanency of modern industry in a strange setting when they see the single Arabian who has
reached the 20-year service mark and the more than 270 who have
been with Aramco 15 years or longer proudly accept their emblems.
In the oil fields and in the refinery, one realizes how adept and eager
the Saudis can be, and, of course, one always imagines that by the relative importance of their assignment he can spot those among the
5,000 plus employees who have had five years or more of service. To
believe that these men could not read their own language and had no
mechanical or technical skill when they began their employment is
difficult.

Some of Aramco's Saudi workers have moved up to become assistant drillers, foremen or supervisors. Others hold responsible, though
secondary, jobs on the business side. A few have reached "senior-staff"
status, with many others on their way to that goal. All of them have
Aramco's training program to thank for their advancement.

Aramco gives wide opportunities to its Saudi employees to broaden
and extend their education toward attaining a professional status by
studying under tutors, and, incidentally, some of the workers tutor
Americans in Arabic. Selected groups take summer-school courses at
the American University at Beirut, and employees who qualify receive
scholarships to Aleppo College and the American University. In all
this professional training Aramco strives to avoid the possibility of the
boys' losing touch with their own country and their own culture;
hence it prefers to use Middle Eastern colleges, at least for under-
graduate work.

Aramco's unique and comprehensive training program has demonstrated that a bright and willing Saudi boy can start work at the
age of sixteen without any schooling or industrial experience, have a
bachelor's degree by the time that he is thirty and receive a regular
salary during the whole time. A major category of Aramco's training,
incidentally, is the development of social and leadership skills among
American and other employees who are responsible for good human
relations. All new American employees are indoctrinated for their
responsibilities in Saudi Arabia by courses which include an intensive

study of rudimentary Arabic, plus further teaching of the language in the field. High-level executives take the lead in learning and in speaking the country's tongue. Americans also are given lecture courses in such subjects as the oil industry and company policies as well as in the history, religion, geography, government, industries, culture and customs of the Arab world and particularly of Saudi Arabia.

Aramco's efforts in the general and vocational educational fields have stimulated education generally throughout the country. The government recognizes the need for more and better schools and is establishing many new ones. Though teachers are scarce, some are being brought in from other countries, especially from Egypt since in Saudi Arabian schools the curriculum is based largely on Koranic teaching. In addition, 300 Saudi Arabs are being educated abroad at government expense, two-thirds of them in Egypt.

Aramco's efforts to care for its employees' health have had profound national results. At Dhahran, Aramco built and maintains a modern 3-million-dollar hospital staffed by about 12 doctors and 45 nurses. The hospital not only treats employees but also the general public. At the company's Dhahran Health Center additional portable buildings had to be set up to handle the great number of outpatients. The company's medical division also operates infirmaries at Abqaiq and at Ras Tanura.

As an outgrowth of company malaria-control operations, the government inaugurated a program to combat mosquitoes under which it provides the materials and labor while the company furnishes technical assistance and supervision. In a country which until recent years enjoyed practically no benefit from modern preventive medical science, dramatic results often follow. Take the case of the Yabrin oasis, a fertile well-watered area, 225 miles southwest of Dhahran and once supporting a population of thousands. Then malaria secured a foothold and gradually killed off or drove away the people, until only a handful remained. An Aramco preventive-medicine team moved in and cleared the oasis of malarial mosquitoes. The area now is being resettled. Extensive work and effective results also have been obtained by DDT spraying in the Qatif and Al Kharj oases, and the company is giving technical assistance to a government community-health project for Dammam. In 1953, inoculations and vaccinations in the government's malaria-control program totaled 36,417.

"Sowing the oil" has brought new construction to such ancient cities as Mecca, Medina, Jidda, Riyadh, Hofuf and Qatif. Though the cities have grown, their architectural style retains the charm of past ages. Most of the change in evidence from petroleum riches, however, lies in the new towns in eastern Arabia which we already have mentioned. Outside the oil fields, progress has been slower than modern-minded Arabs would like, but the trend, at least, is in that direction.

In other words, life in Saudi Arabia has not been revolutionized by oil—not yet. One does not have to go far from Dhahran to see that most of the population still lives much as its forefathers lived, some wandering from pasturage to pasturage with their herds, others living simple, settled lives on date-palmed oases, and all ardent believers in the Koran.

A fair share of the government revenues is spent on social improvement and public works. The newly built railway from the port of Dammam on the Persian Gulf to Riyadh, for instance, was a favorite project of the late Ibn Saud who asked Aramco to do the job. Together with a deep-water harbor at Dammam the 350-mile line was completed recently at a cost of about $63,500,000, with both projects being paid for by the Saudi government out of oil royalties. The transfer by Aramco to the government of the management and supervision of the Saudi Government Railroad and Dammam Port took effect January 1, 1953.

The railroad markedly is affecting the development of the area which it serves. Hofuf, the former capital of Al Hasa—the capital has now been moved to Dammam—is a town of more than 200,000 persons. The inhabitants in that area farm a huge oasis of agricultural land dotted with about 40 new towns and villages fed by underground springs. The railroad and the adjoining Ghawar oil field combine to make the area a thriving community.

The railroad also passes through the agricultural development of Al Kharj to its present terminal at the capital city of Riyadh, but the government plans to extend it entirely across the peninsula to the seaport of Jidda. Managed by Aramco, the agricultural undertaking in the great Al Kharj oasis, 50 miles south of Riyadh, is the most ambitious in Arabia. Here 3,000 irrigated acres are operated by the Saudi Arab government and supervised by American agricultural specialists. With scientists provided by the United States government, Saudi Arabia is sponsoring an active search, in which Aramco cooperates, for additional supplies of water.

The constant birth and growth of new communities in the oil regions finds Aramco fully cooperating with local governments. Typical of a year's activities are the following: a new water well was drilled in Al Thaqbah, and a street layout and plot plan for the town were prepared for the use of government officials. The Rahimah townsite near Ras Tanura was provided with basic water and sewer systems at the company's expense. To give additional momentum to the development of the community when the government sold 275 lots of land here to the public, including Aramco employees, the company undertook the construction of 48 family dwellings near the townsite to be rented to workers. For the new townsite of Rajihah, near Abqaiq, work began on installing water and sewer systems.

One sees the indirect effects of the oil operation in many ways. A number of Arabs, after working and learning with Aramco for a period, leave to start businesses of their own. With Aramco's help, some of them have become contractors and, incidentally, wealthy men. Though contracting, in our sense, is a new concept in Saudi Arabia, it is helping to stir up new developments promoted by the Arabs themselves. A good example is the new power plant, owned on a shareholding basis, in the thriving town of Alkhabar—the same sleepy, little pearling village that Standard of California's geologists first saw when they came ashore.

As fabulous as is the story of oil discovery in Saudi Arabia, therefore, clearly it is being matched by the results of "sowing the petroleum" and by the policy of developing human relations. Perhaps, nowhere else in the world has an equally outstanding job been done in social development and elevating living standards by foreigners going out of their way to extend their technical and business know-how to the peoples of an underdeveloped country. Illiterates have been taught to read and write their own language, while those showing inherent abilities are elevated to positions of responsibility as quickly as they are ready to assume them.

But, reviewing our "sowing" chapters, we fear we have given the impression that all progress in these countries is due directly to the activities of the central governments and the oil companies. This may be true in large degree, but both governments and companies would be open to criticism if they had not, at the same time, stimulated and encouraged small private enterprises. They have. Fourteen years ago Ali din Hussein was a solitary Bedouin tribesman. Today as superintendent he is in sole charge of 30 men and a 2-million-dollar gas separator 20 miles from the nearest company office. Fifteen years ago Mohammed Mutarid was a poor nomad. With company assistance now he is an independent contractor owning 14 trucks, several bulldozers and other heavy equipment. Depending on the contracts in hand, regularly he meets a payroll ranging from 100 to 500 men.

The two cases are not rare. During 1954 Aramco provided technical advice and help in the field of private industries to more than ten different towns of the Eastern Province. These enterprises included ice and cold storage plants, cement block and brick plants, laundries, bottling works, a foundry, stores, office buildings and apartment houses. They are typical instances of the amazing results of "sowing the petroleum" in Saudi Arabia.

And what has "sowing the petroleum" meant to the Bahrainis where the Bahrain Petroleum Company, equally owned by Standard Oil of California and The Texas Company, operates? On the little island more than 10 per cent of all male Bahrainis, or in excess of 6,000, are engaged in the oil industry. They participate in medical, training and employee benefit plans. From their increased purchasing power, local markets have benefited. The country is humming with activity. A network of roads and bridges, modern shipping facilities and a large airport bring the inhabitants into contact with all peoples of the world. The Bahrain government has established a hospital and municipal dispensaries, including a women's division. There also is a mental hospital, which is unique in the Persian Gulf area, and one of the latest medical developments by Bapco is a 67-bed hospital at Awali.

The added comforts of life are by no means limited to employees and their families. Water wells have been drilled by the government for local use in villages. Miles of roads have been constructed by the government and are open to the public. The Bahrain Causeway, another government project, is a major economical installation, connecting the two main islands.

And, as in Saudi Arabia, the impact of oil upon the people through vocational and academic training has been profound.

Chapter 14

IRAQ, KUWAIT AND IRAN SOW OIL

One cannot refrain from contrasting the present sowing of petroleum in Saudi Arabia, in Bahrain Island, in Iraq and in Kuwait with conditions in Iran—where for many years oil also was sown.

Iraq's story of oil development differs from Iran's. The country followed Iran by fully 19 years in appearing in the oil-producing column, the fields were far inland and development was much slower. Only in recent years has the government derived great revenues from petroleum. Indeed, Iran's misfortune proved to be Iraq's gain for her neighbor's shutdown accelerated demand for the Iraqi output.

In 1953 the annual rate of production in Iraq doubled and oil revenues trebled. Under the terms of the 50-50 profit-sharing agreement which received royal assent in February, 1952, the Iraqi government was getting about 45 million pounds a year in oil revenues. Furthermore, the internationally owned Iraq Petroleum Company and its affiliates guaranteed that they would increase production to a minimum level of 30 million tons by 1955—almost as high as that of Iran before the nationalization law was passed—which on the basis of then existing prices would have given the Iraqi government about 60 million pounds.

Obviously these are vast sums of money, and responsible Iraqi officials agreed that measures should be taken to ensure that they not be dissipated through the ordinary channels of government expenditure but, rather, be channeled into long-term investment projects where they would best contribute toward the economic development of the country.

Accordingly, the Development Law of 1950 was passed, placing 70 per cent of the total oil revenues in the hands of a Development

Board which aimed "to enrich the productivity of the soil and enrich the lives of the people." Elaborate precautions were taken to keep its six executive members free from interference by politicians. Members were to be appointed for 5 years and could be removed only if they committed criminal offenses or became politicians themselves. Two of the members are British and American experts nominated by the United Kingdom and United States governments, respectively, in accordance with a request from the government of Iraq. In its own right the board can float loans which the Minister of Finance must guarantee, and once its general programs have been sanctioned by Parliament, the board has wide powers to proceed as it thinks fit. The board's program called for expenditures of over £155 million over six financial years ending 1956.

As strange as it may seem to citizens of the United States, the drawing up of a program to spend several hundred million dollars is no simple matter in many nations. In an underdeveloped country like Iraq, where at its peak the expenditure will reach a level twice as high as the total governmental outlay in 1953 and represent something like a third of the national income, the task assumes prodigious proportions.

On April 3, 1951, Premier Nuri el Said announced that the board had set aside 91 million pounds from oil revenues to be used in a five-year plan covering irrigation, land reclamation, roads, buildings and industrial development. The aims of the numerous projects were of startling magnitude. The first was to regulate the flow of the Euphrates and Tigris Rivers and their tributaries with dams, barrages and irrigation and drainage canals to end the annual floods which damage thousands of acres in the central and southern parts of Iraq and to provide a steady flow of water through the parched summer months which will raise the irrigated area from 8 million to 17 million acres. The second and subsidiary part of the plan was to make use of the enormous quantities of wasted gas—estimated at 25 million cubic feet a year—in the Kirkuk area. In conjunction with large gypsum deposits, the gases would be used to manufacture ammonium sulfate fertilizers, sulfur, carbon black and cement. Large sums also were proposed for roads, hospitals and schools. Parliament approved the plan.

The Development Board's report for 1952–1953 shows a technical, financial and administrative staff numbering 141, including 41 foreign officials. In addition, the board assigned 75 technical men to various government departments to assist in the execution of their projects. Also, under the program, the Ministry of Education has sent 222 Iraqi students abroad for education as engineers and technicians.

In 1951 and 1952 sums of £3,000,000 and £7,000,000, respectively, were sanctioned for the Euphrates and Tigris and other irrigation projects; £2,000,000 and nearly £3,800,000, respectively, for main roads and bridges; £2,400,000 and £2,600,000, respectively, for buildings and institutions, including hospitals and schools; and £1,700,000 and £3,400,000, respectively, for reclamation of lands. In 1952 the board attached "considerable importance to the industrialization of Iraq," and devoted £3,000,000 to industrial projects, including a projected refinery at Qaiyarah, preliminary studies on utilizing Kirkuk's waste gas, and projected studies on steel, cement and textile plants. The grand totals of sanctioned expenditures shown for 1951 and 1952 are £9,364,000 and £20,460,000, respectively.

One cannot help but compare the policy of enlightened self-interest which promises to open the road to a higher living standard in Iraq with the xenophobic mania which was leading to the economic ruin of Iran. Such a comparison, in fact, was commonplace at the time though it suffered from temporary doubt during the Baghdad riots of November, 1951, a period when *coups d'état* were fashionable in the Middle East. But Iraq had a strong man in Nuri el Said, many times Prime Minister. In 1951, while securing for Iraq a rate of oil revenue per ton comparable to any other country in the Middle East, the Premier replied to those who cried for nationalization, "Oil in the ground is nationalized already."

By 1954 the program of the Development Board of the Government of Iraq was showing reasonable progress. Swamps which cover large areas in the delta region of the Euphrates and Tigris Rivers were being drained. Soils encrusted with salt from excessive irrigation were being washed and put back into use. Experimental stations were studying methods of obtaining better seeds and improving livestock through breeding and controlling disease. Better animal-drawn plows were replacing the old ones, which barely scratched the surface and often failed to uproot the weeds. The Agricultural Machinery Administration, an agency of the government, was renting machinery to farmers too poor to buy it, and, though only a small part of agriculture was mechanized, considerable progress in this direction already had been made in the dry-farming area of Mosul and in the new pump-irrigated lands of Central Iraq.

For today's Iraq, isolation is a thing of the past. Roads connect the nation with its neighbors, and their quality is improving even if present motorcar and truck travel is slow and often a tedious process because of ruts and dust. In the chief cities some industries are developing, and the Baghdad sky line shows the smoking chimneys of factories utilizing local raw materials to produce bricks, cotton yarns, soap and cement.

Though education is not yet compulsory and in many rural districts the children cannot attend schools because they are needed in the fields, schools are increasing in number, some of them housed in modern buildings. Under Point Four agreements foreign experts have been called in to help in such activities as agriculture, fishing, engineering, medical services and education. Meanwhile, the young Iraqi are being sent abroad for training. None of these still developing accomplishments would have been possible without the oil revenues.

Another factor promises a profound influence on Iraq's future—the birth and intellectual awakening of a middle class, economically speaking, which includes the lesser white-collar officials who crowd the government departments with little chance of promotion and many workers in stores and industrial enterprises. They want to see more of the benefits of the oil money filter through to benefit the population as a whole.

"In spite of all that the Development Board is doing, it is not popular," S. Van Valkenburg writes in *Focus*.[1] "At present the greater part of the oil money is being used for long-term projects that will eventually raise the standard of living. There is the danger, however, that the people will lose sight of the ultimate advantages; they are impatient to see results. Most of them still suffer from dire poverty, ill health, and ignorance. They would like to see more of the available revenue devoted to immediate relief: better watering facilities and sheep-dipping stations for the nomads, village dispensaries, the training of more nurses, the elimination of stagnant and polluted water, the provision of good water and sewage disposal, slum clearance, and better housing. They would like to see a broadening of the educational

[1] American Geographic Society, January, 1954.

program to teach more people how to cope with their everyday problems and improve their methods of work."

Benjamin Shwadran, writing on "The Oil of Iraq," states: [2] "If Iraqi leaders could withstand the pressures to divert some of the oil revenue to other than long-range capital development projects in agriculture and industry which even with the parliamentary safeguards of the Development Board will no doubt be exerted, and if they should succeed in bringing the social and economic forces of the country in line with the projected objectives of the development plans, they could succeed in raising the Iraqi standard of living to one of the highest in the Middle East. They would then have demonstrated to the other countries of the area the value of an effort of all citizens working for a national objective, and show how the natural resources of a country can be made to work for the welfare of all its citizens."

Evidence of restlessness over the long-term features of the Iraq Development Board's program was reported in June, 1954. "While all the people have heard of the vast benefits to be derived from oil royalties, few have seen any," says a special dispatch from Baghdad to *The New York Times,* July 4, 1954. "A start has been made on the resettlement of landless tenant farmers on government-controlled lands. But thus far only 2,455 families have been moved onto 125,000 acres. For every one touched by these benefits there are thousands who have received nothing and their discontent is being assiduously cultivated and exploited by the handful of active Iraqi Communists and the legion of volunteer assistants mobilized among the frustrated, discontented and vaguely leftist youths."

Iraq, with only 5 million people inhabiting an area of more than 168,000 square miles, is sparsely populated in relation to its oil resources. But Kuwait affords an even more striking illustration of the same characteristic. The rapidly developing sheikdom of Kuwait has one of the highest national incomes per person in the world. With a settled population believed to number about 150,000, the country's oil revenues were running over 50 million pounds annually in 1953.

Only since 1946, the year in which exports began, has oil played any considerable part in the life of Kuwait. Then, after Iran's shutdown, production and exports soared with enormous revenues resulting. But with the Kuwait Oil Company—equally owned by Anglo-

[2] *Middle Eastern Affairs,* December, 1952.

Iranian and Gulf Oil—fully cooperating, the decision of Sir Abdulla Al Salim Al Subah, the ruling sheik, to spend huge sums for the benefit of the people already is showing spectacular results. So rapid a change is occurring both in the commerce and the appearance of Kuwait town itself as to challenge remembrance of conditions as they existed even a few years ago when Kuwaitis struggled to eke a living from desert and sea.

Regarding the oil revenue as a realization of natural capital, the sheik permits a suitable proportion to be allocated for immediate development and conserves the rest for the future through an Investment Board which has been set up in London. Over the next 10 years expenditures of more than 100 million pounds are envisioned in a program for building schools, hospitals, roads, sewage and drainage, a modern harbor and airport, water, gas and electrical services. Inside the walled city a modern road system with roundabouts and car parks is under construction, space is provided for new civic buildings and for the expansion of shops and bazaars. Outside the walls eight residential areas are planned, each to be inhabited by about 6,000 people. Still farther out on the desert an industrial center is being developed, and beyond this point two large areas have been reserved exclusively for health and educational facilities. As a step toward overcoming the most urgent problem—lack of fresh water—a sea-water distillation plant, the largest in the world, is under construction at a cost of £1,700,000.

In outlining some evidences of swift transformation in the sheikdom, C. A. P. Southwell, managing director of Kuwait Oil, refers to the great strides being made in education, where expansion started some time before oil royalties actually were received. A large number of primary schools now exist. A center for secondary and technical education is nearing completion on the outskirts of Kuwait town. Young Kuwaitis also are being sent abroad to study with funds provided by the state and the oil company.

Kuwait Oil Company is playing a large part in the field of technical education. Faced at the start of oil development with a shortage of skilled labor and tradesmen, some years ago it inaugurated a technical training school in which young Kuwaitis, many of them from nomadic tribes, are trained in a number of trades and then go on to training "on the job." The company's center provides facilities for some 300 trainees, but in view of the increasing opportunities for work in the town, a number of the trainees take employment there in other activities. The Kuwaitis have shown great aptitude and diligence in their technical training.

Improvement in public health is another important task already under way. The prevalence of tuberculosis and eye diseases are medical problems which necessitate a large medical service. Around a nucleus of British and Arab doctors, a state medical service is in the process of development, and public-health services spreading out into the villages also are being organized. In Kuwait town a large hospital built only a few years ago is being enlarged, and new hospitals are being built or planned.

Much of Kuwait's present planning and spending implies the recurrent annual expenditure of many millions, particularly for health and educational services and for the operation and maintenance of public utilities. The steady application of part of the large oil revenues to civic and social improvement promises Middle Eastern leadership for little Kuwait in standards of public health, literacy and living within a few years.

"It is, of course, well known that oil companies operating in areas undeveloped technologically have a significance beyond the purpose for which they exist," Southwell told the Royal Society of Arts in London.[3] "They represent not only the economic organization of the West, but its industrial society, and are the sources from which the peoples concerned draw their conclusions about the West. All those who serve in or have a part in servicing these areas must be fully conscious of the need to show the highest standards of technical skill and integrity of conduct to justify the confidence shown by the inhabitants in western partnership in developing their economy.

"Changes in the social structures in Kuwait are occurring at a rapid pace, and in return for the oil the West needs, it has a moral responsibility to offer friendship and assistance in the process of modern development. The aims of the great majority of the Arab people who see good not only in their own, but in Western civilization as well, are to preserve and enrich the Arab heritage, yet to live in a modern world on an equal footing with other peoples without breaking completely with the past.

[3] *Journal of the Royal Society of Arts*, December 11, 1953.

"The conquest of malnutrition and disease and their replacement by better physical conditions of life, are not enough in themselves. Such developments, however beneficial, do not dampen national aspirations; they tend to encourage these through the realization of what technology can do when blessed with valuable sources of raw materials. There is ambition to make up lost ground, for, as developments take place, they are reminded of former times and the greatness of earlier Arab history. Industrial tranquility is difficult to achieve under these conditions, and can only be obtained by the fullest understanding, by the technologists and others of the West, of the Arab viewpoint, by cooperation in the common application to a vital task, and by the elimination of race consciousness in the communities working there."

Noteworthy in conclusion is a comment in the discussion that followed Southwell's address. Said T. Dewhurst, a member:

"During the past few years, we have heard and read a great deal about President Truman's Fourth Point, which is that the more advanced nations should help in the development of the underdeveloped and undeveloped countries, and I think Kuwait provides a most wonderful example of what has been done in the furtherance of that project. In fact, I think the oil industry has probably done more than any other agency to further President Truman's Fourth Point.

"There should also, I think, be greater awareness of the financial hazards of oil exploration, and a greater appreciation of the high administrative skill and the high standard and variety of scientific knowledge and of technical know-how required in order to discover and to develop oil fields to the maximum advantage of all concerned."

What about Iran? Was not petroleum sown there, too?

After the Anglo-Iranian Oil Company had no alternative but to suspend all field operations and shut down its great refinery in Iran in the autumn of 1951, it submitted to its stockholders "an accurate guide to various aspects of the company's operations which have been ignored or belittled in recent anticompany propaganda." [4] In brief, the report showed Iran at the turn of the century as a country rich in tradition, literature and undeveloped resources. Its 9 million people were dependent on a primitive agriculture which, like its society, was

[4] The Anglo-Iranian Oil Company and Iran, a Description of the Company's Contribution to Iran's Revenue and National Economy, and of Its Welfare Activities for Employees in Iran, Anglo-Iranian Oil Company, November, 1951.

unchanged from ancient times. The government's income was only £1,500,000, derived chiefly from a land tax levied on the principle that 20 per cent of the agricultural products was the right of the King.

Neither the Iranians nor the Britisher W. K. D'Arcy nor his English associates who negotiated the 1901 concession could have foreseen the enormous scale of the enterprise which was to arise. In 1950, oil royalties were about 16 million pounds and would have reached approximately 30 million pounds that year if a new agreement offered by the company had not been rejected. Largely in consequence of oil, Iran's revenues had grown to 90 million pounds per annum. The earnings of the 75,000 AIOC employees amounted to 30 million pounds a year and were subject to the Iranian income tax. Flowing to the government from customs duty, excise, income and other taxes coming from petroleum activity was a direct revenue of about 10 million pounds annually. All these factors constituted a large and essential contribution to the Iranian national economy in its modern aspects.

Nevertheless, important as were pounds sterling, the final advantage which AIOC had brought to Iran "were contributions beneficial to present and succeeding generations of Iranians which are unassessable in monetary terms."

The first oil in commercial quantities was found in 1908 in the Zagros foothills. An arid, bare and inhospitable district, it was inhabited by Bakhtiari herdsmen most of whom were nomadic, though some lived in houses of baked mud which, as often as not, sheltered the animals as well as the family. At the head of the Persian Gulf lay Abadan Island, then, for the most part, a sparsely inhabited desert of salty earth, without roads, treated water supply or drainage. Zagros was to see the development of the oil-producing industry in Iran, and Abadan was to become the site of the world's biggest refinery.

During AIOC's 40 years of petroleum activity in Iran, many changes occurred.

At various centers the company built over 21,000 houses for employees along with roads, shops, clubs, schools, cinemas, swimming pools and, of course, such utilities as electric, water-supply and sanitary systems.

Abadan was transformed into an industrial city with all streets lighted and electricity from the Abadan power station made available to the municipality at low cost. In addition to supplying the great refinery with almost as much water every day as the Metropolitan Water Board provides to the whole of London, AIOC at a nominal rate also furnished the Abadan municipality with 1½ million gallons of treated drinking water daily and partly financed the cost of its water system.

Forty years ago Iran periodically was ravaged by epidemics of cholera, plague and smallpox. Malaria and dysentery were endemic, and diseases of the eye—including trachoma which if neglected results in permanently impaired sight and eventual blindness—were prevalent. No organized facilities existed to deal with any disease or to prevent its constant recurrence.

From the beginning AIOC provided its own medical and health services and aimed to develop them for the benefit of Iranians who eventually would operate them practically by themselves. At the time of the company's expulsion from the country, its medical organization consisted of about 100 specialists and medical officers, a nursing staff of more than 90 fully trained sisters and nurses, a school of nursing whose graduates were eligible for Iranian state registration, and, in addition, dressers, dispensers, laboratory assistants and health inspectors. Fifty-seven per cent of the total medical staff and all the labor were Iranian by birth.

At Abadan the company maintained two fully equipped hospitals— the only ones in the town—one with 350 beds for general treatment and the other with 250 beds for infectious diseases, including malaria and dysentery. AIOC also ran modern hospitals at the Masjid-i-Sulaiman and Agha Jari oil fields.

In 1950, 850,000 treatments for trachoma were given. No serious outbreak of cholera or plague had occurred during the last 25 years. When in 1947 a cholera epidemic broke out elsewhere in the Middle East, 120,000 persons were inoculated with serum made in company laboratories. With the cooperation of the Iranian Ministry of Health as many as 10,000 persons per month were vaccinated for smallpox, which had been endemic. In 1943 the company's Preventive Medical Services speedily arrested an epidemic of typhus which had entered the area from the north.

Of 12,100 hospital cases in 1950, employees numbered 6,900 and nonemployees 5,200; of 1,530,000 dispensary cases, no less than 1,026,-000 were nonemployees. Over 3,000 major and 15,000 minor operations were performed, and over 91,000 laboratory and nearly 18,000 X-ray examinations were given.

When AIOC began operations, the percentage of national illiteracy was such that the company had to bring in from overseas all the craftsmen, technicians, clerks and overseers which it required. From comparatively modest beginnings a plan for education reached a point where AIOC rendered assistance to the Iranian Government Department of Education, especially in Khuzistan, the location of AIOC's main activities. It built and equipped more than 30 schools and presented them to the local authorities while continuing to maintain them and to provide housing for many of the teachers. It established adult and apprentice training courses for artisans, process workers, foremen and clerks as well as higher technical and commercial training at the Abadan Technical Institute. The company also trained selected Iranians in the United Kingdom.

Even before 1930, the company operated apprentice-training shops, and from their classes AIOC drew heavily for employees. In 1939 at Abadan the company opened its Technical Institute which gave instruction to students receiving pay allowances, in engineering, science, commerce and language which was equivalent to a Teheran University degree. In 1949–1950 over 1,200 students attended the institute, and in 1950 the company paid the expenses of over 80 Iranian apprentices and students who received training in British works, technical colleges and universities. By 1950 many Iranian chemists, doctors, engineers and administrators were sharing with British colleagues the responsibility of operating and controlling production, transportation and refining. No longer were these operations managed solely by foreign staff workers.

In 1935 only 8 per cent of labor was literate. It was hoped, however, that by 1955 at least 40 per cent would be literate. Increases in secondary education and technical training were encouraging. The cumulative effects of the principle to provide local education for all Iranians and not merely company employees were visible in the country when AIOC left in 1951. With the number of Iranians holding positions of responsibility increasing, both in the technical and administrative fields, the problem of training others was becoming less difficult, since increasingly the Iranians themselves were taking part in training their fellow countrymen.

For centuries before the advent of oil, Iran's industrial fame had rested chiefly on its output of carpets, rugs and pottery, but by far most of the people were workers on the land. Opportunities for regular employment—with its concomitant advantages of steady income and a rising standard of living—were few and far between. The oil industry became the largest and, until 1934 when the late Shah inaugurated a policy of industrialization, the only source of regular employment in the country, providing steady jobs for approximately 70,000 Iranians. All workmen who could not be housed in AIOC accommodations received a special allowance, while those housed were charged a nominal sum which went toward the upkeep of their houses. In order to ensure its workmen receiving full value for their take-home pay in the postwar period of rising prices and shortages, the company built up a supply organization.

Wages were good. The average worker in Abadan earned about 470 rials, approximately £5 5s. 2d., per week; and the average wage of a skilled man was 570 rials—approximately £6 7s. 6d., per week. Less than 1 per cent of AIOC labor was on the legal minimum wage of 280 rials per week—approximately £3 2s. 8d. All employees got full pay for holidays—24 days in the year for annual leave and public holidays—and when absent because of illness. Retired employees received gratuities after they had served for a stipulated period. The scale was considerably more generous than that provided under the labor laws, and the system had been in operation long before retirement gratuities became compulsory. Working hours were less than the legally permitted 48-hour week, being 43½ and 44½ hours, respectively, in summer and winter. Modern methods of accident prevention safeguarded workers, and every worker was insured against industrial accidents and sickness.

By 1951, thousands of Iranians were well rig men, refinery control room or powerhouse technicians, skilled workers in foundries and steel drum works, printers, builders, shipwrights, divers and moving-picture operators. Many of them, though supported by a British staff, occupied responsible company positions. Among the 119 most senior staff employees, 30 were Iranians, and of the more than 18,000 laborers in top-grade classifications, all but 896 were nationals.

The oil workers with their families numbered about 170,000 persons, and when during the war shortages became acute, AIOC undertook the immense task of supplementing the scanty local supplies by importing great quantities of wheat, barley, rice, tea, sugar, meat and cheese, as well as clothing and other necessities. The company installed flour mills, erected grain storehouses, opened shops and, to avoid the extreme inflation of prices then prevalent in Iran, supplemented the wage increases with issues of certain foods free of charge while it sold others well below cost. When inflation decreased, the company ended its issues in kind and replaced them with increased wages, but the food-supply organization remained in being as a powerful stabilizing force in maintaining the value of the employees' pay envelopes. In 1950 no less than 270 million rials—3 million pounds—worth of goods were bought from AIOC shops. Also, in 1951, two food cooperatives—formed in 1947—had over 5,000 members.

To AIOC it seemed that steps should be taken to increase local farm production—an outlook unpromising in the extreme—since most of the land was either desert or, as in the case of Abadan, a salty, sterile waste. Nevertheless, the company encouraged local cultivators by installing and maintaining irrigation pumps free of charge, by initial plowing and the construction of drainage ditches, with the result that 200 acres of hitherto barren land became productive to add considerably to the supply of vegetables in Abadan. The most striking of these agricultural ventures was the reclamation of the salt desert of Abadan where the soil was washed free of salt—100 tons to the acre—by drainage ditches and by irrigation, with the result that where once nothing grew, there appeared a modern farm of more than 1,000 acres. A similar large-scale farm was producing vegetables, cereals, milk and poultry on the once barren plain adjacent to the oil fields, and large tracts were under cultivation by local farmers working under the guidance of AIOC experts.

After contemplating the record set forth by AIOC, it is difficult to imagine how the company could have been expelled from Iran. Perhaps, it is safe to conclude that, while "good works" may prolong, they by no means guarantee the tenure of a foreign company in these uncertain times.

Shortly after the war, a far-reaching development program for Iran, known as the Seven Year Plan, was mapped out by foreign consultants who studied the country's economy. This plan, supported by oil revenues and embracing agricultural and utility projects, was in its initial stages when the shutdown came—an action that brought calamity to Iran. Only after an interim period of three years were Iran's troubles to be overcome (see Chapter 25, The Iranian Oil Settlement), and the nation's oil industry restored to operation and, with it, the "sowing of petroleum."

Chapter 15

A MIDDLE EASTERNER LOOKS AT OIL

Before we could write intelligently about oil in the Middle East, the Aramco people told us, some understanding of the Arabian point of view was necessary. On its part, Aramco long has sought such understanding as essential to doing business with the Middle East. Yet 20 years of living and working with the Arabs had not gained the company a full knowledge of that ancient, desert people.

Desert sands are never still. They are deep, endlessly shifting, often turbulent. And like a calm, placid and ancient sea, the desert can be whiplashed to fury by passionate winds. So with its proud and ancient people.

How does Aramco try to seek understanding? By retaining the services of interpreters, advisers—indeed, it admits, teachers—and by "going to school" to them every day. Among those so employed are European and American scholars who have spent most of their lives in the Middle East and are steeped in its tradition, as well as Middle Easterners themselves.

With Aramco's advice in mind, we talked at length to an outstanding Middle Easterner on four different occasions within four weeks, and this chapter summarizes those discussions.

Our first questions were: "What are the problems of oil companies entering the Middle East? How are the companies meeting them?"

The problems consist of differences between Western and Middle Eastern culture, particularly in law and religion. The laws of the principalities, or sheikdoms, of the Middle East, for instance, go back to and are based on Mohammedan law—the "Shariah" or sacred law. In most of these countries the prince or ruler is the government and has absolute power over life and property. To enter into negotiations con-

162

cerning trade or development in such nations, an individual or company must proceed in accordance with their laws and customs. To continue as a guest in those countries one must abide by their laws and customs just as faithfully. Iraq, Iran, Bahrain Island, Kuwait—all nations under the British sphere of influence—have, to some extent, reflected a Western influence in their laws and customs. But Saudi Arabia is and always has been entirely out of the British sphere of influence. In 1933, when Saudi Arabia admitted foreigners, the country suffered a severe wrench from its past. Three stories, told by King Ibn Saud himself, who ruled Saudi Arabia until his death in 1953, illustrate the severity of the shock.

Story No. 1 concerned the granting of the concession. When in 1933 the King gave Standard Oil Company of California the original oil concession, his inner council members protested, "You are opening your country to aliens who will introduce their way of life." The King replied, "I am letting in the Americans for our people's own benefit in order that they may help us improve our living conditions. Saudi Arabia is a desert. It lies barren and fallow. The Americans may, if they find oil, bring water and life to the desert. What brings water and life to the desert is good. What improves the desert and its people is good. The Americans can bring material prosperity to Saudi Arabia and raise the standard of living here, just as they have in their own country." And to the Americans Ibn Saud pointed out, "To you this oil means trade and profit. To us Arabs it means our bread and water."

Here our Middle Easterner interpolated another story—his own, rather than the King's—in an effort to indicate the depth of the Arab's nature and the character and force of King Ibn Saud in opening his country to foreign oil developers.

In 1948, as a means of retaliation against Palestine, the Arab League voted against the exportation of the Middle Eastern oil supply. Iraq implemented the resolution by cutting the 12-inch pipeline from the Kirkuk field to the great Haifa refinery in Palestine. Despite the great inconvenience and financial sacrifice which Iraq suffered, not a barrel of oil has flowed through the line since then. Later, at a tremendous cost, a substitute line was laid through Iraq and Syria—entirely in Arab territory—to the Mediterranean. In other words, Arabs will make extreme sacrifices—indeed, no sacrifice is too great—*for a cause*, and their feeling against Israel is profound.

In the same year, on the other hand, when the members of the Arab League asked Ibn Saud to stop the flow of oil from Saudi Arabia, his answer was, "Whereas Iraq and Syria are agricultural countries with beautiful green, Saudi Arabia has nothing to live on except oil. For Saudi Arabia the resolution would be tantamount to suicide."

Our Middle Easterner then returned to the King, and recounted Story No. 2 which revealed why Ibn Saud favored Americans. Before 1933 the King had asked the British whether they were interested in exploring for oil, and they had turned down Saudi Arabia as unpromising. They were nonplused, nevertheless, when Ibn Saud granted a concession to Americans, and apparently members of his own council were, too. The King answered the latter's criticism by saying, "Americans are producers, developers. So are the British. But Saudi Arabia is outside the British sphere of influence and wants to stay outside. Whereas Britain is next door," the King finished, "the United States is far away and does not constitute a political danger."

Our Middle Easterner then outlined the history of Arabia, of its nomadic people, the sheikdoms, the ancestral rivalries, the Saudi Arabian boundary disputes—an old situation that has flared up today and is just as acute as ever.

The boundary disputes are deeply rooted in two cultural factors, (1) a nomadic economy based on the camel—migrations in search of pasture, of the "beautiful green"—and (2) in *razzias*. When the heavens became uncharitable and rain did not come, the people resorted to expeditions of conquest in which the strong tried to take what the weak could not defend. Families were pitted against each other, and the feud was inherited by succeeding generations. What you did to me or my relative last year, I'll do to you this year. In Arabia the *razzias* constituted unrest and lack of law and order. The English language contains no literal or even suitable translation of *razzia*. Perhaps the closest word is raid or foray, even piracy, but a *razzia* involves a code of honor, the ancient, deeply rooted code of the desert.

Ibn Saud did an excellent job in quieting the country. Against brigandage and theft he enforced Koranic law in all its rigor. Brigandage meant death; theft, in varying degrees of guilt, cost a hand, both hands, or both hands and feet.

Yet the King would have been unsuccessful had he not provided sustenance for the tribes. He succeeded in eliminating internal strife in the country because his paternalistic government looked after the needs of the people when the rains did not come. And he could care for the people only through revenue from the pilgrimages to Mecca and Medina and from oil, principally the latter. Under Ibn Saud's policies a profound transformation occurred—instead of nomadism, settlement; instead of lawlessness, peace and order. These characteristics are more relevant in Saudi Arabia than in other Middle Eastern countries.

In its more recent aspects the boundary controversy involves Saudi Arabia and Great Britain, with the latter acting as the protecting power of various sheikdoms, emirates or principalities along the Persian Gulf. In former years the activities of the piratical sheiks had created a situation similar to that brought into being by the Moorish pirates along the Barbary Coast of North Africa in the nineteenth century. Britain, however, just before and right after the turn of this century established peace and order in the Persian Gulf, policed, charted, lighted and opened it to trade and navigation. She put the emirs and pirates in their places and suppressed them by the promulgation of treaties. Henceforth, no more piracy, no more mutual invasions. As a result of the truces established among the sheikdoms and between them and the British, the terms of "trucial sheiks" and "trucial sheikdoms" came into use. These refer to the coastal sheikdoms along the Persian Gulf and are under British influence, while the Arabian hinterland is under the family of Saud.[1]

The crux of the boundary controversy is the Buraimi Oasis which the British consider as part of the territory of the Sultan of Muscat, but which is claimed by the House of Saud, now represented by Saud Ibn or Saud I, who succeeded to the crown on the death of Ibn Saud, his father.

It would be unrealistic not to recognize that the situation has become inflammable, principally because of oil—the actual, potential or imaginary reserves buried under the sands of the various sheikdoms—but also because of the growing oil rivalry between British and Americans in the Middle East. In other words, expanding American interests, or

[1] Appendix II, Section 2, Treaties with Middle Eastern Countries and Sheikdoms.

perhaps American ascendancy, in the Middle East cannot help but be challenging to the British who are tied to the trucial sheikdoms. Thus, in the Middle East, complicated tribal or local politics are compounded with international politics.

Story No. 3 concerned Ibn Saud's welcome to the Americans after he had granted them the concession. Quite simply the King told company representatives, "I have given you protection, and you can go about the width and breadth of my country freely, just as my own people. You're like my own children. The land is before you, walk in it."

Our Middle Easterner then related another story—first told by a member of Ibn Saud's council and now in a high post—relative to the council's opposition to permitting the Americans to enter Saudi Arabia. The advisory group objected to the terms of the concession agreement, claiming that 4 shillings gold per ton royalty was too little. Ibn Saud replied, "The Koran says on fertile land, a tithe of one-tenth, on unfertile land, one-half as much. The Americans are offering about one-fourth. Are you unsatisfied with one-fourth when God is satisfied with one-twentieth?"

The Middle Easterner's stories, in sum, emphasize the significant magnitude of the step taken by Ibn Saud in granting the concession. His are a proud and ancient people with an established and ancient culture, with ancient laws based upon an ancient religion. Voluntarily sacrificing their isolationism made a tremendous impact upon them.

But simply stating that Ibn Saud gave Standard Oil of California a concession under agreed terms fails to convey the whole picture. Lacking is the human element. Indeed, the human equation—as so often is true—cannot be minimized in the case of those Americans who—like Columbus shall we say?—landed on the sands of Arabia in 1933 and those who immediately followed them. The Middle Easterner referred specifically to the Standard of California men, the late Lloyd Hamilton, Socal vice-president, and the late Max Steineke, Aramco chief geologist, as being not merely representatives of commerce. They were exceptional human beings, ambassadors extraordinary of good will. No more critical a period can be imagined than the start of the association, the first commingling of American and Arab on Saudi Arabia's sands in the thirties. Nobody then realized the extent of the treasure lying deep under the Arabian desert. No one dreamed how profound would be the impact of its discovery.

That story, our Middle Easterner concluded, should be written. It is a tale of disappointment and hardship, but also of vision, faith and common brotherhood in five years of desert search. Recent though the occurrence was, it ranks as a saga of pioneering.

Our second question was: "How has Saudi Arabia adjusted itself to oil wealth? Do its rulers see that the people benefit?" The substance of our Middle Easterner's discussion follows.

When the oil company came, Saudi Arabia had only one large source of revenue—the annual pilgrimages to Mecca and Medina. The economic impact of oil was terrific, for the Arabian economy, symbolized by the camel and the ibex, was primitive—far more than were our horse-and-buggy days. When the American company came, it established its own airlines, its DC-4's—and now its DC-6B's—flying on regular schedule. It is literally true that the discovery and development of oil precipitated Saudi Arabia from the camel to the airplane, bypassing the railroad and motorcar in one breathless moment without the evolutionary stages that might have given the people time to adjust themselves to change. They must be given time to make that adjustment.

The immense size of the Middle East's oil reserves scarcely is comprehended. Estimated in 1951 at 50 per cent of the world's known reserves, today they are over 60 per cent of the total. After oil had been discovered Saudi Arabians increasingly heard of and became interested in the profits that the Americans made, or were reported to be making. Naturally, they wondered whether they should not get a larger share—as the French say, *L'appétit vient en mangeant*. Rich returns from the oil had whetted Saudi Arabian appetites.

The companies, meantime, were learning that they must revise their concession terms. Beginning in Venezuela, a new policy—a 50-50 profit-sharing plan—was making a bid for universality. The terms in Saudi Arabia were revised accordingly.

The country's sudden oil wealth brought problems. Though oil made a few individuals extremely rich, it cannot be denied that the standard of living as a whole gained because of the general widespread prosperity. Aramco was an important employer of labor and paid good wages. Part of the oil royalty was bound to go for public works, agricultural development, education, health and security against other tribes—all resulting in better conditions for the common man.

Saudi Arabians, at first, could not comprehend the great simple fact that oil is a diminishing, a vanishing asset. Once taken from the ground and shipped out of the country, it is gone forever. If the revenues collected from oil were not utilized in profitable investments, the day would come when the petroleum would be gone with the country having derived little or no benefit from it.

In Saudi Arabia, happily, the authorities reply to those who want to exploit oil quickly and get quick prosperity by saying, "Let's keep some for the future, for our children." More education as to the exhaustibility of petroleum is needed, however, and the oil companies have aided in teaching this truism. In every way possible they are assisting in public-utility projects that will benefit the people, but their efforts suffer from certain general handicaps.

American companies in the Middle East observe the limitations of the law and the sovereignty of the Arab nations. They respect tradition and keep to their policy of having nothing to do with politics. Strictly they adhere to their self-imposed fiat: "We're not in politics; we're in business."

Yet the oil companies operating in the Middle East do realize that they have a mission beyond the efficient operation of their industry. In these countries where poverty is so widespread, they cannot be simply a business company. They have a business *and* a social mission, and they consider that they owe a duty far beyond the obligation of paying royalty on oil to the nation in which they operate.

The results are discernible. The Arabs have been a nomadic people not from choice, but of necessity. They have wandered in search of food. They needed more arable land upon which to settle and raise food. They needed modern transportation. Now they are getting more of both. Saudi Arabia is being transformed before their very eyes.

Our third question to our Middle Easterner was broad in scope: "What primary understandings should the American people and government have about the Middle East and the problems of American companies operating in these countries?" Again a summary of his discussion follows.

Americans must realize, first of all, that the ancient peoples of the Middle East have a point of view that to them is as logical and sound as the American point of view is to Americans and which, perhaps, has deeper roots. Such understanding is difficult to attain. It is not easy for Americans to take seriously the rivalries or feuds of the sheikdoms. Yet to the people involved the points of allegiance and loyalty are of primary importance according to the desert code of honor.

Americans must recognize, secondly, that the Middle East, though low in economic wealth, is inhabited by proud nations with ancient cultural and spiritual traditions which the people regard as their sacred heritage. Whenever moral values dear to the heart of the Arab come in conflict with material values, the Arabian has no hesitancy in sacrificing the latter. Americans, therefore, must be very careful not to minimize in any way the Arab's way of life, or his scale of life, however different it may be.

Despite Kipling, East and West *have* met through oil development in the Middle East—are increasingly meeting. But the Americans should keep in mind the fact that the best that can be hoped for is a compromise between the old and the new. Continuously both sides must try to bring about the necessary adjustments. To maintain understanding and work out solutions when disputes arise, the highest qualities of statesmanship and the greatest ingenuity and skill are required. Patience, restraint and, above all, humanity should characterize the Americans' attitude and action in the Middle Eastern area, and everywhere. They must remember that the "outmoded" human virtues and ideals do work. Behind it all is the basic fact: We all are human.

Third, to try to be clever is shortsighted. In dealing with Arabians, mutuality of advantage and consciousness of common interest should guide American policy. In their relations with the Arabs the oil companies have observed this basic fact. In the common effort of Americans and Arabians to develop oil, Americans must realize that to the Arab the development is a means to an end and not an end in itself. Though much has been done to Westernize the outlook of the Arab— who is quick to learn—no attempt should be made to transplant to the desert the American way of life or the American philosophy of life to the detriment of the Arab manner of life which has a value of its own.

Fourth, Americans would be quite wrong to take for granted that the Arabs see things as they do, or to expect the Arabs to act as they would wish them to. Ways and means to find avenues of agreement between the outlook of the Western and Eastern mind exist, but they have their limitations. While we diligently must seek areas of agreement, we must not try to force the pace or to anticipate the future. In bringing about an increasing measure of understanding between the different outlooks, time is a factor of extreme importance.

Happily, some pioneering spirits are spearheading the caravan. Prominent among them are the scholars and scientists among the oil-company personnel—men of vision and wisdom who are interested in more than the immediate objective of developing some of the material wealth of the Middle East.

Aramco has been in Saudi Arabia for nearly two decades, and long contact with the Arabs has brought home many useful lessons. Aramco personnel are making it a point to prepare themselves in learning the language, customs, culture and traditions of the Arab people. Very strange, but true, is the remark made by one of the officials not long ago, "Aramco is an ideal, manned by idealists, pioneers and adventurers in free enterprise."

Fifth, between Americans and Arabians real cooperation must exist, not condescending assistance. The effort must be a common one.

Briefly our Middle Easterner summarized the ways to understanding between Americans and Arabians: (1) the difference in viewpoint must be recognized; (2) greater understanding must be reached; (3) both peoples must be content with compromise solutions; (4) both must realize the basic, human similarity despite outward differences; and (5) Americans must give cooperative rather than condescending assistance. Compromise, or pragmatism, may not be ideal, but it has worked and will continue to work. Wise men have been brought up in this tradition.

Still not finished, despite his summary, the Middle Easterner authorized a direct quotation: "American greatness, I believe, is in the private initiative and pioneering spirit of its people—above all, in the pioneering spirit to which all Americans, even the humble, contribute. The success of American free enterprise has been far from painless. Indeed, for one that has succeeded, ten have failed. The more resourceful, more daring, more intelligent, it may be said, are the ones that have succeeded. Yet everyone, even the failures, have contributed because trial and error are fundamental to dynamic pioneering. The pioneering spirit is your country's great contribution to the world. And if there is a sense of adoration in American greatness, it is, with me, the efforts of pioneering Americans in foreign lands.

"Many think of foreign oil operations in this light: Here is the oil, served up on a platter. They don't consider the other side of the medal. The hardships, austerity, discipline and sacrifice, not excluding the sacrifice of lives. Not a few American oil pioneers, and pioneers in other fields, have died on the hot desert sands, many have died because of the unaccustomed severity of the life. It costs more than money to create this American success story in foreign oil.

"Yet that success story is the story of cooperative enterprise. While the Americans contribute their science and their modern techniques, the Arabs contribute their resources which a bountiful nature has buried beneath the sands of their desert. They also give their labor and their intelligence. Too, the governments in the area contribute an intangible asset without which no development would have been possible—the determination and ability to maintain order and a rule of law in a land where respect for life and property are secured in ways which—different though they may be from your Western procedures—work satisfactorily in the Middle East."

PART FOUR

WHAT'S THE SCORE?

Chapter 16

CANADA ON THE HORIZON

Before our very eyes Canada demonstrates the time-lag factor which besets oil men operating in foreign countries—the factor of spending much and waiting long before getting returns, if they ever do, on their investments.

Canada, in a petroleum sense, is a delayed United States. Historically, its belated promise shows a time lag of almost a century, for our northern neighbor was at the starting line in the late 1850's along with Rumania, Russia and the United States. Only a few months after August, 1859, when near Titusville in western Pennsylvania Drake drilled the well that founded the United States industry, Canada discovered the Black Creek field in southwestern Ontario. Located in the same area, the Petrolia and Oil-Springs pools, found in 1867, created excitement that suggested Titusville. Subsequent oil booms fevered New Brunswick in 1879 and the early 1900's, and Calgary in southwest Alberta in 1915–1917. But Canadian fields never lived up to their expectations. In many respects Canada's oil position was discouraging—always the prospects were good, always the results were frugal. In the 30 years before 1947 about 2,000 wells were drilled in Western Canada, but only two fields of consequence were found— Turner Valley where production had leveled off, and Imperial Oil's Fort Norman operation close to the Arctic Circle which was of only local significance.

Such was the story until Leduc arrived.

On a bleak February day in 1947—with the temperature 40 below zero—on the flat near the hamlet of Leduc, 20 miles south of Edmonton in the prairie province of Alberta, Imperial Oil struck oil in a deeply buried coral reef. The strike changed everything. The "rush" was on. How many millions were poured into Canadian oil exploration and development from 1860 up to the start of the current boom is anybody's guess. But for more recent years fairly accurate figures and examples are available, and the sums going into the Prairie Provinces of Alberta, Saskatchewan and Manitoba and into the Northwest Territories since Leduc are a matter of reliable record.

As was mentioned in Chapter 2, when the Leduc field came in during 1947, an estimated 125 million dollars already had gone into the previous three decades of Canadian oil effort with relatively small results. Exploration and development from 1947 to 1954 has cost another 600 million dollars and pipeline construction an additional 200 million dollars. Today returns are beginning to come in. But an end to spending is nowhere in sight, for in 1954 Canada was in its eighth year of the world's biggest current oil boom and still was going strong.

For Imperial Oil Limited—70 per cent owned by Standard of Jersey—the Leduc discovery was particularly rewarding. Imperial got its start in 1880 down in the tip of southwestern Ontario during one of that province's periodic booms. A merger of seven small independent refineries operating on the shoestring of Canadian oil, Imperial was encouraged by the then current boom to follow the railroad west. At each fledgling settlement Imperial's storage tank appeared in the usual cluster of station, water tank and grain elevator. But, after overreaching itself in continental expansion, the company found it had no funds for badly needed refining and bulk transport systems. Furthermore, it was badgered by the problem of a reliable crude-oil supply, the greatest part of which had to be brought in from abroad because of successive domestic disappointments. Imperial directors approached Standard of Jersey which, in exchange for majority interest, supplied the needed capital. Imperial then went forward with giant strides—one might almost say with the lumbering but decisive strides of an energetic young man-mountain named Walter Clark Teagle whom Jersey put in as president.

Within the three years until November, 1917—when he was called back to Standard of Jersey to become its youngest president—Teagle had expanded Imperial's Sarnia, Regina and Vancouver plants in Ontario, Saskatchewan and British Columbia, respectively, had completed a new refinery at Montreal and was building another at Dartmouth, Nova Scotia. There was not enough Canadian crude completely to supply Sarnia, whose Canadian runs were supplemented by Mid-Continent crude. Regina ran on Wyoming crude, while Montreal took Mexican oil. But Teagle reached all the way down into Peru for supplies for the Vancouver refinery. Through International Petroleum Company, a wholly owned subsidiary, Imperial took over British producing properties and a small refinery in the South American country. While Teagle was enlarging the Vancouver plant, he did the same for the Talara, Peru, refinery. He was searching for foreign sources of crude oil for Imperial in nations other than the United States in an effort to make Canada independent, if possible, as to raw-material supply. He was dickering for Tropical Oil which was starting the development of its De Mares concession in Colombia—a deal consummated by International a few years later.

In 1917 when Teagle left Imperial Oil Company, Limited, to return to Jersey, Imperial Oil, Limited, as constituted today, was formed with 50 million dollars capital. As Canada grew, Imperial grew. Eventually, it became a completely integrated giant in refining, transport and marketing, and—in so far as possible—in production. Always searching, it spent great sums to turn up fields. In the 14 years after the decline of Turner Valley, from 1933 to 1947, for example, Imperial sank 23 million dollars in that area plus another 7 million dollars between February, 1947—when at long last its faith was rewarded at Leduc—and late the same year when Leduc oil was first commercially marketed.

In recent years many American-owned companies—Texas, Gulf, Cities Service, Standard of California and Socony-Vacuum to name only a few—tried their luck in Canada. The Texas Company, which holds a clear second position to Imperial in Canadian production, incorporated to do business there back in 1928. First conducting marketing operations, the company early in the thirties acquired leases and participated with others in drilling its first well—an unsuccessful venture. The company's later activities in acquiring leases throughout the Edmonton area parallel Imperial's inasmuch as its respective reservations were contiguous to Imperial's at many points. Texas conducts its own as well as joint operations with the McColl-Frontenac Oil Company, a Canadian concern. Even before Imperial's discovery at Leduc, Texaco was doing geological and geophysical work and attempting to evaluate the areas.

The exploratory effort of the Texaco-McColl team was initiated in the first instance by McColl-Frontenac at the commencement of World War II, when the discovery of crude-oil reserves in Canada was pressed as an urgent military necessity. Late in 1939 McColl-Frontenac formed its Exploration Department under the direction of a geologist loaned by The Texas Company, with technical personnel recruited in Canada. Through the war, the search for oil was prosecuted by seismic shooting, geological study and the drilling of test wells. In 1946 four gas fields were discovered in the Pakowki Lake region, with reserves approaching half a trillion cubic feet. When, in November, 1947, Texaco Exploration Company, a subsidiary of The Texas Company, entered the play in equal partnership with McColl-Frontenac, the exploration tempo was increased, more seismic crews were engaged, further land holdings were acquired, and a more intensive exploratory drilling program was initiated. It was not until August, 1949, however, almost 10 years from the starting date, that the companies' first crude-oil production was obtained, on leases in the Redwater field, purchased at a Crown sale. Shortly afterward some sites yielding small production were discovered on the companies' holdings in the Calmar area, a southwest extension of the Leduc field.

At the beginning of 1950, Texaco Exploration Company took over the entire exploratory burden, under an agreement whereby McColl-Frontenac received a "carried" 10 per cent royalty in Texaco's net interest on all lands previously held jointly and the right to acquire a working interest of not more than 50 per cent in any future leases which Texaco might purchase.

At this point the two companies had spent considerable sums of money and had only their Redwater, South Leduc and Calmar production and the Pakowki Lake gas fields to show for it. Convinced, however, that there were still large reserves of oil and gas waiting to be found in Alberta, the companies not only continued but intensified their search, and finally in May, 1951, Texaco had its first good fortune—the discovery of the Wizard Lake field. The field is under 100 per cent Texaco control, since no other operators hold leases within its productive limits. Drilled on a site 1½ miles from a previously abandoned dry hole, the first Wizard Lake well was noteworthy in that it found no less than four productive zones, one of gas and three

Profound change in Saudi Arabia—Aramco's Ras Tanura refinery in the background.

Repair crew keeps oil flowing from Persian Gulf to Mediterranean.

Modern quarters of Aramco employees in shadow of Moslem mosque.

Talking shop at Aramco Craft Training Center in Darhran.

This Aramco employee is one of many with 15 years of company service.

Aramco employees enjoying facilities of company library.

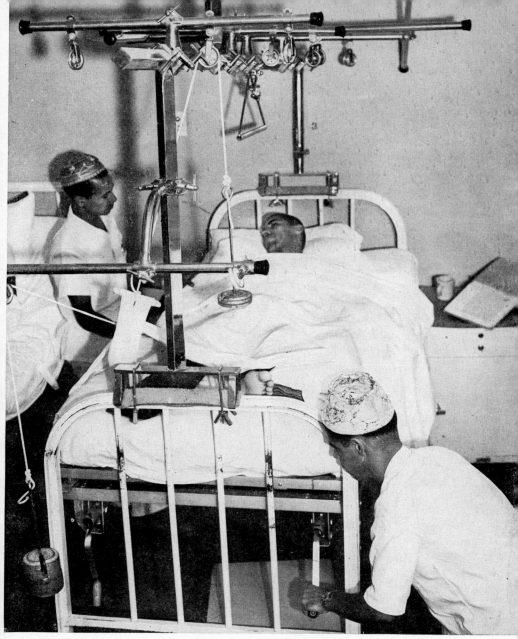

These Saudi trainee nurses at Aramco hospital are conscientious.

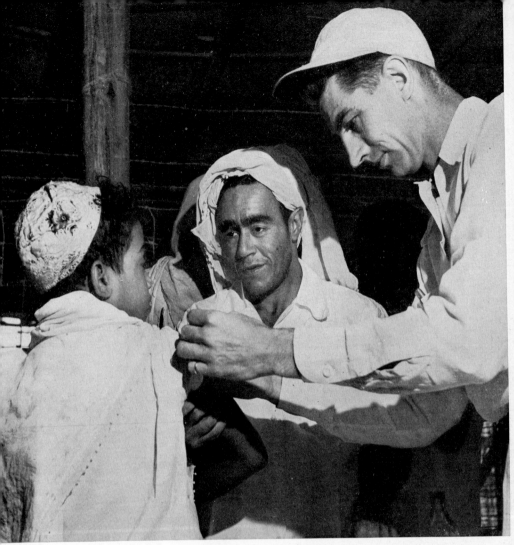

American medical team member inoculates Saudi youngster against smallpox.

Tanker links Middle East with world markets at Shuwarkh, Kuwait.

Morning line-up at Caltex Pacific clinic at Pakanbarn, Indonesia.

Engineer sets dynamite on oil-company road-building project at Klamonafuld, New Guinea.

Venezuelan drillers on well at Jusepin, Eastern Venezuela.

Sign of progress in Venezuela—road building, Carapito to Maturin.

Famous overwater wells in Lake Maracaibo, Western Venezuela.

Creole Petroleum's workers' camp at Lagunillas, Venezuela.

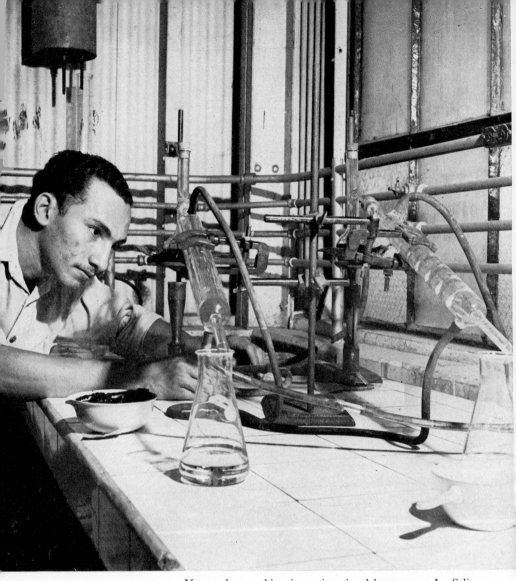

Venezuelan working in engineering laboratory at La Salina.

After-hours study class for illiterate Venezuelan oil workers.

Venezuelan oil worker and family in their company home.

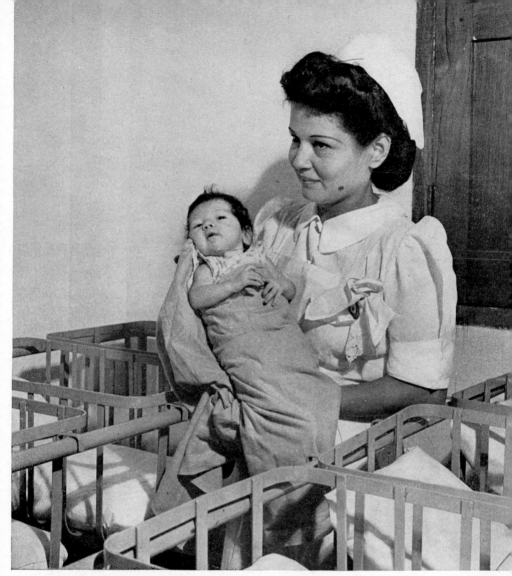

New arrival at maternity ward of Catimas camp, Venezuela.

Aerial view of Barranca Bermija on de Mares concession, Colombia.

Oil freight—familiar sight on Colombia's Magdalena River.

Seventeen pack animals are in this Colombian geological field expedition.

Geologist works in stream bed of dense Colombian jungle.

Company train brings shoppers home from market, Talara, Peru.

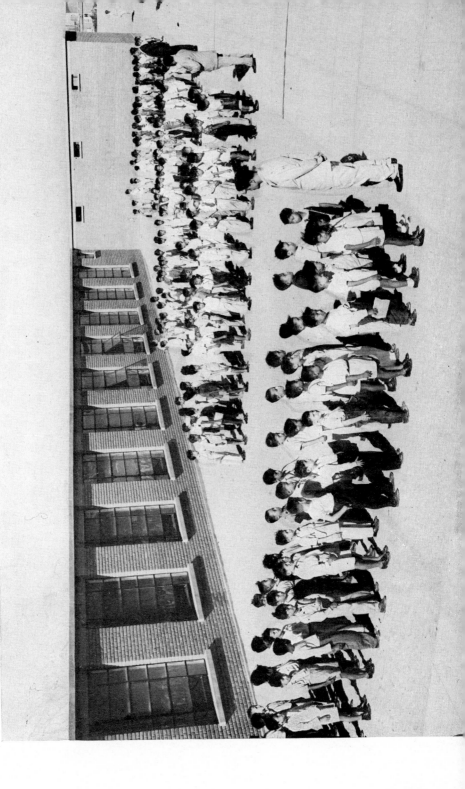

Ready for school—oil workers' children at Talara, Peru.

Leduc well No. 1—discovery that started the Western Canada boom.

Dogs, plane and passengers at Norman Wells field, Canada.

Cold?--Oil worker in the sunlight at Norman Wells, Canada.

Laying the Interprovincial Pipe Line in Canada.

Seismograph exploration expedition pitches camp in Alberta, Canada.

The Trans Mountain Pipe Line crosses the Canadian Rockies.

Warming up the snowmobile for Western Canada field trip.

of oil, and also the thickest section of oil-bearing Devonian reef yet found in Western Canada. This well found 618 feet of oil pay in the D-3 zone, and though one of the highest wells in the field, it was later surpassed by an offset with 635 feet. Here by the end of July, 1953, Texaco had drilled 44 producing wells and the field had yielded 3,309,512 barrels of light-gravity crude. The production rate in August, 1953, was 13,500 barrels per day.

Texaco then went 6 miles southwest to Bonnie Glen where its second important oil strike came in January, 1952, with the discovery of another Devonian reef. The first well in this field, the highest to date, found 700 feet of Devonian reef, of which the top 400 feet was gas cap and the remaining 300 feet oil pay. By the end of July, 1953, Texaco had drilled 39 producing wells, and other companies had drilled 20, and 10 drilling rigs were at work in the field. By this date the field had produced 2,903,197 barrels of better than 40-degree API gravity crude, and the production rate in August, 1953, was 28,121 barrels per day.

These two discoveries suggested the existence of a series of pinnacle reefs, along a southwest trend from the Leduc field and resulted in an intensive oil play throughout the area. Important discoveries have since been made at Pigeon Lake, Westerose, Homeglen and Rimbey, and several prospective wildcats were drilling in 1954.

In the fall of 1951, Texaco laid an 8-inch pipeline from Wizard Lake to Edmonton, and in 1952, it was extended, first to Bonnie Glen and then to Pigeon Lake. In 1953 it became apparent that this line was inadequate to handle the increasing production from the area it served, and a 16-inch loop line was laid from Edmonton to Bonnie Glen. The oil produced from the Wizard Lake and Bonnie Glen fields is being used to supply the requirements of McColl-Frontenac's refinery at Edmonton, completed in the fall of 1951, and surplus is being sold to other refiners in Edmonton.

In addition to development drilling at Wizard Lake and Bonnie Glen, Texaco has maintained a continuous exploratory program, and in mid-year 1954 was operating 12 seismic and two gravity-meter crews in Alberta. Exploratory wells have been drilled in the Peace River area, the Central Plains and in southern Alberta. Some of these have resulted in discoveries of gas at Dixonville, Majeau Lake, Ponoka, and Enchant, black oil at Glenevis, and some interesting shows of oil with the gas at Enchant. Four wildcats were being drilled in the Central Plains, one in the Peace River area and two in southern Alberta. A deep test was drilling in northeastern British Columbia by the Northern Foothills group, in which Texaco shares a 25 per cent interest, with Canadian Gulf, Shell and Socony.

Despite its successes, Texaco Exploration Company shows a loss of $34,700,000 over a period of about six years in its Canadian operations, having expended a total of $58,300,000 and taken out only $23,-600,000. To these figures must be added $13,500,000 for reservations recently acquired and not included above. To explore and develop these will cost many additional millions before there is any possibility of return on the invested capital.

Gulf investigated the oil prospects of Nova Scotia in 1924 and, in the following year, extended its work to include New Brunswick. Finding nothing, the company stopped the job in 1926, but held its properties for a few years pending the completion of deep test drilling by other interests in adjoining areas. They, too, failed to find oil. It was only after years of exploration that Gulf's activities brought substantial results, and the company now is a large producer in Western Canada.

In the early 1940's two American oil companies jointly made two seismograph surveys over a part of Prince Edward Island in the Gulf of the St. Lawrence. Too, they conducted surface studies, and in 1943–1944 drilled a deep test well, but did not strike oil. Without reward, they also did surface work on the mainland of Nova Scotia nearest to Prince Edward Island.

An American company whose name is withheld reported a loss of $1,500,000 in the Turner Valley field, while in the same field a third American company, as another example of time lag in Canada, cited expenditures of almost $2,000,000 from February, 1927, to April, 1939, before it obtained its first revenue. Still another company showed an outlay of $5,400,000 from July, 1941, the date of its first investment in Canada, to September, 1948, plus an additional $2,800,000 spent before commercially marketing oil in June, 1949—a total investment of $8,200,000 in advance of receipts. A fifth American company spent $14,400,000 in Canada from its first investment in February, 1948, until May, 1951, when it sold its first oil.[1]

[1] See Appendix I, Table 4, Large Initial Investment and Long Time Lag.

On a limited scale Socony-Vacuum entered the Western Canada "play" in 1943. Geologists studied the country, seeking structural indications favorable to the presence of oil. After the Leduc discovery well came in, the company stepped up its effort as did others on the scene. After drilling nine dry holes, in 1950 Socony finally made a strike—a producing well about 42 miles southeast of the rich Leduc-Woodbend field.

On July 1, 1953, when Socony-Vacuum's No. 1 Pembina well came in, it opened up not only a new field but a new oil reservoir in the Cardium sand, in west-central Alberta. Socony-Vacuum, with a half interest in the combined holdings of Seaboard Oil Co., Honolulu Oil Corp., Merrill Petroleums Ltd., and Cancoll Oil & Gas Ltd., spudded the discovery well on February 24, 1953. At that time, only three wells had been drilled within a 30-mile radius of the test. The Cardium sand had yielded only showings of gas in the foothills area of western Alberta. In June, 1954, conservative geologists attributed 267,-520 proved and semiproved acres to the field. This included an area some 28 miles long and 18 miles wide with 39 wells completed.[2]

Why was oil not found in quantity in the Prairie Provinces before Leduc—except for an occasional field which fired hopes destined to be dashed with the cold water of drilling failures? The answer lies partly in Canada's inaccessible, rugged and vast reaches and partly in the unpredictability of its geology and oil-bearing sands. The break came when Imperial decided to back a young geologist who came up with a new, or previously discounted, theory—that oil in Alberta might be stored in stratigraphic traps somewhat like West Texas. The best means of testing the theory was by seismograph. Truly Canada is profiting by that latest phase of scientific oil finding—geophysical methods. During the first cycle of oil exploration from 1859 to 1914 oil seeps, divining rods, random drilling and, when science made its bow in the last part of the nineteenth century, surface geology were utilized as the sole means and methods of locating reserves. Then geophysical methods—the use of the seismograph, gravity meter and magnetometer—gradually evolved, to reach their highest utilization only in recent years. Modern exploration embraces all three scientific methods.

Aeons ago, at intervals of millions of years, inland seas covered

[2] *The Oil and Gas Journal,* June 28, 1954, p. 74.

various parts of the North American continent, sometimes stretching from the Gulf of Mexico to the North Pole. Surviving at different levels from various ages, the limestone, sandstone or shale beds of ancient oceans remain today as buried strata, and from Texas to Point Barrow, Alaska, they have been the source of oil.[3]

Beneath the Western Plains of Canada, these sedimentary beds lie flat like layers of a huge geological cake. Six thousand feet below the surface—nearly at the bottom of this series of sedimentary layers—lies one of the oldest beds, deposited hundreds of millions of years ago by a sea of the Devonian Age. Over the limestone and shale strata of this bed once washed a tropical sea from whose tepid shallows great coral reefs rose in long barriers, scattered chains and solitary bastions. Today they remain as gigantic masses of coral limestone embedded deep in the earth between other layers of sediment, and into them vast quantities of oil from the teeming plant and organic life of those long-vanished seas have seeped upward to become trapped.

On the surface little or nothing indicates the presence of such a reef below. Hence Canadian exploration has been almost entirely by seismograph, a method which records the shock waves of dynamite blasts as they are reflected back from successive layers. Careful correlating of the readings with information from cores, outcrops and previous recordings makes it possible to piece together a picture of how the layers lie underground—whether they rise or fall, how thick they are and of what they are made. These data go a long way in determining the chances that oil may have accumulated in pools a mile or more down in the earth.

How successful have oil men been with such scientific methods in their intensive search for "showings" in Canada? They have found oil over a wide area from British Columbia eastward to Manitoba, a distance of over 1,000 miles. They have discovered it in the region stretching from the Montana border 600 miles northward to the Peace River district in the Northwest Territories. Beyond that area the prospects continue good around Fort Norman which boasts an early producing oil field and a refinery almost on the Arctic Circle. Finally, between the Peace River district and Hudson Bay the great Athabaska tar sands await development with reserves which may possibly be

[3] *Standard Oil Bulletin,* July, 1951, p. 11.

several times the total proved oil reserves of the world! Mining these tar sands for oil, however, is economically prohibitive as compared with producing petroleum from buried oil sands.

Simply put, the oil sands which oil men have found in Canada compare favorably with any in the world except the extraordinary producing sands of the Middle East. Recent results have been little short of breath-taking. With reserves of well over 200 million barrels the Leduc field alone multiplied Canada's reserves overnight. By the end of 1952 five major fields—that is, those believed to contain more than 100 million barrels—had been discovered, and Redwater, the largest, was estimated to have reserves of over 600 million barrels. Since Leduc, about 75 other commercial fields with smaller reserves have been added. Furthermore, both the proportion of large to small fields and the number of barrels of new reserves per thousand feet of exploration drilling compared favorably with Texas, the United States' greatest oil-producing state. Not all the new-found oil comes from coral reefs. Canada's fields fall into three categories—coral reefs, sandstones and limestones—and in those categories production is being obtained from six different types of geological formations. At Leduc, Redwater and Wizard Lake coral-reef formation has been particularly fruitful.

Because of these discoveries, Canada's total reserves soared from a mere 45,000,000 barrels in 1946 to 1,950,000,000 barrels in 1953.[4] In terms of square miles of sedimentary basin—which is favorable to oil accumulation—Western Canada is about three times the size of Texas. Geological differences between the two areas make it difficult to estimate whether the Canadian exploration efforts ever will equal those in Texas. Authorities say, however, that if Canada's rate of oil discovery is maintained—actually they believe it will increase in the future—it would be reasonable to believe that by 1960 the country will possess sufficient reserves to support a production of considerably over 600,-000 barrels a day—this compared with 221,000 barrels daily actually produced in 1953 and 20,000 barrels a day in 1946.

Such spectacular progress could come only as the result of considerable effort and vast expenditures. To attract such feverish activity and such sizable investment a factor other than oil promise had to be, and was, present—a favorable economic and political climate. Canada's mineral resources largely are owned by the provinces, not by the na-

[4] *The Oil and Gas Journal*, December 21, 1953, p. 118.

tional government. When it became apparent that the West was in for an "oil play," the provincial governments acted promptly. Drawing on the advice of the oil men, they enacted laws and formulated regulations that would attract both domestic and foreign investment.

As a result, scores, then hundreds of companies joined the handful of old-line concerns like Imperial that had made up Canada's petroleum industry. Practically every large United States producing company not already in Canada rushed to join those already there. All of them—new, old, domestic and foreign—leased great tracts of land for wildcat drilling and in many cases operate jointly to share the risks and costs involved. At the end of 1953 about 500 oil companies were working in Western Canada. The government policy of reserving portions of leased lands for later sale at auction has enabled many operators to enter fields discovered by others, and, of course, participations and farmouts have been frequent.[5]

Not all companies strike oil—or enough oil. No one ever knows what luck he is going to have. To establish whether coral reefs are oil-bearing requires an immense amount of geophysical work, and, of course, the only ultimate test is to drill. The story of the Wizard Lake field in Alberta illustrates the hazard and unpredictability of oil-finding operations in such terrain. The discovery well was only $1\frac{1}{2}$ miles from a dry hole which had been drilled four years previously and which gave no indication of the important structure which lay close by. On the other hand, the fact that Wizard Lake was discovered has more than an intrinsic importance, for it suggests that some of the areas which have been worked over unsuccessfully might be reworked with the possibility of discovering fields of comparable value. In this immense area the scope for future development is almost limitless.

So much for a highlight picture of the advent in the world of a great new oil-producing area. But there is more to oil than production.

When the Leduc discovery well came in, Canada was dependent on foreign sources for 90 per cent of its oil. Leduc, however, lies in far off Alberta, in the western interior, while 90 per cent of the country's population is concentrated in the eastern and maritime provinces. The Prairie Provinces and Northwest Territories are sparsely settled. While British Columbia, west of the Rockies along the Pacific, cannot compete in quantity consumed with the thickly settled

[5] *The Oil and Gas Journal*, December 21, 1953, p. 312.

East, which accounts for two-thirds of Canada's use of petroleum products, nevertheless it has the highest per capita consumption.

To make good the oil strike, therefore, and get the petroleum to refineries and consuming markets required the investment of additional large sums for pipeline facilities. Shortly after the discovery of Leduc, consideration was given to building a pipeline to carry prairie crude to Great Lakes transportation and to middle-western and Eastern Canadian refineries. But this meant over 1,000 miles of pipe—a multimillion-dollar undertaking which caused hesitation. As oil strikes continued, however, not only was the line built, but the planners were emboldened to carry it directly to the East's heart and completed the project in 1954. Others, meantime, dared to undertake the building of a line over the formidable Canadian Rockies and Cascade Range—another multimillion-dollar job.

Founded under Canadian charter and financed by the sale of bonds and capital stock, two companies—International Pipe Line Company and Trans Mountain Oil Pipe Line Company—tackled these projects. To divide the cost and risk Imperial Oil and other Canadian and American oil companies participated as stockholders. Interprovincial's 1,127-mile trunk line from Edmonton to Superior at the head of the Great Lakes was completed in 1950 at a cost of 90 million dollars. From Superior, lake tankers transported the oil to Imperial's large refinery at Sarnia, Ontario. These operations were handicapped, however, since the flow was interrupted during the winters when the Great Lakes are frozen over. In 1953, a 75-million-dollar extension of the line from Superior to Sarnia was begun, and in the following year it was completed. The entire system spans 1,765 miles—nearly half of the North American continent—and from Superior to Sarnia is 30 inches in diameter—the first line on the continent to use such large pipe for moving oil. Interprovincial's line ranks with Tapline's Trans-Arabian—also a 30-inch line—as one of the longest "big-inch" lines in the world. The ultimate capacity of the extension will be in excess of 300,000 barrels a day.

Trans Mountain's 24-inch line was commenced early in 1952 and was completed from Edmonton to Vancouver—718 miles—early in 1953 at a cost of 93 million dollars, after a herculean and dramatic job of line laying over mountains, across streams and through forests of a grandiose, highly scenic but utterly wild region. A United States incorporated subsidiary of Trans Mountain was building extensions of the line from the Canadian border into the state of Washington in 1954. The initial capacity of the Trans Mountain's line—120,000 barrels a day—was raised to 150,000 barrels daily by the addition of a pumping station in mid-1954, and the company states that by adding more stations ultimately it can move approximately 300,000 barrels per day.

An additional and important aspect of the Canadian petroleum story is natural gas, large reserves of which were discovered in connection with petroleum exploration in Alberta. Early in 1954 Trans-Canada Pipe Lines and Western Pipe Lines, two competing companies, amalgamated and announced a project involving the building of a main trunk line to transport natural gas from Princess, Alberta, to Montreal—a 350-million-dollar undertaking expected to be completed in 1955.[6]

Added to expenditures for development and transportation, the expansion of refining activities in Canada probably represents an investment of over 200 million dollars—a sum which raises the actual expenditures since the 1947 Leduc discovery well to an estimated 1 billion dollars plus.

By 1954 Canada's dependence on foreign oil had been reduced to 50 per cent of requirements as against 92.2 per cent in 1942. Thus Canada moves swiftly to petroleum self-sufficiency. More than that, Canadian crude oil is beginning to feed new refineries across the border in our Pacific Northwest, a region which long has been an importer from California and, more recently, from the Middle East. Indeed, speaking before the Alberta Petroleum and Natural Gas Conservation Board on March 9, 1954, L. C. Stevens, production vice-president for Socony-Vacuum Exploration Company, envisioned a day not far distant when Canada would be sending oil to California—now forced to import to meet its requirements.

Canada's great rise from almost nowhere to a place in the galaxy of oil-producing countries, of course, is primarily important to Canada itself. The oil boom has contributed greatly to Canada's thriving economy. Speaking of this fact in faraway Turkey, Max W. Ball, formerly director of the Oil and Gas Division of the U.S. Interior Department said,[7] "I recently addressed a convention in Alberta, Canada's leading

[6] *The New York Times*, January 9, 1954.
[7] Address before the Geological Society of Turkey, Ankara, May 20, 1953.

oil producing province. . . . The Premier of the province spoke before me. He said that the province has received $70,000,000 in rents, royalties, and bonuses from oil in the past six years. He also pointed out that, whereas a few years ago the Canadian dollar was at a discount of 10 per cent *vis-à-vis* the American dollar, it now enjoys a premium of 2 per cent. He emphasized that the growth of the Canadian oil industry had played a large part in bringing this about. I had learned about that premium. When I gave the girl at the cigar counter an American dollar she gave me back change for 98 cents. And this, please note, was in a free market; neither currency is controlled. When my turn came to speak, I brought together the Premier's separate statements and drew an obvious conclusion: that the 2-cent premium on the Canadian dollar was worth more to the Canadian people every month than the $70,000,000 Alberta had received in six years. The indirect benefits from oil development are so much greater than the direct revenues that a country—any country—could better afford to give away her oil resources than to have them undeveloped."

G. L. Stewart, president of Imperial Oil Limited, points out that though oil is important in its own right, as is any other industry, its role as an opener of frontiers is the feature of the industry that appeals to Canadians. Canada's development has been a succession of frontier industries—the cod fishing off the Atlantic coast, then the fur trade, timber, railways, grain, mining and electrical power industries. All of them have opened new horizons, have led to new industries and have increased population. Kitimat, Labrador and Leduc are not important solely for the aluminum, iron and oil that will come from these developments, but for the other industries that will almost certainly follow on their heels.[8]

"It's worth remembering that this investment in oil began to flow at a time when the prairies were losing population," Stewart said. "Farm mechanization had grown rapidly during the thirties and early forties. There was not the same need for men on the land, while the need for men in the cities—chiefly cities outside the prairies—was very great. . . . Under the circumstances, the discovery of oil could not have come at a more auspicious time. It meant a billion dollars or so worth of new opportunity in an area which badly needed it. . . .

"Before the discovery of oil at Leduc, Alberta ranked second in

[8] Address before Empire Club, January 15, 1953.

prairie population, with 30,000 fewer people than Saskatchewan. Five years later it had reached top position, with a lead of 107,000 over its eastern neighbor. Not only has Alberta grown more rapidly than the other prairie provinces, but it has outpaced Canada as a whole, rising 17 per cent against Canada's 14 per cent. Rather more interesting than the gain in Alberta's total population are the changes in occupation during the five years. For example, 26 per cent more people found jobs in manufacturing and the mechanical trades. There was a one-third rise in the number of people managing or owning businesses. This is, broadly, what one would expect in such a period of expansion—a growth in manufacturing and the establishment of new businesses."

With its estimated 3-billion-barrel reserve—including an estimated 1 million barrels for Pembina—Canada, in 1954, is no Middle East with its 78 billion barrels, no United States with its 29 billion barrels, nor even a Venezuela with its 10 billion barrels. Yet our northern neighbor looms large on the oil horizon. From new fields, through new pipelines and out of new and bigger refineries, oil and petroleum products are flowing in impressive quantities. But Canada must await the test of the drill and the completion of even larger facilities before the results of the enormous expenditures now being made will be known. Even then the story will be incomplete. For only by finding a world outlet for its oil can Canada fulfill its great oil promise. Those are economic considerations which the country must face even though it has arrived and still is going strong.

The importance of Canada's arrival—if you will—lies not merely in its great oil potentiality. Its strategic location is tremendously vital. A great new, and in all probability enormous, source of oil has been found in the North American continent. Over and above economic pressures, the conditions of Free World defense conceivably might speed Canada's development.

Chapter 17

REFINERY EXPANSION: AID TO EUROPE

The postwar era has seen great expansion—and, therefore, great expenditure—in foreign countries. Not only has this growth occurred in the departments of oil-field development and pipeline transportation but also in refineries and in marketing facilities, including world tanker fleets. It would be difficult to appraise—let alone to express in terms of United States dollars—the aggregate outlay of funds since World War II for these purposes, but, more than that, in terms of Free World recovery and security this remarkable growth is beyond calculation. Increasingly, the truism that "Wars are won largely on a flood of oil," applies to the arduous task of winning the peace.

Because of economic pressures since World War II, companies have taken certain steps to keep abreast with the increased consumption of petroleum products as well as to protect their already large refinery and marketing investments abroad. These pressures have played a major role in the rapid rehabilitation of the European community. Refining and marketing expansion have exerted a somewhat similar influence in the Far East, and refineries in Venezuela have been built under interesting special conditions, while the substantial growth of Canadian plants has been in keeping with the sensational oil discoveries in the Prairie Provinces, measured by the growing pipeline facilities. In this Free World recovery and expansion, American oil companies have been important participants and contributors. In 1938, outside of Russia, foreign refineries ran a total of only 1,669,000 barrels of oil daily, 30.9 per cent of which was credited to American-owned refineries. By 1953 they averaged 4,704,000 barrels daily, of which the American-owned average was 43 per cent, admittedly a somewhat

inflated figure because of the shutdown at Abadan, Iran, of the
world's largest refinery owned by the British Anglo-Iranian Oil Company.[1]

Actually, over the years the American percentage of participation
in foreign refinery runs has not changed materially and continues to
average 40 to 50 per cent of the total in the Western Hemisphere and
20 to 30 per cent in the Eastern Hemisphere, a remarkable record in
view of the magnitude of the refinery expansion abroad in both hemispheres.[2]

The swift-moving drama of change in foreign petroleum-refining
capacity has made many countries—and is making many others—increasingly independent of petroleum-products imports and even has
resulted in certain countries, which formerly were heavy importers,
becoming exporters. As affecting the Middle East's oil development,
Eastern Hemisphere refinery expansion has been the unheralded key
to the reversal of the historic flow of oil from West to East. Once
on an import status, the Eastern Hemisphere now not only supplies
most of the requirements for crude oil and refined products in that
part of the world, but has become a substantial supplementary source
of crude oil for the refineries of the United States and other Western
Hemisphere countries, a fact reflected in the record of United States
petroleum exports. Annually during the 1920 to 1929 period United
States exports accounted for 32.6 per cent of the average annual foreign
petroleum demand; in the next 10-year period—during which Middle
East oil discoveries first stimulated Eastern Hemisphere refinery building—our exports decreased to 19.6 per cent of the total, and in the
eight-year period of 1946 to 1953 to only 9 per cent.[3]

In 1938 United States exports of crude and products—largely refined
products—totaled 193,728,000 barrels, or 21.1 per cent of the foreign
demand. In 1953 the volume, though still at the sizable figure of 146,-
258,000 barrels, was only 6.7 per cent of foreign demand. Moreover,
in 1938 United States imports of crude and products—largely crude
oil—were 54,308,000 barrels, while by 1953 they had increased to 383,-

[1] Appendix I, Table 6, Estimated Crude Runs to Stills at Refineries Outside
the United States.

[2] Appendix I, Table 11, Estimated Foreign Free World Refinery Runs by Area.

[3] Appendix I, Table 7, Total Foreign Petroleum Demand versus United States
Exports.

157,000 barrels. In 1938 products imports accounted for nearly 52 per cent of the total while in 1953 crude imports were nearly 62 per cent of the total.

The monetary value of petroleum imports and exports reflects the change not only of ratio but also of character of the product—that is, whether refined or crude. In 1938, exports were valued at $390,-216,000 and imports at $39,456,000; in 1952, exports were $799,-908,000 and imports $691,044,000; in 1953, exports were $690,936,000 and imports $761,760,000. Thus in the last year the value of imports exceeded that of exports.

Beginning in 1948 the United States ceased to be a net exporter of oil.[4]

The drama of foreign refinery expansion began in 1939.

As the year 1938 drew to a close, the Western Hemisphere was meeting all consumer requirements for oil products and, in addition, was exporting most of the products needed by the highly industrialized countries of Western Europe. But 1939 saw a series of major crises, the first, of course, being the outbreak of World War II. A huge and steady flow of petroleum products to Allied war industries and to fighting forces throughout the world was an absolute necessity. It was provided largely by the United States which supplied nearly 6 billion of the 7 billion barrels of oil needed to win the war. Victory brought only the briefest of lulls, for in the United States the sudden removal of wartime restrictions soon released a long-pent-up civilian demand for oil. More cars, trucks and buses crowded the roads, more planes winged the skies. Greater numbers of farm tractors tilled the soil and aided in harvesting crops, more diesel locomotives flashed over the rails and increased numbers of oil burners heated or powered homes and factories. From farms and suburban homes came a soaring demand for bottled petroleum gas. And to meet the mushrooming market the oil industry had plants and equipment which, because of wartime restrictions on normal expansion, were a full five years behind the times.[5] Not only did the industry have to replace worn-out and obsolete equipment, but it had to build additional capacity at a time when both materials and men were scarce and costs were high. And if mount-

---

[4] Appendix I, Table 8, Exports and Imports of Crude and Products by the United States.

[5] Thirteen Crowded Years, *The Lamp*, March, 1952, p. 2.

ing demands were not hopelessly to outspeed the industry, it had to replace and expand at top speed. Oil men in the United States faced many and difficult postwar problems, but, at least, they did not have to contend with bomb-ruined cities or displaced and starving populations. American oil facilities were intact, ready to expand. How different were large areas of Europe and Asia!

Looking back to the winter of 1945, we recall that millions of Europeans were starving and freezing in the cellars of their ruined homes. Their traditional source of warmth had been coal, but with the end of the war little coal was to be had. The mining industry was too badly wrecked, its transport too severely battered to provide coal on anything like the prewar scale. To warm its people, to power its reviving industries, Western Europe turned to oil.

But oil, too, was lacking, for, when the bombing ended in 1945, most European refineries were only twisted, burned and gutted ruins. Bulk oil plants and terminals practically had been leveled, their storage tanks collapsed and fire-blackened. Hundreds of tankers were in Davy Jones' locker. Tank barges had sunk at their loading docks. Railroad tank cars had been blasted to bits or had vanished into thin air, to be found months, even years, later wandering over half the railroads of Europe.

But the worst obstacle of all for the resumption and expansion of the oil flow to Western Europe was the dollar shortage.

Producing but a trickle of oil itself, Western Europe always had imported the bulk of its supply from the giant refining industries of the United States and the Caribbean area, which in turn ran largely on United States and Venezuelan crude oil. A much smaller portion of Europe's oil had come across the Atlantic as crude to be turned into usable products by the few relatively small refineries in England and on the Continent. Crude oil was cheaper than refined products, and refinery workers could be paid in their own currencies. Obviously, the bigger the refinery capacity, the larger the dollar saving in meeting vital oil needs.

The first job in postwar Europe, of course, was to repair and recon-struct the existing war-damaged plants. Several American companies, such as Standard of Jersey, Socony-Vacuum and Texas, were left with bomb-wrecked or dismantled refineries. Before the war Standard of Jersey's 10 refineries in Europe had turned out finished products at the rate of 60,000 barrels daily. On V-E day all these plants combined could not refine a single barrel of crude oil. How well and how rapidly the industry accomplished the first step is revealed by the fact that in 1946—the first year after the war—the output of these refineries had reached 55 per cent of their prewar level, 73 per cent in 1947, and 103 per cent in 1948.[6] Jersey's record of recovery was handicapped in 1948, however, when the Rumanian government expropriated the company's newly rebuilt refinery at Teleajen. This incident was only one of many which eventually brought complete frustration to all companies attempting to continue their operations in countries that lie behind the Iron Curtain.

But, superb as the job had been, simply rebuilding existing plants did not meet the problem. The coal shortage threatened to become permanent, and increasing numbers of consumers wanted to switch to oil—seemingly the demand was limited only by the availability of oil-burning equipment.

In the prewar years Europe's use of residual fuel oil had been confined almost exclusively to ocean-going ships. But, after the war, this heavy black fuel began to replace coal in rebuilt office buildings, hotels and apartments. In reconstructed factories, mills and power plants, it helped the recovering countries to overtake and pass their prewar production rates. Transportation, too, was using much more oil than in the prewar years. In a continent so deeply penetrated by the sea and so laced with a network of navigable rivers and canals, slow-moving coasters and barges carried most of Europe's bulk freight. So generally were these vessels converted to residual fuel and diesel fuel that in a few years some of Britain's coastal colliers were burning fuel oil under their boilers, even though their holds were loaded with good steam coal. In addition, entire fleets of fishing boats were dieselized.

The swelling postwar use of oil also became increasingly apparent on Europe's roads and highways. In Italy, hundreds of thousands of buzzing motor scooters suddenly created a demand for a special fuel, consisting of gasoline and lubricating oil and supplied ready-mixed at service stations. Both German and Italian countrysides echoed with the rush of big long-distance trucks and buses. Elsewhere on the

[6] Up from the Ashes, *The Lamp*, September, 1951, p. 2.

Continent, and in the British Isles, most of the prewar truck traffic
had consisted of light pickup and delivery vans. The war was not
long past before these small highway users were moving over to
make room for massive 10-ton carriers. And with the lowering of
frontier barriers, international trucks and buses began to travel in
almost all directions.

Agriculture was still another major contributor to Europe's great
demand for oil. Shortages of labor, losses in draft animals, and changes
in farming methods made it necessary to mechanize agriculture to
restore production to required levels.

But how could these high petroleum-consuming and largely non-oil-
producing "soft-currency" countries—all gravely afflicted with a "dollar
shortage"—afford to buy the volume of petroleum products needed to
assure continued recovery when most of their imports came from the
"hard-currency" countries of the United States and Venezuela and
had to be paid for in dollars?

Obviously, the answer was for Europe to create a petroleum-refining
industry of its own. Even before the war, such a trend had been in evidence as a result of (1) the discovery of great new oil reserves in the
Middle East and (2) the increasing political demand in non-oil-produc-
ing or small oil-producing countries to establish home oil industries.
The latter urge stemmed from a desire to substitute imports of the
cheaper crude oil for the more expensive petroleum products and also
a wish to build up jobs for nationals.[7]

But so critical was the exchange problem that for all practical purposes the dollar shortage alone was all that was needed to create a
European refining industry. Recognition of the problem was an essential element in the Marshall Plan, and, from the start, a large increase
in Europe's refining capacity was one of the cornerstones of the
European Recovery Program. Stimulating the undertaking also were
the availability of local labor for both the construction and operation
of refineries and the provision by some countries—notably France and
Germany—of duty protection for the express purpose of supporting
refining investments.

The Economic Cooperation Administration, which directed the
Marshall Plan, recognized that petroleum was one of the key com-

[7] *American Oil Operations Abroad*, p. 113.

modities, if not *the* key commodity, of the European Recovery Plan. Between April 3, 1948, and November 30, 1950, ECA issued commodity procurement authorizations to the value of $9,400,000,000 of which $1,070,000,000—or more than 11 per cent—was for petroleum and petroleum products. Of the principal Marshall Plan commodities, petroleum and petroleum products easily occupied fourth place in dollar value.

E. Groen, Secretary of the Netherlands Government Office for Petroleum, reporting on petroleum results of the Marshall Plan for ECA before the Third World Petroleum Congress in 1951, said,[8] "Fairly soon after the end of World War II, the American companies made no small contribution—by supplying their traditional share in the market—to the reactivation of the European economy."

Standard of Jersey and Socony-Vacuum and Caltex, on their own and using their own money, launched extensive refinery-building programs in Europe. To provide the equipment and services available only for United States dollars—and, to some extent, to expedite construction schedules—the companies made substantial direct dollar investments in anticipation of subsequent dollar dividends. Thus the financing of refinery construction by American companies resulted in huge saving to the countries of dollar outlay and helped to effect swift and direct European recovery.

The United Kingdom affords an illustration of how effective in this respect was the European refinery-building program coordinated under ECA. Producing little crude oil any place in the United Kingdom, Britain is a "have-not" nation so far as petroleum is concerned. Traditionally, she accepted the importation of oil products as a matter of course. In 1938, the last prewar year, Britain imported 82 per cent of its oil in the form of finished products, and nearly half of it came from the Caribbean region. After the war, however, with her ability to earn foreign exchange severely reduced by damage to her exporting industries and by liquidation of her overseas investments, Britain rapidly approached the point where she could not bear much longer the

[8] The Significance of the Marshall Plan for the Petroleum Industry in Europe—Historical Review of the Period 1947–1950, E. Groen, Secretary of the Netherlands Government Office for Petroleum and Delegate to the OEEC Oil Committee, before the Third World Petroleum Congress, The Hague, May 27 to June 7, 1951.

dollar outlay necessary to purchase oil products without courting disaster.[9]

Fortunately for Britain, she had access to new fields of the Middle East which were located in the sterling area and did not require dollar expenditure as in the case of Western Hemisphere oil. But to utilize this Middle East crude, more refinery capacity was needed. Refineries existing in the United Kingdom at the close of World War II provided a nucleus on which to build.

As far back as 1945, the British government and the country's principal oil companies began to consult on the possibility of expanding existing refineries so as to supply Britain's mounting needs from Middle East sources. By 1949, much construction was in progress. Standard of Jersey—through Esso Petroleum, Limited, its British affiliate—modernized and expanded at the cost of 100 million dollars its refinery at Fawley, Hampshire, England, increasing its capacity from a prewar figure of 18,000 barrels a day to 140,000 barrels to make it one of the largest refineries in Europe. The Fawley refinery was completed in September, 1951.

In 1950, through its British affiliate, Vacuum Oil Company, Limited, together with Powell Duffryn, Limited—whose vast British coal properties had just been nationalized by the Labour Government—Socony-Vacuum became interested in building a 40-million-dollar refinery at Coryton, on the Thames River estuary about 25 miles east of London. The plant was put on the stream in May, 1954.

According to estimates, by September, 1953, the investment in British refineries since the war had amounted to the equivalent of nearly half a billion dollars. If Britain had not been able to utilize Middle East crude in this fashion, its 1952 oil imports alone easily might have cost the equivalent of $1,333,000,000. In actual fact, 1952 oil imports, including ocean freight charges, cost only the equivalent of $937,000,000. Moreover, since the refinery-building program still was incomplete, no assessment of its full effects will be possible until at least the latter part of 1955.

The cooperation of the oil companies aided Britain in overcoming her critical currency problem in still other ways. They made large purchases of goods and materials in Britain for expanding that nation's refining and marketing facilities and those in other countries as well.

[9] Oil's Role in Britain's Struggle, *The Lamp,* September, 1953, p. 2.

American companies ordered tankers from British shipyards. Standard-Vacuum Oil Company, for example—which operates principally in the Far East and in which Jersey has a 50 per cent interest—spent some of its accumulated pounds sterling on the construction of two 26,500-ton supertankers. On delivery in 1954, the ships in themselves would add the equivalent of more than 8 million dollars to the value of British exports, and six other big tankers are being built for Esso Petroleum and Esso Transportation Company at a cost of 26 million dollars. When the vessels enter service under the British flag, they will save dollars in tanker charters. The Texas Company and Caltex also have gone a long way toward the same program of saving dollars in connection with new tankers built for use principally in the Eastern Hemisphere.[10]

Refinery construction itself stimulated a wide variety of activity in construction materials and processing equipment, such as steel pipe, steel plate for tanks, metal valves and fittings, electric motors, pumps and control instruments. In 1945 the output of goods manufactured in Britain for the oil industry was valued at 58 million dollars, and virtually all was for export. By 1951 the production for domestic use and export combined had risen to 235 million dollars. In some instances, entirely new industries were created to serve the refineries—a million-dollar plant, for example, now turns out catalyst for cracking units of British refineries.

In refinery by-products the highly industrialized British economy also found materials which formerly had to be imported; quantities of sulfur, for instance, are being derived from the characteristically sulfurous Middle East crude. And Britain is emerging with a rapidly growing petrochemicals industry the annual output of which exceeds 85 million dollars. Built on waste gases from the refineries, the industry turns out products which replace another category of dollar imports.

All these developments had the net effect of substantially improving that crucial set of balance-of-payment figures which confronted every postwar British government. They were anxiously watched by the governments of all Western nations which were vitally affected by British economic stability. By the end of 1952 Britain had succeeded in turning her 1951 balance-of-payments deficit, amounting to 402 million pounds sterling, into a surplus of 170 million pounds. Said Geoffrey

[10] Appendix I, Table 10, World Tank-ship Fleet.

Lloyd, British Minister of Fuel and Power, to the House of Commons in 1953, "Of all the fuel and power industries, oil is making the greatest contribution to our balance-of-payments."

A British Government's Balance-of-Payments White Paper, covering the years 1947 to 1953, revealed the declining importance of United Kingdom oil imports from the dollar area. In 1947 they totaled 52.6 per cent of all oil imports; but by 1950 the opening of United Kingdom refineries had reduced the figure to 32.2 per cent. The loss of Iranian oil and the Abadan refinery pushed up imports to 45.1 per cent in 1951, but then a steady decline set in, and in the last half of 1953 imports from the dollar area were a bare 19.0 per cent of the total. In this context it should be noted that American oil companies are treated as residents of the dollar area, even when they are operating outside it.

Commenting on these figures, the *Petroleum Times* of London said,[11] "The fact that these totals are now as small as they are, and that the United Kingdom's needs are met for so small an expenditure, is actually something of an economic miracle."

Moreover, the per-barrel dollar cost to the British Treasury of dollar-area imports has been brought into line with that of sterling oil. The United Kingdom's purchasing and substitution of dollar operations to sterling, mentioned earlier in this chapter, made the lower dollar cost possible.

As of 1953, of all foreign areas Free Europe records the outstanding refinery expansion, a five-and-a-half-times growth in capacity since 1939 as compared with a 2.6 increase in all foreign refineries.[12]

Some European countries, in fact, have built refinery capacity above their domestic needs and have become exporters of petroleum products—this despite the fact that the ECA never intended to encourage refinery expansion beyond that for which a home market reasonably might be expected under normal competitive conditions. When Sir Herbert Merrett, chairman of Powell Duffryn, Limited, spoke at the opening of the Socony-Vacuum's Coryton refinery, he recalled that before World War II only one-fourth of British demand was met by home refining. "Today," he said, "the island is an exporter

[11] *Petroleum Times*, London, April 16, 1954, p. 362.

[12] Appendix I, Table 11, Estimated Foreign Free World Refinery Runs by Area, 1939–1953.

of refined oil and its refining industry [capacity] is second in size to the United States."

As Britain's refining capacity rose to a point over and above her domestic needs, nearby Western European nations offered a normal market for her surplus. Thus this activity has aided Britain in its struggle for economic survival not only by reducing the dollar content of her imports but also by increasing the value of her oil exports. In 1949, the United Kingdom exported, largely to Western Europe, the equivalent of 25 million dollars' worth of oil products. In 1951, with more new refineries "on stream," oil exports reached 84 million dollars and even had edged ahead of coal, traditionally the backbone of the British export trade. In 1952, oil exports exceeded coal by some 8 million dollars, for a total worth of 147 million dollars.

Italy, however, affords the outstanding example of postwar refinery building above local requirements. Among the factors that created this situation were that nation's strategic location on the supply line between the Middle East crude supplies and large European markets, her large low-cost labor supply and her adequate investment funds. Surplus products from Italian refineries are being marketed in Northern Europe, but not without difficulty.

But oil men in the foreign business profess themselves not to be disturbed by some imbalance of capacity against requirements resulting from the fabulous refinery building. With the completion of refinery projects under construction, they say, it is apparent that the rapid growth of refining capacity can be expected to decline to a rate approximating that of requirements. Surpluses which have been built up in some of the European countries have found an economic outlet in other European and North African areas which lack adequate refining capacity. And the ever-growing industrial capacity of European countries will bring continuing increases in consumption which, in turn, will catch up to what today appears to be an overexpanded capability to produce. They point to gains in per capita oil consumption in foreign countries in recent years. In 1952, in free foreign areas, petroleum demand averaged only 1 barrel per capita, as compared with 17 barrels for the United States. But the rate of gain abroad between 1947 and 1952 was double that of this country.[13] As more

[13] Appendix I, Table 12, Per Capita Petroleum Demand by Principal Countries.

and more people experience the contributions of petroleum to better living, oil men can see nothing to stop an increasing use of oil products per person.

Here, as we shall see, lies the key to petroleum's role of destiny in the fortunes of the Free World.

Chapter 18

REFINING—WANTED BY EVERY COUNTRY

The appreciable growth of refining capacity since World War II has not been limited to Europe. In the Far East—for our purposes the area is that "East of Suez" from South Africa through India, Australia, the East Indies and Japan—many new refineries were constructed or are being built. South America—particularly Venezuela—presents much the same picture, and, since the development of indigenous crude supplies in the Prairie Provinces, the enlarging of old refineries and the building of new ones proceeds at a vigorous pace in Canada.

Essentially, the growth in refinery installations since the war's end has its origin in conditions which, basically, are similar to those which American oil interests encountered when they first engaged in foreign refining. In that experience they built refineries when they met one or more of the following situations: (1) where local refining was attractive purely on an economic basis exclusive of artificial regulation—usually close both to production and market; (2) where local refining was unattractive purely on an economic basis, but was made so by a tariff against imports; (3) where local refining was unattractive purely on an economic basis but was forced into being by a high protective tariff and a system of import license; and (4) where local refining was forced in countries with large crude-oil reserves, either developed or potential, by making the operation obligatory as a part of securing or holding concessions for exploration and development.[1]

Though the reasons for the growth of refining remain the same, the emphasis has shifted. In the case of the expansion of European

[1] *American Oil Operations Abroad*, p. 113.

refineries the dual factor of exchange rates and the urgent need for recovery caused many countries to desire self-sufficiency in producing their domestic petroleum products. And, regardless of the fact that most of them had little or no oil production, they developed their own refining industries thanks to the role played by private industry.

In connection with the Far East, South America and Canada, each country, whether a prolific producer or a nonproducer, pressed hard to establish domestic refineries—in certain instances seemingly in defiance of pure economic law. For the great producers, the reasons were national pride, the theory that the country should share the profits of refining as well as of crude-oil sales and the urge to create jobs in a manufacturing as well as in a producing industry. Nonproducing nations simply wished to substitute the lower-cost crude oil for the relatively high cost of petroleum-product imports and to provide jobs in a new industry. These influences, of course, still exist.

But over and above such pressures stands that of a rising demand for petroleum throughout the world. Where we are accustomed to think of oil consumption only in relation to the industrialized or so-called developed countries, the oil people see petroleum as a potent force, as an indispensable commodity in the awakening and advancement of underdeveloped countries. Building so many refineries throughout the world makes business sense under conditions where slight rises in per capita consumption over large areas would mean soaring volumetric increases in consumption. In India and Pakistan, for example, petroleum demand edged upward from 0.06 barrel per person in 1947 to 0.09 barrel in 1952, representing the difference between 23,500,000 and 39,800,000 barrels, or an increase of 70 per cent. Between 1947 and 1952, Free Eastern Hemisphere countries experienced a 62 per cent growth in per capita oil consumption, as contrasted to an average of about 38 per cent in foreign Western Hemisphere countries. Canada, in 1952, was the largest per capita foreign consumer, attaining a level of 11.5 barrels, as compared with 17 barrels in the United States. Efforts to determine the results of the underdeveloped nations' burning desire to improve their condition in terms of increased petroleum consumption have long-range economists sharpening their pencils.

Indicative of the restoration and growth of refineries since the war is the fact that Eastern Hemisphere plants processed 2,311,000 barrels daily in 1952 as against 836,000 barrels in 1946.[2] In the same period Free Europe's refinery runs rose from 145,000 barrels to 1,452,-000 barrels daily. In Middle East plants the daily average flow grew from 640,000 barrels in 1946 to 829,000 barrels in 1950, but dropped to 669,000 barrels in 1951 and 455,000 barrels in 1952, thus reflecting the cessation of operation in September, 1951, at Anglo-Iranian's Abadan refinery—the world's largest refinery with a rated capacity of 500,000 barrels a day—but also the offsetting factor of increased runs by other plants in the area.

The refineries which the American-owned companies, the Bahrain Petroleum Company and the Arabian American Oil Company, have constructed in the Middle East properly fall into the class of those built principally because of the economic advantages of having them close to large indigenous foreign production. Located on Bahrain Island, the Bahrain refinery originally was constructed in 1936 because of the economic advantages of refining Persian Gulf crude locally for the market requirements east of Suez instead of supplying them with products shipped all the way from the United States. As this market grew and World War II required heavy petroleum production for the Allied nations, a number of additions were made to the plant which in 1946 processed more than 90,000 barrels daily. In 1954 Bahrain refinery's rated capacity was 185,000 barrels a day. Though Aramco's construction of a 50,000-barrel refinery—completed late in 1945—at Ras Tanura in Saudi Arabia also was authorized primarily to help the war effort, secondary considerations were the benefits accruing to the Saudi Arab government and the increased products that would be available for commercial outlets after hostilities. Enlargements since the war have given this plant a rated capacity of 189,000 barrels a day. American company plants in the Middle East area were accounting for 381,000 of the total 455,000-barrel runs in 1952 because of the shutdown of the British-owned Abadan refinery.

Other Eastern Hemisphere countries, such as India, Australia, Indonesia and Japan—some of them left with war-damaged plants—showed the remarkable recovery and growth in refinery runs, increasing them from 51,000 barrels in 1946 to 404,000 barrels in 1952.

[2] Appendix I, Table 11, Estimated Foreign Free World Refinery Runs by Area.

One of the most significant postwar economic developments in India has to do with a refinery project contracted for with American private interests—significant not only because of the importance of India's affirmative action, but also because of the nature of the agreement, which guarantees against nationalization. Under the agreement signed November 30, 1951, by the Indian government and the Standard-Vacuum Oil Company—equally owned by Standard of Jersey and Socony-Vacuum—the company contracted to build an oil refinery on Trombay Island in Bombay Harbor at a cost of 35 million dollars. Representing the first action of independent India in opening up the country to foreign private investment, it is believed to be the first instance of a country specifically guaranteeing foreign investors against the nationalization of their properties for a period of years.

In 1948, when the negotiations began, such an outcome seemed highly improbable, for among India's leaders, an influential group looked with disfavor on the admission of foreign capital, partly out of sheer suspicion, partly because of the feeling—natural under the first flush of independence—that India should go it alone in financial affairs. At the time Western capital, in turn, was skeptical of India as a promising climate for sound investment. With a relatively new government no clear pattern of past experience on which to chart probabilities for the future was present. In the background loomed the specter of possible nationalization or at the least considerable doubt concerning the freedom with which management would be left to operate the business and thereby assure an equitable return to the stockholders. During the exchange of viewpoints which preceded the final agreement, the doubts and fears that beset both sides gradually were dissipated.

The terms of the agreement provided many long-sought assurances: that the refinery would be immune from nationalization for a period of at least 25 years, that no import duty would be placed on crude, that the company would never be required to sell products at a price lower than the import cost of refined products, and that 75 per cent of the stock in common shares would be reserved for the operating company with the balance being offered in cumulative preferred shares to Indian citizens. The company also was granted exemptions from certain provisions of India's industrial laws. The net result of these assurances was to leave financial and managerial control in the company's hands, thus allowing full scope for the unhampered development of the enterprise.[8]

News of the agreement attracted considerable attention in India and in other countries. Most of the investment was to be in the form of private capital dollars from the United States and committed only after careful and searching consideration of all the facts. The commitment was made by the management of a large international business enterprise—men who weigh all the risks involved and evaluate the opportunity of earning a reasonable return for their shareholders on the sum ventured.

Several other significant points were noted by India's press and by her political and industrial leaders, as well as by industrialists in other parts of the world. Easily the largest single postwar investment of private American capital to be made in India since that nation became independent, the venture was looked upon as an expression of confidence in India's stability and its prospects for further economic progress. Secondly, the construction and operation of a 35-million-dollar refinery of itself would be a major transfusion into India's industrial arteries, for the spending of that sum would mean substantial purchases of materials and services in India as well as new payrolls affecting many workers.

Still other benefits which the project would bring to the people of India were listed as foreign-exchange savings for the government of India, greater national security, provision for the Indian public to invest in the enterprise, and a definite program of training which gives Indians new skills in oil refining and technology and provides opportunities for them to qualify for responsible technical and administrative posts. Involved also was the construction of a new and ultramodern headquarters office building in Bombay for Stanvac's marketing staff and a further expansion of marketing facilities throughout India, calling for an additional outlay of 10 million dollars. All these programs were under way in 1952, and the refinery was scheduled for completion by 1955. A wholly modern plant of 25,000-barrel daily capacity, it will be capable of filling approximately 30 per cent of India's petroleum-products needs. Thus Standard-Vacuum, the successor organization of the Standard Oil Company which had begun serving India over 60 years before, which had introduced the kerosene

[8] J. P. Saigel, Oil and India's Economic Life, *The Lamp*, December, 1952, p. 2.

for India's millions of lamps—indeed, which had introduced the lamps themselves—became the company to introduce oil refining to the nation.

Refineries in the East Indies are in the category of those contiguous to oil fields, for East Indian countries represent one of the world's substantial producing areas. In Indonesia, Standard-Vacuum Petroleum Maatschappij, an affiliate of Standard-Vacuum Oil Company, has been operating in all departments of petroleum activity since 1923. Today 96 per cent of its 14,000 employees are Indonesians, and the company long has been identified with the industrial progress of the country. On the Musi River, 8 kilometers downstream from Palembang is Sungei Gerong which was unoccupied marshland in 1923. On the same spot today stands a vital industrial city, centered around Standard-Vacuum's oil refinery which produces an average of 50,000 barrels daily. Through other affiliates Standard-Vacuum also operates refineries in Australia and Japan.

The Caltex group, owned jointly by The Texas Company and Standard Oil Company of California, has a 50 per cent interest in three refineries running about 35,000 barrels a day in Japan and a 40 per cent interest in a 22,000-barrel-a-day plant building at Sydney, Australia. In 1952 Caltex began construction of a 13,000-barrel-a-day plant near Manila in the Philippines.

Even before its oil-discovery boom of 1954, Australia was enjoying a substantial refinery-building program which called for the expenditure of 100 million Australian pounds (80 million pounds sterling) by 1956. Sources outside the country are supplying 80 per cent of the funds. Speaking at a ceremony opening the new 10-million-Australian-pound Shell refinery at Geelong, Victoria, on March 18, 1954, J. W. Platts, a managing director of the Shell group, said: [4] "This large inflow of capital is of great importance to Australia, but its supreme national importance is not as widely known as it might be. There is nothing sinister about capital seeking investment in other countries. In a lifetime of business I have not known a case where foreign investment in a productive enterprise or essential service has been anything but a beneficent influence. Australia enjoys preference in the capital market owing to its stability and justice but, in Australia, profits now allowed

[4] *Petroleum Times,* London, April 16, 1954, p. 364.

on petroleum investment are too small to earn even a minimum interest on the capital employed and, if a reasonable return is not offered, other industries and perhaps other countries may get the funds for which, granted level terms, Australia would have a preference. With response from the Commonwealth and State Governments, in their interest and in that of the petroleum industry, the difficulties will find a fair solution." Crude oil for Geelong comes from the Middle East and from the Seria oil field of British Borneo, both virtually 100 per cent sterling sources of supply.

The expansion of foreign refineries in Venezuela and Canada—the first, long one of the world's largest oil-producing countries and the second, the most promising new producer—calls for special attention.

In the early days of Venezuela's petroleum development Shell and Lago (Standard of Jersey) established refineries off the Venezuelan coast on the Dutch islands of Curaçao and Aruba, respectively. At about the same time a few refineries were erected in Venezuela, but they possessed nothing like the capacity of the Curaçao and Aruba plants which grew to giant size over the years. The disparity in refining capacity caused succeeding Venezuelan governments so much pain that, when the Venezuelan Petroleum Act of 1943 was offered, there were proposals to place a provision in the new law requiring companies which held concessions to commit themselves to building refineries under certain conditions. The oil companies countered with a proposal to construct refineries voluntarily. Creole originally agreed to build a 40,000-barrel-a-day plant, and the proposal was formalized in the company's Amuay refinery agreement with the government. Other companies made like agreements for building new refineries of various capacities.

The Dutch island refineries have a capacity of 675,000 barrels a day. In 1950, the five large refineries in Venezuela—two owned by Shell, two by Creole and one by Gulf Oil, the latter partially owned by a Texas Company subsidiary, together with several small refineries and topping plants—had a capacity of 220,000 barrels daily. By 1954, the figure had been more than doubled and stood at 448,000 barrels a day.

The intensity of Venezuela's desire to build a home refining industry, and the realism with which those in charge of its petroleum affairs regard the situation in relation to world oil competition is revealed in the Report of the Minister of Mines and Hydrocarbons for 1953, in the following: [5]

"The quantities of crude oil refined domestically during 1952 and 1953 were 20,191,173 cubic meters and 23,958,388 cubic meters, respectively. A gradual increase in domestic refining can be noted in these figures which slowly but surely, in keeping with the fervent national desire, is felt year after year in that important phase of national industry. . . . Such figures demonstrate eloquently the continuity and firmness of the emphasis with which—within the inappropriate picture which results from world refining structure and from the very historical and intrinsic nature of our oil industry which in world balance has played a prevailing role of crude oil supplier—the Government maintains the thesis that the greatest possible quantity of nationally produced crude should be refined within the country.

"This problem must be viewed objectively, in the light of the obvious facts of world competition, in so far as crude oil supplies are concerned, and of the no less true fact of the disproportionate evolution in world refining. Middle East production increased even more in 1953. The incessant exploratory activity maintained in these countries located on the immense geosyncline of the Persian Gulf, has recently resulted in the greatest discoveries of reserves ever recorded. Just one of the newly discovered fields in Saudi Arabia adds more to world reserves than those attributed statistically to the United States. In Canada also, where there has been feverish exploratory activity in recent years which has resulted in attracting abundant specialized capital investments, proven reserves have been enriched by important discoveries. . . . In Peru, Colombia and Argentina, definite steps have been taken to stimulate investments of private capital and in Mexico exploration and export have received special attention.

"Programs calling for the erection of refineries have been emphasized everywhere. Europe, without yet having completed its own, has a surplus refining capacity which is wasted, or only partially utilized, as long as the Abadan refinery is shut down. . . . Important refineries are being constructed in Australia, India, the Philippines, Aden, etc., and, in South America, in Brazil and Peru.

"Circumstances such as these must, then, be taken into consideration;

[5] *Memoria y Cuento Año 1953*, Ministerio de Minas y Hidrocarburos, pp. xviii, xix.

not to weaken the strength of the Venezuelan thesis, but to give it its correct place in world reality and to better evaluate the considerable relative merit inherent in its gradual fulfillment."

Canadian refinery growth is shown by the nation's refining runs of 379,000 barrels at the end of 1952 as compared with 195,000 barrels in 1946.[6] On June 30, 1953, Canada possessed 39 oil refineries, 29 of which were in the western provinces. Total Canadian crude-oil capacity as of that date amounted to 475,000 barrels daily, and Canada ranked second in the world as to the number of refineries, the United States standing first with 352.

Of course, Canada's great refining gains are a concomitant to the country's emergence as a major oil-producing nation, but the effect of her oil development has spread across the border to the Pacific Northwest of the United States where a new refining industry served by Canadian and Far East oil is growing up. Speaking on July 18, 1953, at the opening of General Petroleum Corporation's new refinery at Ferndale, Washington—the first refinery in the area—B. Brewster Jennings, president of Socony-Vacuum, General Petroleum's parent company, told the Washingtonian audience that fundamental change in the petroleum economy had required a reexamination of the historic pattern of refinery location on the Pacific Coast. No longer could California—the historic supplier of the region—fill even its own territorial needs.

"Washington and Idaho are bounded on the north by Canada; Oregon is only 200 miles from it," he said. "If crude oil produced in British Columbia, Alberta or even Saskatchewan is the cheapest and best crude from which to supply the fuels so essential to the region, there must be truly compelling reasons if the Canadians are to be denied the market and you are to be denied the use of that economical source of oil."

The record of petroleum-refinery expansion since World War II is clear evidence that truly every nation wants a petroleum-refining industry.

[6] Appendix I, Table 11, Estimated Foreign Free World Refinery Runs by Area, 1939–1952.

Chapter 19

DOES FOREIGN OIL PAY?

Does foreign oil pay?

In Chapter 2 we aired, rather monotonously we fear, the heavy risks and costs, losses and long time lags inherent in overseas exploration and development. Quite properly, the long listing provokes a question something in the nature of, "Just what is the score in foreign oil development anyhow?"

Before attempting to answer, we must look at available figures on foreign oil investment. At once the great growth becomes apparent. In 1919 American investments in all departments of foreign oil activity—producing, transportation, refining and marketing—aggregated no more than 400 million dollars. By 1939 the figure had risen to 2½ billion dollars.[1] Estimates for 1953 indicate that a total of 4½ billion dollars was invested in petroleum activities abroad.

In surveying the scene one becomes impressed with the discovery of how big American foreign oil activities are in comparison with our other foreign activities. Of all United States investments abroad, those in petroleum rank close to the top in the main subdivisions given in the U.S. Department of Commerce, *Survey of Current Business*, which reports by industrial groups on the worth of American direct investments. Exceeded only slightly by "manufacturing," direct petroleum investment in 1952 was $4,291,000,000, or 29 per cent of the $14,819,000,000 aggregate—this compared with $3,390,000,000 in direct petroleum investment in 1950 and $1,074,000,000 in 1936. In the last-named year petroleum investment accounted for only 16.1 per cent of the $6,691,000,000 aggregate.

In 1952 of American investments in all enterprises, those in oil com-

[1] *American Oil Operations Abroad*, 1947, p. 1.

AMERICAN DIRECT INVESTMENTS ABROAD BY INDUSTRIAL GROUPS

(In millions)

	1952	1951	1950	1943 *	1936
Manufacturing	$ 4,920	$ 4,352	$ 3,831	$2,276	$1,710
Petroleum	4,291	3,703	3,390	1,393	1,074
Transportation, communication and public utilities	1,469	1,431	1,425	1,390	1,640
Mining and smelting	1,642	1,317	1,129	973	1,032
Trade	966	883	762	654	391
Agriculture	626	642	589	503	482
Miscellaneous †	869	762	662	674	362
Total	$14,819	$13,090	$11,788	$7,863	$6,691

* 1943 figures as of May 31, 1943.
† Includes finance, insurance, and miscellaneous.
Source: 1952 and 1951 U.S. Department of Commerce, *Survey of Current Business*, p. 6. 1950, 1943 and 1936, U.S. Department of Commerce, *Direct Private Foreign Investments of the United States (Census of 1950)*, Table 13, p. 49.

prised 15.6 per cent of the total in Canada, 27.4 per cent in Latin America, and 24.8 per cent in Western Europe.[2]

Bearing firmly in mind the startling growth of foreign oil investment—from only 400 million dollars in 1919 to 4½ billion dollars at the end of 1953—let us consider the answers that the oil men give to the question, "Have American oil companies' operations abroad since World War I paid off? Do they show a net profit or a net loss?" Some oil people believe that an over-all recapitulation for the period would show American oil operations abroad to be in the red. Others state that the books would reveal approximately an even break or a slight net profit. Still others disagree and claim that substantial profit would be shown. The score, unfortunately, cannot be toted. Existing oil companies might be able to figure out where they stand, but the records of scores of other American oil concerns which have engaged in foreign exploration, development and marketing only to lose their shirts have gone with them to the junk heap.

[2] Appendix I, Table 13, Summary of Relative Direct Oil Investment Abroad.

Those who believe that American companies show an over-all loss since World War I base their opinion on an intimate knowledge of the operations of extant companies, both large and small, and also on their recollection of the companies which folded or were absorbed after sinking undeterminable sums in foreign operations. They take into consideration also comparisons with the average yield of venture capital in wildcat, exploratory and development operations of a comparable nature in domestic operations which, while varying greatly over the years, have, they believe, averaged out profitably. Over the last 34 years—from 1919 through 1953—this group believes that domestic operations of this character would show a return of 6 to 7½ per cent. This average, they say, has been made possible by the relative lower outlay necessary in domestic operations, even considering the geographically remote, formidably rugged and geologically stubborn areas and terrain which are characteristic of this type of operation in the United States.

As compared with foreign operations, the principal differences in domestic operations are (1) the availability of skilled labor; (2) the obviation of the necessity to assume paternalistic and municipal functions, such as providing homes, commissaries, utilities and certain services usually provided by local government services, and (3), and importantly, generally more favorable laws.

On the basis of all the handicaps of foreign operations—and figuring that their money invested in similar operations at home would have yielded at least 6 per cent, which they compound in the case of time lag—these oil men are convinced that American foreign oil operations unquestionably would show red ink. They also express the startling view that, if an impossible auditing were made of those ghostly ledgers, which are gone or are in moth balls, perhaps only two companies would be in the black. These companies began operations on a foreign-trade basis in the late 1870's and in the 1890's, respectively. At first they shipped domestically produced and refined oil to foreign markets, which undoubtedly was a profitable operation, and then as foreign production began to develop they were in a position to change their markets from American to foreign sources. So much for the doubters.

Those who believe that the score since World War I is on the profit side—while admitting that the experiences of most companies in Mexico and in South America in the twenties and thirties were costly and that world-wide exploration netted few companies in existence through both decades anything but disappointment and loss—nevertheless believe that the record of the last 15 years more than balances the picture.

At this point, then, for the benefit of nervous stockholders and members of the general public who might have read the early chapters of this book, if we have given the impression that American oil operations have not been profitable since World War I, it is only fair to offer evidence that the score may not be so poor as unwittingly we may seem to have indicated.

In this connection, the August, 1952, issue of *Survey of Current Business,* published by the U.S. Department of Commerce, contained a pertinent article titled "Income on International Investments in 1951," from which the following information is quoted: "The record production of petroleum abroad by United States–controlled companies in 1951, together with additional earnings from refining, transportation and marketing facilities, brought total petroleum earnings abroad to nearly $1,000,000,000. Income remittances to the United States did not keep pace with earnings, and in fact there was a decline in remittance from Latin America, partly because much larger amounts remain undistributed. However, part of the undistributed earnings was made available to the parent companies through remittances on intercompany account, and thus entered the balance of payments as capital inflows rather than income receipts." The article also included the following summary:

DIRECT INVESTMENT INCOME RECEIPTS—1946–1951
PETROLEUM INDUSTRY

Year	Total from All Foreign Areas
1946	$ 204,000,000
1947	323,000,000
1948	472,000,000
1949	487,000,000
1950	705,000,000
1951	741,000,000
Total for 6 years....	$2,932,000,000

If for the 6-year period 1946–1951, income receipts from United States oil company investments abroad amounted to $2,932,000,000, profitable operation is indicated during those years at least. One must remember, too, that most of the American companies engaged in foreign operations also are active in the domestic industry. In addition to income receipts from investments abroad, therefore, United States oil companies importing crude and refined products probably have realized profits on some of the domestic transportation, refining and marketing of that part of their imports which may be attributed to their overseas investments. Most likely, the companies also have realized profits from the export of crude and refined products from the United States to their foreign branches and related companies. In other words, a part of the profit included in domestic earnings logically could be credited to foreign operations.

In October, 1951, *Survey of Current Business* published an article similar to the one just quoted. Using that data—in which return on investment was considered as including dividends, interest, reinvested earnings, branch profits and related material—a study by the Stanford Research Institute for the Chamber of Commerce of the United States showed that the percentage return on American direct investment abroad by various industries in 1951, was as follows: manufacturing, 13.2; petroleum, 20.6; transportation, communication and public utilities, 3.5; mining and smelting, 13.0; trade, 16.2; agriculture, 20.5; and miscellaneous, 11.4—average, 15.7. A similar calculation for 1950 showed the return from petroleum at 18.4 per cent—the highest for any division—as compared with an over-all return on all investment of 14.1 per cent.[3]

But any calculation of returns on foreign investments is a complicated and controversial matter. The Balance of Payments Division of the Department of Commerce informs us that they compute their returns on book values as they appear on the books of the foreign enterprises, but converted into United States dollars in accordance with standard accounting practice. Thus the fixed assets represent present depreciated values converted into United States dollars at the rate at which they originally were acquired, while the net current

[3] *U.S. Tax Incentives for Private Foreign Investment,* Chamber of Commerce of the United States, 1952.

assets are converted at the current exchange rate which seems most applicable. This method of valuation has serious limitations which are well known and which apply about equally to the valuation of the stockholders' equity in domestic enterprises. Any rate of return computed from accounting statements of profit and loss and assets and liabilities would, of course, be subject to all the qualifications of standard accounting practice, and the interpretation of the ratios would be a matter of opinion.

Because of the special character of foreign investments as compared with domestic enterprises—particularly with respect to their industry distribution and their interrelationships with the domestic earnings of the parent companies—the Balance of Payments Division makes little use of these rates of return in its own analyses. Nor does the oil industry accept these calculations as representative of the usual accounting concept of return on investment because of the serious shortcomings of available data on United States investments abroad and on the income received therefrom.

From annual consolidated earning statements of American oil companies, it is possible to estimate income from the two sources—domestic and foreign. The profitability of foreign operations is indicated. Combined net income of 35 American oil companies amounted to $2,258,-000,000 in 1953, divided as follows: $1,589,000,000 from domestic operations and $669,000,000 from foreign operations, according to the Chase National Bank.[4] It is interesting to note that, of the 35 companies included in the analysis, 28 (checked) engage in direct or jointly owned foreign operations.

    √ Amerada Petroleum Corporation
    √ Anderson-Prichard Oil Corporation
    √ Atlantic Refining Company (The)
    √ Cities Service Company
    √ Continental Oil Company
    √ Gulf Oil Corporation
    √ Honolulu Oil Corporation
      Houston Oil Company of Texas
      Lion Oil Company

[4] *Financial Analysis of the Petroleum Industry for 1953*, Frederick G. Coqueron, Petroleum Analyst, Chase National Bank, New York.

Louisiana Land and Exploration Company (**The**)
Mid-Continent Petroleum Corporation
√ Ohio Oil Company (The)
√ Pacific Western Oil Corporation
√ Phillips Petroleum Company
√ Plymouth Oil Company
Pure Oil Company (The)
√ Richfield Oil Corporation
√ Seaboard Oil Company
√ Shell Oil Company
Signal Oil and Gas Company
√ Sinclair Oil Corporation
√ Skelly Oil Company
√ Socony-Vacuum Oil Company
√ Standard Oil Company of California
√ Standard Oil Company (Indiana)
√ Standard Oil Company (New Jersey)
√ Standard Oil Company (Ohio) (**The**)
√ Sun Oil Company
√ Sunray Oil Corporation
√ Superior Oil Company (The)
√ Texas Company (The)
√ Texas Gulf Producing Company
Texas Pacific Coal and Oil Company
√ Tide Water Associated Oil Company
√ Union Oil Company of California

Gross investment of the 35 companies in property, plant and equipment as of December 31, 1953, aggregated $27,290,423,000, divided as follows: $24,043,109,000 domestic and $3,247,314,000 foreign.[5]

A comparison of the earning and operating data of 30 American oil companies over the years 1944–1953, from the same source, while not dividing domestic and foreign earnings, does separate crude-oil production and refinery runs, and thus reveals the striking growth of foreign activities.

Should doubt still remain as to the question of America's foreign-oil book balance since World War I, none can exist on the score that foreign countries of the Free World have derived, and are deriving, dividends, both economic and social, from petroleum private enterprise. And the record seems to show that stockholders can felicitate

[5] Appendix I, Table 14, Gross and Net Investment of 35 American Oil Companies, Domestic and Foreign, 1953.

SUMMARY OF FINANCIAL AND OPERATING DATA OF 30 OIL COMPANIES FOR THE
YEARS 1944–1953

Year	Earnings				
	Total income	Operating costs and other charges	Capital extinguish-ments	Net income	Net income per cent of total income
	Million dollars				Per cent
1944	7,308	5,893	776	639	8.7
1945	7,326	5,750	976	600	8.2
1946	7,549	6,024	763	762	10.1
1947	10,483	8,392	872	1,219	11.6
1948	14,728	11,653	1,146	1,929	13.1
1949	13,892	11,261	1,224	1,407	10.1
1950	15,574	12,577	1,258	1,739	11.2
1951	18,307	14,706	1,511	2,090	11.4
1952	19,458	15,671	1,767	2,020	10.4
1953	20,543	16,412	1,937	2,194	10.7

Year	Operations					
	Net crude production			Crude runs to stills		
	Domestic	Foreign	Combined	Domestic	Foreign	Combined
	Thousand barrels per day					
1944	2,433	464	2,897	3,682	487	4,169
1945	2,526	543	3,069	3,766	514	4,280
1946	2,531	654	3,185	3,873	569	4,442
1947	2,718	723	3,441	4,164	603	4,767
1948	3,043	846	3,889	4,690	644	5,334
1949	2,671	906	3,577	4,570	671	5,241
1950	2,784	1,077	3,861	4,943	797	5,740
1951	3,209	1,303	4,512	5,549	872	6,421
1952	3,272	1,420	4,692	5,626	914	6,540
1953	3,364	1,498	4,862	5,915	913	6,828

management for pursuing a policy of enlightened self-interest. The big answer to the question, "Does foreign oil pay?" is simply this—it is paying our nation to have American-controlled companies develop vast crude-oil reserves at strategically located points in friendly countries all over the world. Altogether the answer is interesting and satisfying.

Chapter 20

CARTELS AND COMPETITION

Is there a huge international oil cartel that stifles competition in foreign oil? Considerable airing of the subject took place in 1952.

Early in the Presidential election campaign in the summer of 1952, the Select Committee on Small Business of the United States Senate released a report prepared by the staff of the Federal Trade Commission and titled *The International Petroleum Cartel*.[1] Previously, President Truman and the State Department, realizing that the report might be harmful to the United States in connection with delicate Middle East relations, had kept the document in a classified status.

This report—which was prepared without giving the oil companies a single hearing and without the approval of the Senate Committee or of any governmental body or agency even by the Federal Trade Commission itself—charged that five American companies, Standard of New Jersey, Socony-Vacuum, Texas, Standard of California and Gulf, and two foreign oil companies, Royal Dutch–Shell and Anglo-Iranian Oil, constituted a gigantic international oil cartel.

Largely as a result of the preparation of this report, the then attorney general of the United States began, during the same period, a grand-jury investigation of the international oil business to determine whether there had been a violation of the United States antitrust laws. Early in 1953, the grand-jury investigation was terminated by the government for reasons of national security and a civil action alleging antitrust law violation was substituted. In 1954 this action still was pending. Meantime, a Federal court invalidated subpoenas served against the two foreign companies.[2]

[1] *The International Petroleum Cartel, Staff Report,* August 22, 1952, U.S. Government Printing Office, 1952.
[2] *National Petroleum News,* December 17, 1952, p. 3.

At the time the cartel case was filed, another government suit, known as the ECA or MSA cases, was filed against Standard of Jersey, Socony-Vacuum, Texas and Standard of California for allegedly overcharging for Middle East oil which was delivered to buyers in Marshall Plan countries in Europe and in connection with which the Economic Cooperation Administration (later known as the Mutual Security Administration and now called the Foreign Operations Administration) provided dollar financing.

The accused American companies emphatically deny that they belong to a cartel, and those accused of overcharging in the ECA cases also deny that allegation,[3] declaring that the price controversy in the latter cases was a technical matter which had long been under discussion and negotiation between the government and the companies. When either question in controversy goes to trial, the companies are prepared to defend their position vigorously. In the meantime, the government's charges and the companies' amended answers provide material for those who wish to go into the questions in more detail.[4]

Few people—few government officials—realize how staggering and damaging these published charges and court actions have been to the companies and to the United States. How many of us fully comprehend that the cartel litigation implies that the American companies will undo or redo all that they have accomplished in agreements and trade relations in Middle Eastern countries? How many Americans see this as a potential threat to our position in the Middle East? How many of us know that the mere filing of the suits has damaged our prestige there and elsewhere?

In denying the charge of being a participant in a cartelized industry, and in pointing out the role that American companies have played in building up strategic oil defense in the Middle East, The Texas Company says: [5]

"The effect of the competition of Texas and its affiliated companies in the foreign field has had far-reaching and beneficial effects for our

[3] *The New York Times*, July 11, 1954.

[4] Amended Answers of The Texas Company, Standard Oil Company of California, Standard Oil Company (New Jersey), Socony-Vacuum Oil Company and Gulf Oil Company, U.S. District Court, Southern District of New York, Civil Action No. 86-27, September, 1953.

[5] Amended Answer of The Texas Company, U.S. District Court, Southern District of New York, Civil Action No. 86-27, September 21, 1953, p. 16.

country also. The strain on United States oil reserves represented by shipments formerly made by them to Eastern Hemisphere countries from the United States is ended. Their reserves of foreign oil constitute a backlog to supplement United States production in the event our own reserves become insufficient to supply our needs. Through the efforts of these companies, the United States has potential access to billions of barrels of oil abroad, located in strategic places and vital to our military forces, which it would not otherwise have had. It also has the potential use of pipe lines, tankers, and other transportation facilities and of refineries, terminals, and marketing facilities abroad. As has been repeatedly demonstrated, our Government has but to speak and these vast resources and facilities are at its command to meet national emergencies. . . .

"Texas' ventures in the foreign field are hardly those of a company willing or content to accept the status of a participant in a cartelized industry. Its whole record is completely inconsistent with such a charge. Texas, and the companies in which it has an interest, believes in the principles of fair and equal competition which our antitrust laws are designed to promote. It is those principles, combined with aggressiveness, technical skill, and good fortune in finding oil, which have made it possible for Texas to become an active and effective competitor in the foreign field. It has never abandoned them."

And Standard of Jersey, in raising the question of the ability of the United States government to regulate business conditions in the Middle East through the instrumentality of our antitrust laws, avers that the attack against the companies "has in fact already prejudiced American interests" there. "Could we," the company asks,[6] "expect the King of Saudi Arabia, or the King of Iraq, to accept the supremacy of a decree of a United States court which would void or modify a concession agreement adopted by his royal decree? Or which in effect dictated to him the number and ownership of producing companies which he might engage to produce his oil? Or which operated to reduce his royalties from his oil?

"The answer lies not only in the evident considerations of sover-

---

[6] *Joint Oil Producing Ventures in the Middle East—Their Status under United States Antitrust Laws.* A submittal by Standard Oil Company (New Jersey) to the attorney general's National Committee to Study the Anti-Trust Laws, December 31, 1953, pp. 29, 30, 31.

eignty," Standard of Jersey continues. "It takes on additional content from the political and economic nature of the Middle East countries. Most Western business methods and concepts are without meaning in the Middle East. The corporation was unknown there until very recent years. Local business is conducted according to ancient Islamic law supplemented by the dictates of monarchs, like the late King Ibn Saud, who has been described as a 'desert prophet,' 'not a modern or even a medieval man but one of the last great figures of the Old Testament.' In the end, it is monarchs such as he who determine the nature of the economic and political institutions of the countries. Once the method by which oil is to be produced has been elected by the monarch, it is impossible to believe that he will abandon that method because of a United States court's view that it is not compatible with a competitive economy.

"Thus, regardless of action taken by our courts, the joint producing venture will doubtless remain in the Middle East. The British, the Dutch and the French, the Iraqis and the Saudi Arabs will see to that. We would accomplish nothing except great harm to ourselves by insisting that American companies comply with standards to which their foreign competitors are in no way obliged to adhere. This would simply strait-jacket American companies in their oil operations in the Middle East and put them at a disadvantage with foreign concerns which are free to deal with Middle East countries according to the wishes of those countries. It may in the end lead to the forced withdrawal of American business interests from operations in those countries with all the damage to the interests of the United States which that would entail.

"The fact that the United States cannot, through the medium of its antitrust laws, effectively deal with business conditions in the Middle East States where the ventures operate does not leave it powerless to prevent conduct prejudicial to United States interests. This country is at all times free to employ its immense political power and prestige through diplomatic channels to persuade the Middle East Governments to recognize legitimate United States interests in Middle East petroleum. But persuasion through the State Department is one thing; it is quite another for the United States to institute under its laws judicial proceedings in which intimate internal affairs of the Middle East

States are exposed in public litigation and made the subject of attempted control by a United States court. . . .

"Attempts by the United States to enforce its antitrust laws in such manner as to control the economic institutions within Middle East countries can only inspire the impression that the United States has abandoned the traditional policy for which it has received great credit with such fruitful results. Such action will inevitably be interpreted as a new form of economic imperialism, since the Middle East Governments and peoples cannot be expected to appraise our motives except in terms of the effects of our actions upon them. The irritation generated by our attempt to extend our antitrust laws into areas where their own economic interest is paramount would be intensified by the fact that the challenge is not only to the economic interests but to the political sovereignty of the countries involved.

"Once cast in such a role the United States faces grave perils. Not only would the prestige of American companies abroad be seriously damaged, but their ouster could result. Nationalism, when aroused by such an act of foreign interference, takes easy refuge in the policy that industry and other economic activity should be locally handled. The result is turbulent agitation against the resident commercial enterprises of the offending nation. Russian Communist activity is struggling to fertilize the area for just this. Its tactics are designed to use the banner of nationalism in the Middle East countries in order to weaken and drive out Western influence. These petroleum-producing countries, with their politically unsophisticated peoples and strong nationalistic yearnings, are logical prey for such tactics. Their nationalistic fervor, especially in this nascent period, develops momentum and intensity when large foreign petroleum companies are involved, since such companies are of course developing the principal national asset of those countries.

"Jersey believes that the current attack against the oil companies has in fact already prejudiced American petroleum interests in the Middle East. The prestige and respect which the companies have so earnestly worked to establish have been damaged by the challenge to the ventures. The allegations of antitrust violations are interpreted in the Middle East as official and outright repudiation by the United States of the behavior of its own nationals in the conduct of their business in that area. What is incorrectly thought to be a profound lack of confidence by the United States Government in its own companies has created grave distrust of the companies in the countries where they do business. Deserted and repudiated by their own Government, as they appear to be in the Middle East mind, the American companies are marked as fair game for attacks and hostile action by different nationalist, Communist or religious factions, which would not occur if the companies were thought to have the full backing and confidence of their Government.

"The stakes, moreover, transcend the private investments and the potential gains of the American oil companies in the Middle East. Cultivation of the good will of the Governments and peoples in that area has been and should remain a major United States objective. It is imperative that, situated as they are just outside the Iron Curtain, they be our friends as well as our allies."

Obviously the cartel suit has done the American companies no good in an area where "face" means so much.

"To think that a few politicos, basing their action on superficial reading, or study, believe they can un-do or re-do things that it has taken long and evolutionary and understanding daily contact to establish, doesn't make sense," a Middle Easterner told us. "The filing of the suits in 1952 against the American oil companies operating in the Middle East did tremendous damage. Under attack was the price structure which has been worked out for Middle Eastern oil through the evolutionary stages of trade in which this area, by carefully judged considerations of commerce, has been fitted into and has taken its place in the world oil market.

"To understand the implications of this attack from the Middle Eastern point of view, Americans must realize, first, that the economy of Saudi Arabia and several other Middle Eastern countries is primarily based on oil, on royalties paid in accordance with this established price structure. These oil royalties are the peoples' bread and butter. To the Middle Easterner, it is not only incredible but it's presumptive and untenable in international law, that an American court be asked to rule on this price structure in a way that takes into consideration only the interests of the American consumer. What about the Saudi Arabians to whom oil is bread and butter?

"If a suit seeks to destroy or carries the threat of destroying this price structure, what can the Middle Eastern countries think other than that the American government is hostile? Moreover, because of the charges made in the suits, American companies lost face in an area where face means much. The suits were one of the biggest blunders in the history of American foreign relations—only accountable to inexperience, fortuity, vanity. Anything American companies do abroad, is in the name of America—a responsibility they fully and deeply recognize. In this light, anything discrediting to the companies is fratricide."

As recently as September, 1954—over two years after the filing of the cartel suit—B. Brewster Jennings, president of Socony-Vacuum, said that "regardless of the final disposition of this case, we probably shall never know the full extent of the damage to America's position in foreign oil resulting from these charges.

"In view of our record of keeping the United States government informed of our business overseas, as well as the fact that the government often encouraged us to go abroad in the first place," he remarked,[7] "I think you can imagine our shock two years ago when cartel charges were brought against several American oil companies operating abroad. These charges were based in many instances on activities which had been thoroughly discussed with appropriate government officials. For that and other reasons, the action seemed to us completely removed from reality. Had there been a cartel—and we firmly deny that there was or is—it would have been the first cartel in all history to expand production even faster than rapidly rising demand for its product."

Jersey's statement quoted above reveals the intensity of competition in international oil. "Regardless of the action taken by our courts, the joint producing venture will doubtless remain in the Middle East," it says, and adds, "The British, Dutch and French, the Iraqis and Saudi Arabs will see to that." To our way of thinking the puzzlement of most persons who search for the answer to the question, "Is there a huge international cartel, comprising seven big British, British-Dutch, and American companies, that stifles competition in world oil?" stems from two sources. One naturally registers, first, that these companies together account for the largest percentage of world production and refining. Then, second, one asks, since it is no secret that

[7] Address before The Los Angeles World Affairs Council, September 29, 1954.

these same companies are partners in certain joint corporate operations, "How can they be joint partners and still compete?"

The facts as to the "bigness" of the companies are these:

In 1952 five American, one British and one British-Dutch company—including the operations of their consolidated subsidiaries and their interests in nonconsolidated companies—produced an estimated 2,260,-000,000 barrels, or 55 per cent, of the Free World's total output of 4,109,000,000 barrels of oil. These figures, of course, include United States output. In the sense that they produce, refine, transport and market oil in many countries of the world, all the companies listed in the accompanying tables are international in scope. And all but one—Anglo-Iranian—also engage in large producing and other operations in the United States which, except for the brief "John Bull" shortage scare period after World War I, always has held firmly to the "open-door" policy at home as well as advocated it abroad.[8]

ESTIMATED CRUDE-OIL PRODUCTION BY INTERNATIONAL OIL COMPANIES, 1952

Company	Million barrels	Thousand barrels per day	Per cent of total
Standard (New Jersey)....	656	1,793	16
Royal Dutch–Shell........	488	1,333	12
Gulf Oil.................	285	779	7
Texas Company..........	253	691	6
Standard California.......	213	583	5
Socony-Vacuum..........	185	507	5
Anglo-Iranian *..........	180	491	4
	2,260	6,177	55
Others..................	1,849	5,050	45
Total..................	4,109	11,227	100

* Company's production in Iran shut down throughout 1952.
Source: Private sources.

These seven companies also accounted for an estimated 57 per cent of the Free World's refinery runs in 1952.

[8] A Case History of Oil-shortage Scares, *Our Oil Resources*, 1950, p. 329.

ESTIMATED REFINERY RUNS BY INTERNATIONAL OIL COMPANIES, 1952

Company	Million barrels	Thousand barrels per day	Per cent of total
Standard Oil (New Jersey).	701	1,915	17
Royal Dutch–Shell........	607	1,659	15
Texas Company..........	261	714	6
Socony-Vacuum..........	249	679	6
Standard Oil California....	215	588	5
Gulf Oil.................	182	498	5
Anglo-Iranian *...........	107	293	3
	2,322	6,346	57
Others..................	1,719	4,696	43
Total..................	4,041	11,042	100

* Company's refinery in Abadan shut down in 1952. (See also Appendix I, Table 15, Distribution of Operations of Seven International Oil Companies by Principal Free World Areas, 1952.)
Source: Private sources.

From the accompanying tables one notes that American Standard of Jersey and the British-Dutch Royal Dutch–Shell group are almost neck and neck in the crude production and refinery runs that they control, with the former leading by a few percentage points in both cases. Notable, too, is the fact that British Anglo-Iranian, despite its elimination from Iranian production and the shutdown of its great Abadan refinery, still was able to account for 4 per cent of the Free World's output and 3 per cent of the refinery runs.

How does it happen that so few companies control so much of the Free World's oil production and refining capacity? The answer supplies a partial explanation to both sides of the puzzle—bigness and joint operations.

In earlier chapters we have detailed the costs and risks, economic and political, involved in doing business abroad and have explained the genesis of joint practices in producing operations. When it costs about 10 million dollars even to begin the first phases of petroleum

development in an undeveloped country, when it takes years before
first revenues can be anticipated, when special skills and know-how—
the products of long experience—are required, and when, in the final
analysis, facilities for transporting and marketing petroleum in world
trade are essential to the enterprise, then patently the growth and
methods, the bigness, of international oil companies become under-
standable as evolutionary processes dictated by capital requirements
and business judgment.

Then, we believe that there are other little-understood factors in
this evolutionary process which account for the presence of a few
outstanding companies in foreign operations. These factors we shall
call (1) geographical scope of operations and (2) vintage.

As to the geographical scope of operations, probably only because
they *do* operate in many countries could the five outstanding American
oil companies have made the headway that they did in face of the
severe restrictions on currency exchange which the governments of
"soft-currency" countries have imposed. Royal Dutch–Shell and
Anglo-Iranian Oil do most of their business in sterling, and though they
do have sizable hard-currency expenses, these are nothing as compared
to those of the American companies. In carrying on business in nations
short of dollars, through affiliates scattered over the globe, big American companies can select their purchasing of supplies of every description, a fact which has helped them to maintain their positions in
European markets against competition from foreign companies less
hampered than they by the strait-jacket of currency controls.[9]

As to vintage, to succeed in doing business in a foreign country
a company must thoroughly know that country's laws, its peoples and
its customs—knowledge gained only by the aging of time, experience
and patience. Perhaps the unsung heroes of American foreign operations are the local managers who are alert when conditions are active
and favorable and who have the patient ability to sit it out through
the dull and adverse periods. A word of praise must be added, too,
for the board at home which in the dull and adverse period votes
affirmatively on the question, "Shall we stick it out a little longer?"

What we call vintage may be as important in the scheme of things
as huge financial resources. Standard-Vacuum's recent 35-million-
dollar, 25-year agreement with India tempts us to speculate along this

9 Bridging Barriers to Trade, *The Lamp*, November, 1953.

line. A Standard-Vacuum affiliate has been in India since 1890, and we wonder if, through the years, the company's books might not show long columns of red ink, interspersed only occasionally with black. But when opportunity came, the company, having lived with and dealt long among the Indians, was in the position of an old and trusted friend and was given the chance to try out the venture and to profit by it. Patience in sticking it out and in accepting the political time lag finally have paid in more than one country.

Now, as to the interrelated activities of these companies in joint operations, in certain cases, as we have seen, two or more companies of different nationalities conduct operations jointly through affiliates. Iraq Petroleum Company, for instance, is an internationalized concern embracing British, British-Dutch, French and American companies. Kuwait Oil Company is equally owned by a British and an American company. Standard-Vacuum,[10] owned half by Standard of Jersey and half by Socony-Vacuum, operates in the Far East and holds a part

[10] Though it became a corporate entity only in 1933, Standard-Vacuum traces its beginning back to before the turn of the century when clipper ships were sailing out of New York and other Atlantic ports with case lots of kerosene for the new market that was China. The salesmen of the Standard Oil Company of New York (Socony) used metal kerosene-burning lamps with glass chimneys to open up this territory, and sold them at a price the humblest Chinese farmer could afford. Before Socony's entrance into the Chinese market, and subsequently into others in the Orient, millions of people had obtained illumination only with smoky animal or vegetable oils. Another pioneer in the East was the Vacuum Oil Company which specialized in lubricants. Before the turn of the century it was developing its business in South Africa, Australia, New Zealand and some of the port cities of the Orient. For many years these two concerns operated independently.

Several years before Socony and Vacuum joined forces, Jersey Standard had developed crude supplies and refining facilities in the Dutch East Indies but had no nearby marketing operations. The complementary positions of the two organizations in that area soon became apparent, and in order that each might serve the market more effectively and improve its competitive position—one in relation to crude supply and refinery output, the other in relation to attaining a nearby market—they formed the Standard-Vacuum Oil Company and transferred to it their properties in Australia, South and East Africa, India and the Far East. Standard-Vacuum's activities are carried on both directly through regional divisions and through subsidiary companies. The subsidiaries manage their own businesses, and the various divisions of Standard-Vacuum have their own managements which are self-sufficient in administering their operations. Besides being good local policy, decentralization simplifies the mechanics of operation, for Stanvac does business in about 50 different countries or territories, each with its own laws and government and with many different languages and local customs.

interest with Shell in a producing operation in New Guinea as does Caltex,[11] equally owned by Texas and Standard of California. Jersey and Shell affiliates have built oil-field-to-port roads together in Venezuela. At the present writing, negotiations aimed at reopening Iran's oil industry (see Chapter 25) are under way between the government of Iran and a consortium which includes Anglo-Iranian, Royal Dutch–Shell and Compagnie Française des Pétroles and the five leading American companies operating abroad. The pact which seems to be materializing is almost exactly of the same nature as that which established the internationalized Iraq Petroleum Company—an undertaking launched with the blessing of the United States government, though not officially fostered by it. (See Chapter 25, The Iranian Oil Settlement.)

As we have seen in Chapter 2, joint ownership and operation of producing properties is historically "old stuff" in the United States industry. Moreover, since the adoption of a national oil-conservation policy, we have in the United States an increasing number of producing operations which are jointly engaged in by numerous oil enterprises, large and small. These consist of unitized operations of oil fields where the oil is taken in kind by the respective parties

[11] The Caltex group, owned jointly by the Standard Oil Company of California and The Texas Company, sprang from California's producing successes in the Middle East and The Texas Company's long building of foreign marketing outlets. Born during the Spindletop boom in Texas of the early 1900's, Texas, officially formed in 1902, is a latter-day example of the early independents which challenged Standard Oil not only at home but abroad. As early as 1905 Texas organized a company for foreign trade with a terminal at Antwerp, and in 1910 established an export department which soon expanded company product sales in Europe, Africa and Latin America. By 1926 Texas could point to the fact that its products sold in 46 states—a record unequaled by any competitor—and that it had expanded its foreign markets into New Zealand and the Philippines. By the mid-thirties the company had a large marketing organization and a thriving business east of the Suez, but possessed no source of supply in that area. Hence Texas was most interested when promising oil sources became available in the Middle East. Standard of California had production on Bahrain Island and in Saudi Arabia and a small refinery at the former place, but no marketing organization or facilities. In 1936 the consolidation of Texas' marketing facilities east of Suez with the producing and refining interests of Socal on Bahrain Island led to the first formation of the Caltex (California Texas Oil Company Ltd.) Group, owned 50-50 by Texas and Socal (see Chapter 5). In 1947 Caltex purchased the distribution facilities of Texas in Europe and North Africa. The Caltex Group today operates widely in the Eastern Hemisphere and Latin America and is engaged in every branch of the oil industry.

concerned and individually sold. The propriety of these operations is not now questioned by the Antitrust Division of the Department of Justice as competition remains, and conservation—the main purpose of unitization in the United States—is greatly promoted. Though the main purpose for the existence of joint producing operations abroad often is to share the risk of the venture, the only real difference is that foreign operations are on a substantially larger scale.

There is obvious inconsistency in government policy when the State Department encourages joint American oil-company operations abroad as in the cases of Iraq and Iran—while the Department of Justice attacks such agreements as cartelization. There is palpable inconsistency in government policy when one department of the government approves conservation, involving unitization under state conservation laws, and another files antitrust actions against companies in foreign trade because of actions involving the same principle.

Are we to believe that the epic "world struggle for oil" [12] is over,

---

[12] The struggle of American companies for a share in foreign oil dates, in its modern phases, from World War I. Pushing further back into history, however, it seems almost as if American companies invaded and took over foreign markets without a struggle beginning in the 1870's. The reason? Simply because the world's outstanding development of petroleum resources occurred in the United States—this country produced 60 to 70 per cent of the world's oil and was the world's refining center.

The first challenge to American supremacy grew from a small and isolated beginning—a Netherlands trader sitting in his office in Batavia and dreaming of developing Dutch East Indies oil and giving it a world market. For Royal Dutch started in J. B. August Kessler's little Dutch East Indian oil-producing company, with the world's longest name, the Koninklijke Nederlandsche Maatschappij Tot Exploatatie Van Petroleumbronnen in Nederlandsche-Indie (Royal Dutch Company for the Working of Petroleum Wells in Dutch East Indies), organized in 1890, and Shell started in the early Dutch trading interests of Marcus Samuel, a Britisher, who in 1897 formed Shell Transport & Trading Company. In 1907, Henri Deterding, Royal Dutch's managing director, and Sir Marcus Samuel, later Lord Bearsted, brought about an amalgamation of the oil-producing and refining interests of Royal Dutch with the transport and marketing facilities of Shell, enabling the organization to offer severe competition to Standard Oil and other American interests in foreign markets. The second challenge had equally small and isolated beginnings—the British gold miner, D'Arcy, dreamed of developing Middle East oil and giving it a world market. Already we have told, in Chapter 5, how these dreams materialized in the Anglo-Iranian Oil Company, the development and present ramifications of which doubtlessly have surpassed D'Arcy's most optimistic visions.

[*Continued on page 232.*]

that world oil has been cartelized? [13] A brief search of "ancient" and recent history indicates that the competitive struggle, though changed in form, is unchanged in essence. Competition in the *sale* of the oil produced always has existed. It is still intense.

In 1950, for example, American oil companies were charging that regulations governing the receipt and use of sterling in the "soft-currency" countries, which felt the need to close the gap between their dollar receipts and their dollar expenditures, were giving Anglo-Iranian and Royal Dutch–Shell a discriminatory advantage.[14]

Again, in expanding their operations abroad American oil companies are meeting the stiffest competition from Royal Dutch–Shell and Anglo-Iranian. Look at Anglo-Iranian—suddenly expelled in September, 1951, from Iran, the company's chief source of crude and refined products. Anglo-Iranian's share of crude-oil production in Kuwait, Iraq and Qatar increased during 1952 to 536,500 barrels per day, compared with 347,900 barrels from these sources in 1951. During 1953 this figure rose to about 733,000 barrels. AIOC's 1952 offtake from Iraq was nearly doubled because of the commissioning of the new 30-inch pipeline from Kirkuk to the Mediterranean.

AIOC has extended exploration in various parts of the world—in Papua; in Nigeria; in Tanganyika and Zanzibar, where concessions have been obtained and surveys begun; in the Gulf of Paria, where test drilling is to begin; in Sicily, where surveys are encouraging; and in the Persian Gulf.

Chief items in AIOC's refining expansion were the 80,000-barrel-a-day Kent refinery near London, which started operating early in 1953, the 62,000-barrel Kwinana refinery in Western Australia and the 100,-

---

[Continued from p. 231.]

By the end of World War I, the world struggle for oil between Royal Dutch–Shell and Anglo-Iranian Oil on the one hand and Standard Oil and independent American oil companies on the other was on in earnest. The growth of Royal Dutch–Shell, including its invasion of the United States, alarmed American officials during the shortage scares of the early 1920's, as did that of the Anglo-Iranian Oil Company at the same time, particularly in light of the apparent advantages they held by virtue of the British and Dutch "closed-door" policy in the Middle and Far Eastern countries under their control or influence.

Strong representations by the United States to the Netherlands government managed to open up the Dutch East Indies to American concerns.

[13] Appendix I, Tables 16 to 22, showing American-controlled production and reserves.

[14] Dollars, Sterling and Oil, *The Lamp*, March, 1950, p. 2.

000-barrel Aden refinery. The completion of these and the expanded output of existing refineries will give Anglo-Iranian by 1955 a total refining capacity of about 600,000 barrels per day. Not only will this allow for an appreciable extension of product sales, which in 1952 were about 460,000 barrels per day, but it will provide a chain of refineries well placed to supply its markets throughout the Eastern Hemisphere.

In 1953, the company's tanker fleet totaled 151 ships of 1,934,000 dead-weight tons. Under construction or on order were 27 additional ships totaling 618,000 dead-weight tons, comprising 12 tankers of 32,000 tons, 12 of 16,000 tons and three of 14,000 tons. The company continued to utilize about 2,000,000 dead-weight tons of tanker shipping on charter.

In sum, despite the complete loss of oil from Iran, as against the 107,100,000 barrels exported during the first half of 1951, Anglo-Iranian's 1952 sales of over 670,700 barrels per day of crude oil and refined products were only 8.6 per cent below the 733,600 barrels of 1951. The company achieved this volume by expanding its own resources, by hiring refining capacity, which processed a daily average of 62,900 barrels of its oil, and by purchasing nearly 146,700 barrels a day, mainly in the form of refined products. Purchases of crude oil were discontinued early in 1952, as Anglo-Iranian's *own* supplies from the Middle East were increased. Sales in the second half of 1952 ran 11 per cent ahead of the second half of 1951, and in 1953 almost attained the pre-Iranian nationalization level.

Furthermore, as the expanded exploration, production and refining activities and facilities just mentioned come into fruition, Anglo-Iranian presumably will be in a position greatly to increase future sales in many parts of the world. Such moves are independent and made by a company with the resources to make them possible. They are no part of an international cartel. Neither Royal Dutch–Shell nor American companies are consulted as would be the case if a cartel existed. Neither Royal Dutch–Shell nor American companies share in Anglo-Iranian sales as would be the case if the operations of these companies were cartelized. Indeed, it is interesting to quote the following from the 1953 annual report of Anglo-Iranian Oil: "As forecast last year, severe competition has been experienced in all our markets, and trading conditions have been far from easy. Particularly was this so in our Continental markets where to the pressures caused by a surplus of refining capacity has been added the new factor of a resumption of exports of Russian and Rumanian oil. It is, therefore, satisfactory to record an over-all increase in sales by our Continental subsidiary and associated companies of 10 per cent compared with 1952."

The fact of Anglo-Iranian's swift comeback *as a competitor,* after what might well have been considered a mortal setback since 1951 when the company lost in one blow its 610,000-barrel daily Iranian production and products from the world's biggest refinery, becomes obvious. But that is not all. Not to be forgotten is that in the initial stages of this remarkable comeback the government of the United States itself played a role. Immediately upon the loss of Iran our government rallied 19 American companies engaged in foreign operations to join the Foreign Petroleum Supply Committee to make up the loss of Iran. (See Chapter 23, Oil and Free World Defense.) The Korean War was at a critical stage. This loss had to be replaced. Moreover, as it could not be expected that American companies competing with each other and with big foreign companies would join together with Anglo-Iranian and Royal Dutch–Shell in an agreement such as that involved in the program, the Petroleum Administration for Defense procured in advance a clearance for them by the Department of Justice to the effect that they would not be liable to prosecution under the antitrust laws for entering the agreement.

Yet a year and a half later the Justice Department filed suit against five of the participating companies charging them with being part of a cartel with Anglo-Iranian and Royal Dutch–Shell. Not merely was a civil suit filed against them but initially a grand jury investigation was started, often a preliminary to criminal action.

One sees, therefore, immediate evidence of inconsistency. The State Department and the Department of the Interior, as represented by PAD, on the one hand urgently impressed the oil companies into this agreement as a national defense need, but the Department of Justice—which consented to the agreement among competitors—on the other hand turned upon them. The agreement itself is not involved in the action. But the inconsistency remains.

In fact, it would appear that the cartel charges show the Justice Department itself inconsistent. True, it may be argued that the mere fact of giving the companies clearance did not imply or presuppose the existence of competition. But this argument, it seems to us, becomes fallacious because if a large cartel, comprising the American "Big Five" and the British and Dutch "Big Two," did exist no such arrangements involving elaborate and complicated shifts and pooling of products and transportation as were necessitated would have been required. The cartel would have been able to act simply intramurally to solve the situation.

Nor does the above discussion touch on the obvious question as to the unfairness of entering action—civil and especially grand jury— against American companies which, when called upon, were in a position to render vital service to their country in time of emergency and did so. The bigger question is that our government, because of inconsistency, undermines the very objective it is seeking, namely, strategic oil security.

To summarize, competition in the Free World's markets, the so-called world struggle for oil between companies, marches on! It continues despite certain internationalized joint ownership among rivals in the exploration, producing and refining departments.

So far as competition among international oil companies is concerned, the companies contend that it is inherent in the struggle. The struggle, they say, is simply a manifestation of a situation where all companies need crude oil for their refineries so that they can make the products to sell at a profit in a highly competitive market. They point out that as soon as crude oil jointly produced is taken by individual companies for their own refineries, as soon as petroleum products— which may have been produced at jointly owned refineries—are ready for the market, the competition becomes visible to all. In the case of gasoline, it manifests itself in the rival filling stations nudging each other on streets and roads wherever one goes all over the Free World.

Today, then, the struggle for a share in the world oil goes on but is tempered with experience, knowledge and hard fact. Experience has taught oil companies of whatever nationality that foreign development entails huge costs and unusual economic and political risks. Knowledge derived from the spreading usages of petroleum has given nations and oil men a new concept of the role that petroleum plays in the world today and will play tomorrow. Hard fact points out that, in an uneasy era, ready oil sources are required insurance for the Free World.

Moreover, as we shall see in Chapter 21, Resurgence of Foreign Oil Investment, far from being stifled competitively, the foreign oil field is wide open. By no means do the American Big Five have everything their own way.

Chapter 21

RESURGENCE OF FOREIGN OIL
INVESTMENT

After World War II a resurgence of American oil-company activities in foreign countries occurred which is without parallel since the World War I postwar period. In 1954 it still was in full swing and far greater in magnitude and scope than the upswing that followed the first world conflict. From it is emerging an internationalized American oil industry.

In a sense the United States oil industry, as we saw in Chapter 1, long has been relatively international both as to its operation and as to the interrelationship of its foreign supplies to domestic markets and its domestic supply to foreign markets. But today's outright transformation of the industry from domestic or local to international stems from two major developments: a changed world—a world which requires that to preserve the peace we must be prepared for war—and a changed oil world.

Despite the large percentage of foreign oil production credited to the American Big Five, those companies never have been alone in the field, as witness the large array of companies in Mexico during the late teens and twenties, in Venezuela during the twenties and thirties, and more recently the participation by almost every sizable company producing oil in the United States in the Canadian rush. Nor is the scramble by many American companies for a share in foreign oil confined to comparatively nearby countries. Instead, as the following notable examples show, it reaches far into the Middle East, Africa and South and Central America, and in Chapter 2 we already have seen something of these activities in the Far East and of the "rush" that is on in Australia.

237

Shortly after the war, Ralph K. Davies—a former Standard of California vice-president who had served with distinction as deputy to Secretary of the Interior Harold L. Ickes, United States Petroleum Administrator during hostilities—came up with the American Independent Oil Company and put a group of 10 American individuals and companies into the oil business in the Middle East. They were J. S. Abercrombie Company of Houston; Ashland Oil & Refining Company of Ashland, Kentucky; Davies himself; Deep Rock Oil Company of Chicago; Globe Oil & Refining Company and Lairio Oil & Gas Company, both of Wichita, Kansas; Hancock Oil Company of Long Beach, California; Phillips Petroleum Company of Bartlesville; Signal Oil & Gas Company of Los Angeles; and Sunray Oil Corporation of Tulsa. They own American Independent Oil Company, which on June 28, 1948, secured from the Sheik of Kuwait a concession in Kuwait's undivided half interest in the Saudi-Arabia-Kuwait Neutral Zone. The Neutral Zone is a tiny square of desert of about 2,000 square miles on the Persian Gulf, plus islands and territorial waters in the Persian Gulf. Within less than a year—on February 20, 1949—J. Paul Getty's Pacific Western Oil Corporation of Los Angeles signed a concession with Saudi Arabia, covering that nation's half of the zone. After having drilled five dry holes and having performed extensive exploratory operations at a cost in excess of 30 million dollars, joint operations, conducted by American Independent, brought in a discovery well on April 13, 1953, and have drilled in others since. Pipeline and dockage facilities have been built.

Neutral Zone oil—the first in the Middle East to be developed by so-called independent companies, that is, companies other than the major international concerns—was seeking, in 1954, to share in the Middle East development and in the world market. Davies hailed the Neutral Zone's first shipment of oil, scheduled to leave for Japan on January 5, 1954, as a "milestone in the history of independent oil enterprise abroad." [1] Incidentally, in 1952 Pacific Western acquired a half interest in five exploration permits covering 700,000 acres in the Republic of Lebanon but, after drilling a dry hole during 1953, abandoned its interest.

An old, but long inactive, hand in foreign activities, Cities Service

[1] *The Oil and Gas Journal,* December 21, 1953, p. 101.

Company appeared in the Middle East in 1953 with a concession embracing the entire province of Dhofar in the Sultanate of Muscat and Oman, which borders Saudi Arabia on the Arabian Sea. Subsequently a one-half interest was assigned to Richfield Oil Corporation of California.

Early in 1954 in Israel, close to oil and asphalt seepages known as far back as Biblical times, a joint venture of three companies—Jordan Exploration Company, Lapidoth-Israel Petroleum Company and Israel Oil Prospectors, partly backed by foreign capital, most of which was from the United States—began drilling near the village of El Ghor, 52 miles southeast of Jerusalem in the Dead Sea. Also among American interests doing exploration work in Israel is William F. Buckley of New York—whose Pantepec Oil is an old-timer in Venezuela—with his Israel Oil Licenses and his Pan-Israel Oil Company.

When, on February 3, 1954, A. A. Curtice, president of the Conorada Petroleum Corporation, signed an agreement with Dr. Helmi Baghat Badawi, Egyptian Minister of Commerce, for a 30-year concession of over 72,000 square miles of the Western Desert of Egypt, he projected another group of American oil companies into Africa, the fringe area of the Middle East. Jointly owned by the Amerada Petroleum Company, Continental Oil Company and Ohio Oil Company, Conorada was formed in 1948. The company agreed to spend at least 8 million dollars within the next six years in exploring the wildcat territory where Britain's gallant Eighth Army finally turned back Rommel in 1941.[2] Before operations started, however, Amerada decided not to participate. Then, early in May, 1954, Raymond V. Whetzel, veteran foreign manager of Cities Service, obtained from Egypt an exploratory concession covering about 15,000 square miles in a territory adjacent to and west of Conorada's, and it was learned that Cities Service and Richfield Petroleum were participating in the Conorada Western Desert concession on the following basis: Continental Oil and Ohio Oil, each 27½ per cent and Cities Service and Richfield, each 22½ per cent. Negotiations were reported under way to bring both concessions under joint operation.[3] In addition to its Egyptian venture Conorada previously had acquired exploration rights over an area of about 36,000 square miles in British Somaliland, in north-

[2] *The Oil and Gas Journal*, February 8, 1954, p. 74; and February 15, 1954, p. 106.
[3] *The Oil and Gas Journal*, May 13, 1954, p. 62.

east Africa, where another United States concern, Moriqui Exploration Company of Los Angeles, also held concessions which cover 12,000 square miles.

Sinclair Oil, another old hand in foreign oil exploration, though inactive in the field for many years except in Venezuela, surged back in 1945 with a concession covering all of Ethiopia, where it has drilled several test wells. Sinclair Exploration, its operating company, also acquired rights in adjacent United Nations–administered Somalia and subsequently sold a half interest to Conorada.

Just as energetically have American oil companies sought concessions and exploratory permits in South American countries since the war. In Venezuela, despite the large percentage of foreign oil production credited to three big companies—Standard of Jersey, Shell and Gulf—several other American concerns of considerable stature have been producers for a number of years. In this group are Sinclair Oil, with its 66½ per cent owned Venezuela Petroleum Company; Atlantic Refining, with its Venezuelan Atlantic Refining Company; and Phillips Petroleum as well as the smaller American-controlled Pantepec Oil Company and the American Maracaibo Company which rate pioneer status in the country since their operations date from the early 1930's. Both The Texas Company and Standard of California have been persistent explorers and developers in Venezuela, and following World War II all companies stepped up their exploratory and development operations in that nation. Without doubt other companies would have entered Venezuela but for the government's policy, effective since 1945, of not granting new concessions.

A previous operator only domestically, Union Oil Company of California is another large American company which recently and vigorously has entered foreign search. One of several American companies to enter Peru during and after 1952, it acquired holdings in the Sechura Desert area, on the coast south of the Chira River as did Conorada, Richmond (Standard Oil of California) and Peruvian Gulf Oil (Gulf). Still other American-controlled companies which have acquired rights elsewhere in Peru are Peruvian Pacific (50-50 Cities Service and Richfield Oil), Texas and Richmond (Standard Oil of California) and a group consisting of the Texas Gulf Producing Company, Kendall Refining Company and Bay Refining Company.[4]

[4] *The Oil and Gas Journal*, January 4, 1954, p. 160.

Mention might be made, too, of Union Oil Company's earlier contract with Costa Rica—made on November 9, 1951—which opened more than 2 million acres in Limón Province and 2½ million acres in Guanacaste Provinces to immediate prospecting.

In June, 1946, Floyd Odlum, president of the Atlas Corporaton, a New York investment firm, was quoted in Buenos Aires as having reached, in association with Dresser Industries of Dallas, an "agreement in principle" with the Argentine government for the development of production and the construction of a pipeline. He revealed the formation by Atlas and Dresser of Petro-Argentina, a Delaware company, to operate the expected contract.[5]

We have said that almost every sizable American oil-producing company has joined the Canada "rush." Amerada, Continental, Ohio Oil—the components of Conorada—singly and in other joint operations with other companies are three who are in the thick of it. Continental, for example, is joint owner of the Hudson's Bay Company which was reactivated after the Leduc well discovery in 1947. In that year Hudson's Bay held about 5 million acres of prospective land in Alberta and other provinces, and since that time it has made important oil and gas discoveries. The reactivated firm also holds a stock interest in the Interprovincial and Trans Mountain Oil Pipe Line companies.

The J. Paul Getty interests, too, are in Canada through both Pacific Western and Tide Water Oil and through associates which include Ohio Oil. Exploring 9 million acres in Saskatchewan, the Tide Water group was credited with seven discoveries in 1953.

Holding exploratory rights covering 3½ million acres in the provinces of Alberta, British Columbia and Saskatchewan and, in addition, owning oil and gas leases covering 300,000 acres, Phillips Petroleum is an active operator in Canada as are Sinclair, which scored its first Canadian production in 1952, and Union Oil of California which has been successful in developing natural-gas reserves in the Peace River area of northern Alberta.

Thus, since the war, some of the so-called independent American oil companies have been reaching into, or stepping up, foreign activities. The listing just made is not complete in either companies or countries. Probably, for instance, of the approximately 500 identifiable companies which have production or extensive reservations of land

[5] *The New York Times,* June 12, 1954.

awaiting development in Canada, two-thirds are wholly or partly United States owned.

Furthermore, independent American companies are represented among those exploring for oil in a few European countries, and some have joined the Australian "rush." Only in the Far East do they appear not to be present. In all the prospective areas of the world, however, the large international oil companies are engaged in intensive and expensive oil exploration and development.

Obviously, American oil companies, large and small, would not have expanded operations into foreign territories so extensively without sound economic reasons for doing so. Regardless of what the reasons may be, they all have their basis in the fact that alone among the countries of the world the United States has developed a great, a rounded, petroleum industry, embracing every field of operation—exploration, production, transportation, refining and marketing. Favored from its start by a bounteous supply of oil within its borders, the position of eminence held by the American industry cannot be fully comprehended unless one sees it in perspective with the pigmy size of the oil industries of other nations. A highly technical industry in all its branches, know-how is essential to oil activity in all its branches. America has that know-how, and it is not confined to a small group, but is possessed by thousands of persons with scientific and technical talent and specialized skills in each department. Other countries may have respectable representation in one or two branches, but in the over-all picture of oil technical know-how the United States cannot be approached.

To comprehend the dimensions of the American industry, moreover, one must take into account the specialized manufacturing, supply and servicing industries which have been built up around it—the United States steel mills which alone can make certain "big-inch" pipe, the contracting firms with the modern equipment to lay the pipe, the specialized companies that can build complete refineries and the concerns equipped and staffed for geophysical surveying. Thus, wherever there is oil enterprise, American know-how and American equipment always have been in demand. In this sense, the American oil industry is equipped to—and does—conduct an international business.

That American oil know-how is hired by foreign governments and by foreign companies on a wide scale is not generally known.

They employ American experts to write petroleum laws and regulations, to make preliminary surveys of oil prospects, to carry on actual drilling and producing operations on a contract basis, to survey for and build pipelines as well as to construct and, sometimes, to operate refineries. Max Thornburgh, and the then partnership of A. A. Curtice and Herbert Hoover, Jr., helped to draft Venezuela's Petroleum Law of 1943 which first posed the 50-50 government-industry profit-sharing principle. More recently Max W. Ball advised Turkey on its new petroleum law. De Golyer & MacNaughton, geologists of Dallas, have been employed from time to time by the Mexican and other governments for special studies. These are but a few examples of the availability and employment of American skills as a consequence of the high development of the United States oil industry. As against the government's Point Four program paid for by taxpayers, they illustrate another side to sending technical assistance to undeveloped countries where services are bought and paid for by the client on a business basis.

The key to the resurgence of foreign oil activity lies not alone in American companies seeing a need—if not immediately, then in the not too distant future—to bolster their supply position in caring for mounting United States requirements. The picture is broader than that. Oil men envision a vast increase in world demand which they are eager to stimulate. They want to share in it and are broadening the scope of their operations to do so. Moreover, the shifting patterns of development and the interrelationships of world oil sources are spurring them on.

All this is a part of the fact that the transformation of the American oil industry from a domestic or local scale to an international one stems, as we have said, from a fresh set of causes—first a changed world, and second, a changed oil world.

Simultaneously many countries have awakened to the importance of developing whatever oil resources they may have. Their first impelling motive is to attain as close as possible to self-sufficiency in crude-oil sources. Second, underdeveloped countries look with envy on oil-rich Venezuela, Saudi Arabia and tiny Kuwait and would like nothing better than to have a similar opportunity to "sow the petroleum." Certain nations have sought self-sufficiency through a nationalized oil industry, through a government-owned company which excludes foreign capital from participation, though sometimes employing American or other foreign specialists as consultants or operating experts. As is evidenced by the 1952 oil production of the principal countries having such government-owned companies, their record is not impressive:

Country	Enterprise	1952 production, thousands of barrels
Mexico......	Petroleos Mexicanos (Pemex)	78,903
Argentina....	Yacimientos Petroliferos (YPF)	19,851
Colombia....	Empresa Colombiana de Petroleos *	12,793
		111,557

* The De Mares concession in Colombia was operated by International Petroleum through August, 1951, when it reverted to the Colombian government. But all Colombian oil production is not government-owned. Other countries with government-owned production are Brazil, Bolivia and Chile.

The Free World total of 11,227,000,000 barrels for the same year contrasts sharply with the nationalized industry total of 111,557,000 barrels shown above.

With the notable exception of Iran, since World War II an increasing number of countries have tended to make it attractive to foreign oil companies to invest in and initiate the development of their petroleum resources. All of them are jealous to retain full control of their national resources—in all countries the nation owns the subsoil and to that extent oil *is* nationalized. Nevertheless, it has not been solely a case of United States or other foreign capital going forth to invest in oil rights all over the world as a matter of necessity. The activity has been encouraged by an increasing number of foreign governments themselves. Capital has gone where it has found encouragement, and the "where" includes one or two surprise countries such as, notably, Argentina.

Conorada, Cities Service and Richfield went into Egypt only after the Egyptian government enacted a new and more favorable law governing oil exploration. Several major companies—among them Standard of Jersey, Socony-Vacuum and Royal Dutch–Shell—had carried out geological and geophysical work over parts of the Western Desert in the immediate postwar years, but an unfavorable legal situation created by the passage of the 1948 Egyptian mining law, along with the corporate law requiring majority stock offering to Egyptians and Egyptian directors, caused the companies to withdraw. In 1949, indeed, Standard of Jersey, after 10 years and an expenditure of some 16 million dollars abandoned its entire exploration program in Egypt. With Anglo-Egyptian Oil Fields (Royal Dutch–Shell), active in the country since 1910, accounting for all the country's 1953 output, and Socony-Vacuum participating on a 50-50 basis with AEOF production in two Sinai fields discovered since the war, Egypt worried over declining production and lack of interest. By passing the 1953 mining law and abrogating the 1948 corporate law, however, the government succeeded in securing foreign interest in Egypt's oil prospects. The new mining law, specifically, sought to encourage exploration of the Western Desert by granting more liberal terms for that region.

When the Turkish National Assembly passed its new 1954 petroleum law (see Chapter 11), among the concerns attracted to it were not only the large international companies, such as Standard of Jersey, Socony-Vacuum, Gulf Oil, Royal Dutch–Shell and Caltex, but also Conorada, Cities Service, Canada Southern Oils and others.[6]

Jordan Exploration, Lapidoth-Israel Petroleum, Israel Oil Prospectors, Israel Oil Licenses, Pan-Israel Oil and others were drawn to Israel by the attraction of the terms in the country's petroleum law of 1952. Major international companies, however, are not in Israel.

Though Venezuela has not granted any new oil concessions since September 26, 1945, in 1954 the government decided to open up new land for exploration.[7] Of the present total acreage under concession, 57 per cent is held by the three dominant companies—Creole, Shell and Mene Grande (Gulf, International and Shell). Meanwhile, the elapsed years since Venezuela last granted concessions have allowed time for the conversions of all exploration acreage to the exploitation phase as provided under the 1943 oil law. Conorada, Superior

[6] *The Oil and Gas Journal*, March 15, 1954.
[7] *The Oil and Gas Journal*, October 25, 1954.

Oil and Cities Service, among others, are expected to enter Venezuela. A huge new investment of several hundred million dollars is anticipated.

Union Oil of California and other companies which went into Sechura Desert exploration in Peru did so in response to the country's petroleum law of 1952. International Petroleum (Standard of Jersey) had developed the country's major production in the coastal La Brea–Parinas field, but the new law sought to open two new tracts—one, the Sechura Desert to the south of La Brea–Parinas, and the other to the east of the towering Andes near the border of Brazil among immense jungles where the headwaters of the Amazon River begin their 2,000-mile descent to the Atlantic.

Colombia's petroleum law of 1952 encouraged new foreign investment. Though a government-owned company took over the historic De Mares concession upon its expiration on August 25, 1951, International Petroleum (Standard of Jersey)—the concessionaire for 35 years —commenced a new career in the country under a contract which permits it to lease its old De Mares refinery, to continue to market oil products and to explore a number of other areas throughout the country.

Colombia's *la reversion De Mares* deserves a brief digression for it came at exactly the same time that Iran repudiated a contractual obligation embraced in a long-term concession. In Colombia, nationalization of the expiring De Mares concession was by orderly process, by reversion. In Iran, nationalization of the existing D'Arcy concession was by emotional process, by riot. In the first case little was heard of the matter, in the second all the world read the headlines. Suitably celebrated with ceremonies far up the Magdalena River at Barranca Bermeja, the reversion indicated that a private company could enjoy a mutually beneficial contractual relationship with a government for the full term of the contract and then could reach amicable agreement on the conditions of a new relationship "shaped by present circumstances but secured by mutual confidence rooted in past experience." Above the signatures of government, church, army and labor representatives, as well as of officials of the company, the Minister of Development solemnly declared that "he had received for the Colombian nation, and to its satisfaction, all the properties involved in the reversion." [8] As a result of Colombia's Act of Reversion and her policy of

[8] *The Lamp,* March, 1952.

encouraging new ventures by foreign capital, not only oil companies but United States concerns in other fields have begun to expand their operations in that nation.

Atlas Corporation's reported concession in Argentina is contingent on that country's Congress confirming a 25-year contract under which the company would take over operations from the government-owned YPF of three of the six proved oil fields in Neuguen Territory. Under Argentina's long-standing policy of nationalization, the producing operations of Standard of Jersey and Royal Dutch–Shell—which carried on integrated operations in Argentina—declined or disappeared through the years since only YPF was allowed new acreage. Indications of a change in Argentina's policy came in 1953 when high administration officials declared that foreign private capital would be given an opportunity to participate in the petroleum industry. More recently, President Peron has said that pride in the nationalized oil industry was "false nationalism." [9]

Other countries which have nationalized their petroleum industries have endeavored to secure foreign capital for use in expanding their petroleum activities without compromising their nationalist policy or prejudicing their national operating company. Providing such an example is Mexico, where American Independent has a 53⅓ per cent interest in contracts negotiated with Petroleos Mexicanos covering exploration and development operations in southeastern Mexico.

This desire among nations for self-sufficiency, for developing their oil resources for internal revenue as a means to raise living standards has become a world obsession. If it is not yet a world movement, it constitutes a definite new oil trend which, as we have seen, is drawing more American companies into foreign operations.

Moreover, national policy in countries which recently have modernized their petroleum laws frankly invites and looks for multiple participation of foreign oil men and companies. The lawmakers want development by small, as well as by large, international oil companies. In Canada the Alberta province's "goal and policy" for oil and gas includes provisions to take all reasonable steps necessary to encourage orderly development and "to establish prospecting and leasing regulations designed to effectively prevent monopoly and encourage individual enterprise." "Only by the existence of wholesome rivalry,"

[9] *The Oil and Gas Journal*, June 7, 1954, p. 82.

says the statement, "where free and competitive enterprise is carried on can we expect to get the most active development." And in Canada wide participation has been achieved. How to reach this accomplishment in countries where costs and risks are exceptionally high and where companies are called upon to assume paternalistic functions is a trick of the first order. Nevertheless, it is the universal objective. And there is visible evidence, as we have seen, of the world's Big Seven having increased competition.

PART FIVE

PROBLEMS AND PRESSURES AND POLICY NEEDS

Chapter 22

RUSSIA HAS OIL

Russia has oil. But her self-sufficiency in petroleum is relative. On a commercial production basis she has had oil since 1863, only four years after United States petroleum went into the market. Until the advent of Mexico's "Golden Lane" of the teens and twenties and Venezuela's Maracaibo Basin of the thirties and the fabulous Middle Eastern fields of the thirties and forties, Russia habitually ranked second in output to the United States and sometimes a rather close second. From 1898 through 1901, she even came out on top, but that was in the Kerosene Age and not too important in the modern world.

Of real importance, today, however, is the seeming anomaly that with a population of 201,000,000 and an average annual oil production of 1,050,000 barrels a day Russia is self-sufficient, while the United States with a population of only 157,000,000 and an average output of 6,466,000 barrels daily is not self-contained. The apparent contradiction deserves explanation since it points at once to the Soviet Union's certain strength and to its profound weakness in comparison with the United States and the Western World. Indeed, the comparison points up with startling vividness and cold realism a true picture of Communist Russia today, for the nation consists of millions of deprived people—have-nots in the truest sense of the term—over whom is superimposed a ruthless military machine for which every foreseeable provision, including petroleum, is made.

As of 1952 an everyday American consumed 17 barrels of petroleum a year, a Canadian 11.5 barrels, an Englishman 3.2 barrels and a Frenchman 2.5 barrels. But a Russian used only 1.7 barrels of petroleum annually. It should be borne in mind that, at the time, Great Britain and France were rationing gasoline to the public as an economic

251

measure. In ordinary circumstances, the per capita use would have been much higher had the Britisher and Frenchman been able to buy and use motorcars in the normal free fashion. By contrast the Russians have no such freedom in any case.

Moreover, as the figures clearly reflect, on a comparable basis with the United States and the Western World the Russian people do not have the motorcars and the drudgery-saving machines which provide comforts, conveniences and pleasures. Instead, since the Bolshevik Revolution of 1917, Russia has been transformed into an industrial nation of huge and unknown capacities, into a country of heavy industries devoted to equipping a war machine. The Soviet's oil development has gone forward, therefore, with a military purpose primarily, if not solely, in mind, while civilian uses have been excluded completely or restricted almost entirely. Therein rests the answer to the anomaly of Russia's self-sufficiency and our lack of it. Less than ours, though it is, practically all the Soviet's oil goes to direct or indirect military use while a large proportion of ours goes to raising the civilian standard of living. Thus the Soviet Union can be counted as strong and, at the same time, as weak, for real strength lies essentially in a free, individually comfortable and prosperous people. In other words, while Russia is self-sufficient militarily, her weakness lies in persistently depriving her people of the benefits of an industrial economy which she has eloquently proved herself capable of building. What this might portend in the way of internal discontent would be a book unto itself, but it is less vital to our story than Russia's present oil position in relation to her aggressive military aims.

To the surprise of no one the secrecy that surrounds Russia's industrial development holds in respect to her petroleum activities. The same gaps and question marks are present in Soviet oil statistics as those which existed when, in 1954, the United Nations published its *Fifth Annual Statistical Year Book*, a voluminous survey which, on a global scale, covered everything from the sums that nations were spending for defense to the amounts of fertilizer they were using in agriculture.[1]

At least as significant as any figures in the report were those which it did not contain—the statistics relative to day-to-day living

[1] See Appendix I, Bibliography of More Important Sources of International Statistics on Petroleum.

in the Soviet Union and its satellites. The yearbook's 578 pages and 182 statistical tables, covering some 130 countries and territories, are studded with such notes as "all world figures exclude the U.S.S.R.," or "excluding Albania, Bulgaria, Mainland China, Czechoslovakia, Eastern Germany, Poland, Rumania and the U.S.S.R." The exclusions are explained on the ground that the figures were not available.

Even in the few instances when some Communist information has been given, United Nations statisticians have treated it skeptically. The yearbook noted, for instance, that revised United States budget estimates for the fiscal year 1953–1954 indicated a reduction of nearly 5 per cent in defense spending as compared with the previous year. In the Soviet Union the amount specified as for "defense" in the 1953 budget was approximately 3 per cent lower than the "corresponding item" for 1952. But, the survey pointed out that Russia's total budget increased 15 per cent from 1952 to 1953 and "most of the increase" was allocated to "unspecified items."

Since coming into power Soviet rulers officially have announced important new oil discoveries and have claimed substantial expansion of their refining industry as well as the construction of many new refineries. Oil authorities agree that Russia has made important gains in production and reserves, but are apt to look skeptically at her occasional claims as to fantastic reserves. On the other hand, to Russia's oil production and refining capabilities must be added those of the countries which she has drawn behind the Iron Curtain since World War II. The Communists began their doctrine of seizure in 1917 when the Bolsheviks took over and nationalized private oil properties without compensation.[2] They have extended it to all their satellite countries.

Petroleum producers in the territory which Russia has taken over are Rumania, Hungary, Poland, Czechoslovakia, Albania and the Russian-occupied portion of Austria. Yugoslovia, another oil-producing country, broke away from Soviet domination in 1948–1949. In the Iron Curtain countries oil properties owned by the United States and other foreign interests were confiscated and brought under the control of Soviet-dominated companies. The case of the MAORT Gas Trading Company well illustrates the manner of a phase of Russian oil expansion. Seized on September 24, 1948, by decree of Hungarian

[2] *American Oil Operations Abroad*, p. 89.

Prime Minister Lajos Dinnyes—"in order to prevent willful sabotage of production of crude oil, which is of first-rate importance from the viewpoint of national economy, and in order to secure undisturbed production"—the company was owned by the European Gas & Electric Company, over 90 per cent of whose stock was held by Standard Oil Company (New Jersey). After many years of exploration it had discovered substantial fields prior to World War II. The strike had made Hungary with Russia, Rumania and Poland the sole European countries that were self-sufficient in oil. The Hungarian government had gained a hundred times as much in revenue and royalties as the owners had received in dividends. The company, furthermore, had met all costs of development, supplied the technical skills and assumed all the risks.

Prior to the seizure in 1948 the company's American executives in Hungary were arrested, imprisoned, maltreated and forced to sign "confessions" of sabotage. When finally released from prison, they were expelled from the country. Then the Hungarian government published and distributed a booklet which attempted to prove its unfounded accusations against the company and its executives. The booklet, needless to say, was based on false evidence, forced "confessions" and deliberate distortion of facts, and was nothing more than a part of the Hungarian government's propaganda campaign to justify the seizure.

The United States recognized the facts of the case, and in a note dated November 30, 1948, the State Department informed the Hungarian government that this nation viewed the seizure as "wholly arbitrary and unwarrantable [and] emphatically rejects as false and malicious in their entirety the charges of 'sabotage' which the Hungarian authorities have made against the owners and officials, [and] looks upon the Hungarian government's course and manner of proceeding in this matter as an encroachment upon American rights and interests in Hungary, for which the Hungarian government must bear full legal and financial responsibility." [3] Further representations have failed to obtain any satisfaction from the Hungarian government.

In 1947 the combined daily average production of the countries

[3] *Standard Oil Company (New Jersey) and Oil Production in Hungary by MAORT*, 1931–1948, European Gas & Electric Company, New York, December, 1948.

whose oil properties had been appropriated by Russian-owned companies amounted to about 110,000 barrels. Moreover, their properties, some of which, notably those of Rumania and Poland, were among the oldest commercial oil fields in the world and included refineries which previously had marketed their products widely in Western Europe. In 1953 Russia and its controlled areas were credited with an estimated crude-oil production of 1,258,500 barrels daily [4] and with estimated reserves totaling 9,740,000,000 barrels, divided as follows: USSR 9,000,000,000; Austria 200,000,000; Rumania 400,000,000; Hungary 55,000,000; and others—these figures include Yugoslavia and China—85,000,000 barrels.

In China, the extensive marketing properties of the Standard-Vacuum and Caltex were seized by the Chinese Communist Government after it completed its conquest of the mainland in 1949, and, in 1954, it was reported that the assets and properties of the former had been turned over to the Soviet-owned Kwong Hwa Petroleum Company.[5]

With Communist China launching an aggressive military economy supported by Russia, her oil potentialities must be considered along with Russia's. Though state petroleum development is given wide publicity in Mao Tse-tung's press, estimated production is infinitesimal, averaging only 3,000 barrels a day in 1953. Any sizable reserves are yet to be proved. Hence, it would appear that for some time to come China's war machine must get its oil from Russia and from what imports it can manage to buy from Free World countries. Meanwhile, civilian demand must wait. From an oil point of view China may be said to rank as Russia's greatest liability.

Conservative estimates in 1953 placed the production of the USSR and its satellites at an average of 1,315,000 barrels of crude oil and other hydrocarbon supplies a day.[6] Scattered reports suggest the reasonable assumption that refinery expansion has kept step with production. Russia's releasing for export of larger volumes of refined products in 1953 would seem to strengthen this assumption.

While no data have been released concerning the consumption of

[4] See Appendix I, Table 1, World Crude-oil Production, 1947–1953.
[5] *The Oil and Gas Journal*, September 13, 1954.
[6] See Appendix I, Table 28, Estimated Oil Production of USSR and Satellites, 1953 and 1948.

petroleum in the Soviet bloc, it is generally believed that the civilian use of petroleum is highly restricted. In the 5 years preceding World War II the petroleum demand in all the countries now Russian con-trolled—excluding China—was increasing at the average rate of about 11 per cent a year. Assuming that in the past 5 years the total Soviet demands—including essential needs, military uses and military stock-piling—were growing at the same average level, in 1953 requirements would be in the neighborhood of 1,200,000 barrels daily. Thus, with production averaging 1,315,000 barrels daily, it would appear that the Soviets may have a surplus of about 100,000 barrels a day which they could sell on the Free World markets.

This being the case, it is not surprising that petroleum should have figured prominently in the Soviet Union's "trade offensive" of 1953–1954. At about the time of the Korean armistice of July 27, 1953, Russia attracted world attention with a flurry of new trade agreements with non-Communist countries. A second flurry occurred around the end of the year. All told, the USSR concluded trade agreements with France, Greece, Argentina, Denmark and Iceland, then with India, Belgium, Norway, Sweden and Finland. With Israel and Japan, as well as with some of the countries already mentioned, Russia also made barter deals. Furthermore, she renewed agreements with Iran and Afghanistan and signed a "payments agreement" with Egypt. In the early part of 1954 the Soviet Union had trade agreements with more Free World countries than at any other time in the postwar period. Prominently publicized by Russia was its desire to buy con-sumer goods, commodities which the Free World never has withheld from her.

In August, 1953, meantime, behind the guns of a "power" statement, Premier Malenkov introduced the Soviet Union's "new economic policy." Addressing the Supreme Soviet, he made repeated claims of Russian strength and progress. He said that the United States had no monopoly on the hydrogen bomb, for example, and added that such facts "are shattering the wagging of tongues about the weakness of the Soviet Union."

Nevertheless, in his discussion of consumer goods he gave a reveal-ing picture of weakness. "The urgent task," Malenkov said, "lies in raising sharply in two or three years the population's supply of food-stuffs and manufactured goods, meat and meat produce, fish and fish produce, butter, sugar, confectionery, textiles, garments, footwear, crockery, furniture and other cultural and household goods, in raising considerably the supply to the population of all kinds of consumer goods." To attain these ends in "two or three years," he announced a program of expanding consumer goods manufacture. "We shall continue to develop, by all possible means, heavy industry and transport," he stated. ". . . we must always remember that heavy industry constitutes the basic foundation of our socialist economy, because without its development, it is impossible to insure further growth of light industry, increase productivity of agriculture, and the strengthening of the defensive power of our country." The Russian premier, in other words, asserted that the consumer program would not displace basic industrialization, but that both would progress simultaneously.

With its combined "trade offensive" and its "new economic policy," obviously the Soviet Union sought to convey the impression that since, at last, it was sufficiently strong militarily a better day was dawning for the consumer. Similar moves were made in satellite countries.

Prominent in the items offered for sale or barter was Iron Curtain oil. By the end of 1953, Russia's treaties and other agreements included oil exports to the approximated total of only 15,000 barrels of crude oil and its products daily, chiefly to Finland, the Scandinavian countries, Italy, Argentina and India.[7] Since then business in prospect at that time might have raised Soviet oil exports to Free World areas to about 100,000 barrels a day.

Naturally, the Free World oil industry was curious to know the meaning behind Russia's move. It had some history to fall back on. Back in the Kerosene Age, in the early part of the century, Russia was an exporter of petroleum products and competed with the United States and Rumania for European markets. But during World War I and the period immediately following the Bolshevik Revolution, Russian exports virtually disappeared from the European markets. Oilmen see the present situation as not unlike one which developed in the mid-twenties. At that time, the Communists were in dire need of machinery and equipment of all categories, and the one commodity which they had readily available for export was petroleum. They or-

[7] See Appendix I, Table 29, Estimate of Possible Oil Exports from Soviet-controlled Areas.

ganized the Russian Oil Products Company, established offices in the principal consuming countries of Europe and by various methods, principally price cutting, recaptured and expanded their prewar oil markets. At the same time, incidentally, the Rumanian oil industry had been rehabilitated after war wreckage and was finding some important new reserves, and Poland also had a small exportable surplus. Today the products of these countries—now all satellites—and particularly those of Rumania undoubtedly figure in the Soviet Union's export deals.[8]

In 1926 Russian oil exports averaged a little over 31,000 barrels daily, and by 1932 they had climbed to a peak of about 123,000 barrels. By that time, however, the new Russian industrial economy, already denied some petroleum because of the high priority given to exports, reached a point at which either the export trade or the economic development had to be curtailed. After 1933, then, shipments from Russia declined consistently, and by 1938 they averaged only 21,000 barrels daily. Simultaneously the Rumanian oil industry was progressing to the point of developing substantial surplus petroleum supplies for export, and competitive pressures from this source coincided with those from Russia. In 1926 Rumanian exports amounted to 31,000 barrels daily, or about the same volume as shipped from Russia. When, in 1932, the Russian oil trade reached its peak of 123,000 barrels daily, the volume shipped from Rumania averaged about 100,-000 barrels a day.

Oil people see Russia's reemergence in world markets today as indicative of her need for food instead of as in her previous "offensive" a desire for machinery and equipment. The supposition is heightened by the fact that her barter agreements in large part have stipulated the receipt of food products in exchange for oil.

From an oil marketer's standpoint, today's question is not delimited to Russia's direct ability to export oil. Rather, it embraces all Iron Curtain countries. And marketers admit that the new Soviet exports pose some real competitive problems—perhaps more in the light of potential pressures than in the comparatively small volumes being shipped currently. Assuming that the Soviets dispose of 100,000 barrels daily in 1954—an optimistic assumption—the total would represent

[8] See Appendix I, Table 30, Exports of Crude and Products by Russia, Rumania and Poland, 1926–1938.

only 1.5 per cent of all foreign demands. But small volumes can cause serious competitive impacts in some countries. The products which ultimately would be shipped to Iceland and Finland, for instance, represent nearly the entire consumption of those countries. In other words, Russia would capture these entire markets. The volume of residual fuel oil included in the Finnish trade agreement conceivably might be higher than local demand; then Finland might trade the surplus within the framework of her tripartite agreements. Thus Russia might displace present marketers in Scandinavian countries. Her fuel-oil sales to Norway represent about half of the consumption of that country; she is pressing sales in Sweden and Denmark. Stemming from East Germany's great need for food and from West Germany's desire for additional petroleum products, oil exports from East Germany and Austria to West Germany are increasing. Russian oil, therefore, presents problems out of proportion to the total quantity involved.

Moreover, in world markets Soviet Russia is a price cutter. The expansion of Soviet oil sales in the twenties and thirties resulted in bitter price wars with established oil groups, a bitterness made more intense by the fact that the Bolsheviks had neglected to settle for the foreign oil properties which they had seized after the revolution. As with all her exports at that time, the USSR was interested more in total receipts of foreign exchange than in high per-unit profits; hence she could and did cut prices. Though established companies earnestly sought to meet the competition and save their markets by underselling the Soviet monopoly, nevertheless Russia won back an important place in world oil markets. But—and this is a point the oilmen stress today—having done so, she withdrew. The inference of this action at that time was that she had achieved her immediate purpose of acquiring needed machinery and, further, that the fuel demands of continued industrial expansion precluded the continuation of exports.

Will Russia repeat her past performance? Her barter deals are a form of price cutting. If the Kremlin so decides, the Soviet bloc, though still short of certain specialized refined products, probably has the capacity to make substantial oil exports for at least some years. Whether the bloc will step into world markets in an important way, as the USSR did in the twenties, is not known. To participate today to the extent that they did in 1932, when they accounted for 14.5 per cent of total foreign demand, Russia and her satellites would have to export ten times the maximum quantity which is estimated to be involved in the agreements already made—an unlikely possibility. Most oil people, indeed, think that Soviet shipments may never reach the commitments in the deals which, optimistically, she already has made. Also, on the basis of simple historical fact, buyers might well ask themselves how long they can expect to rely on Soviet oil. Who can predict the moment when the dictates of the Kremlin—whether they be economic or political—will override the dictates of the market place and the oil suddenly will be whisked out of reach?

From a propaganda point of view, of course, Russia's invasion of foreign markets has a value all its own. To the world it appears that the Soviet has "oil to burn" or "oil to give away"—that her petroleum self-sufficiency has expanded to exportable proportions. A sharp contrast this to the United States which is forced to import! The Russian action has a peculiar value in bolstering her claim of "now we are strong enough," for petroleum is a strategic material of high priority. Yet, obviously, every barrel of oil shipped out of the Soviet Union is a direct repudiation of the Kremlin's line to its people. If oil is so plentiful why not stimulate the manufacture and use of domestic oil burners and of pleasure automobiles? Why not implement by action rather than by propaganda the slogan of "a better day for the consumer"? In this connection, it should be noted by contrast that in 1953 the British tore up their gasoline ration books.

Quite possibly Russia's petroleum move is a necessary part of her "trade offensive." She *does* have *some* oil—and some manganese and gold as well—which she can sell. Reporting on the results of her first year's efforts, Harold E. Stassen, director of the Foreign Operations Administration, labeled the Soviet bloc's drive a flop. In 1953 Russian trade with the Free World declined, despite her highly publicized trade offensive, her unusual imports of consumer goods and her unusual exports of gold, manganese and oil.[9] Though 1954 might possibly show slightly better results, "the impression that a historic increase in East-West trade is taking place, seems hardly justified." The best explanation for the selection of petroleum, manganese and gold as export articles, the report indicated, seemed to be simple—hard pressed for

[9] *East-West Trade Trends*, Foreign Operations Administration, Fourth Report to Congress, May 17, 1954.

adequate exports, the Kremlin decided to use a fraction of certain commodities which it had and knew that the world wanted.

But no one doubts for a moment that, in the case of oil at least, the Kremlin duly has regarded its military self-sufficiency before taking to world markets.

In Chapter 23, Oil and Free World Defense, some attention is given to the predominance of Free World petroleum over the Soviet-controlled supply. According to authorities, Russia has some of the most promising oil territory in the world; yet, in spite of a vast market of consumers eager for a better way of life or, should we say, a driving military urgency to develop the potential, her production does not nearly approach our own. No one is free to look for oil in Soviet Russia. The state runs the industry on a cut-and-dried basis dictated by the needs of the Red Army. Dr. Leonid P. Smirnov, former chief arctic geologist for the Soviet government and a man who traveled widely in Russia from 1925 to 1942 answers the question, "How does Russia stand on oil?" as follows: [10]

"We must bear in mind one very important fact: In Russia oil is not used for civilian automobiles. It is not used as a fuel in industry, almost all of Russia's oil goes to the Red Army. There are few gasoline stations in Russia . . . not even any paved highways except those strategically placed near the frontiers. All gasoline-burning trucks and autos belong to the government. Industrial plants burn coal; electric power stations work on brown coal and even peat. The average Soviet citizen cannot buy gasoline; he may buy only kerosene for his cook stove and benzene for his cigarette lighter. . . .

"A large part of it [oil] is stockpiled [for the military]. Because transportation is always scarce in the Soviet Union, the Russians have sought to build up sources of oil in all strategic parts of the country. They now have oil in the west. They have oil in the east. They have oil in the south. They have oil in the Arctic. I have first-hand knowledge of many of the newer oil basins, because I helped discover them.

"About 40 per cent of Russia's oil comes from the Baku region, in the Caucasus, which has been producing since the time of the Czars. My news from the Soviet Union indicates that the Baku has lost its first place in production, but I think this is only temporary. Many favorable new structures are being drilled in the shallow Caspian Sea.

[10] Soviet Oil: The Inside Story, *The Flying Red Horse*, Summer, 1953.

In the Baku are six major refineries and many pipe lines. Oil from the Baku region, plus oil from the Ukraine and from the satellites, supplies the Red armies in the west.

"In Turkestan are several smaller basins which supply oil to the armies in the south. In the interior of Russia is the great new Second Baku basin, which now accounts for about 40 per cent of Russia's oil production. I took part in its discovery when I was chief geologist of the Southern Urals. This basin is similar to the Oklahoma basin; it is especially rich in Permian reefs and Devonian beds.

"The Second Baku region has been developed from the Caspian Sea for more than 800 miles northward, but it actually extends all the way from the Caspian Sea to the Arctic and north to Franz Josef Land. There are at least 20 refineries and more than 1,000 miles of pipe line in the Second Baku area. One pipe line goes across the Ural Mountains into Siberia.

"Throughout the tremendous area of Siberia many oil basins are being explored; some are now in production. In south-central Siberia, in the Lake Baikal region, is an ancient depression. Rotary drilling was begun here in 1932. The region is now producing.

"After World War II some German plants were brought to this area to produce oil from the abundant soft coal and shale, an expensive process which our reserves in the United States have enabled us to avoid. One such plant near Irkutsk has a yearly capacity of 10,500,000 gallons of high-quality aviation gasoline. Labor from nearby concentration camps is being used to build new refineries.

"It was decided 23 years ago that the Far Eastern army must have its own oil supply. At the time Russia entered the war against Japan in 1945, this army was supplied for a prolonged war. They certainly did not expend very much oil in their few days of fighting the Japanese, and they have been continuing to build up oil supplies ever since.

"The most important oil area in the Far East is on Sakhalin Island. Proved reserves there are about 350,000,000 barrels; perhaps ten times that amount ultimately will be found. Before World War II production on Sakhalin was about 3,500,000 barrels per year; it could be as high as 21,000,000 barrels now.

"Oil basins are on both coasts of the Kamchatka Peninsula; the most favorable basin is on the west coast. Rotary drilling was started in 1938; production on Kamchatka could now be from 1,500,000 to 7,000,000 barrels per year. There are four large refineries in the Far East and a pipe line from the Sakhalin fields to Vladivostok.

"But it is in the Arctic—closest to the United States—that the Soviets are most rapidly expanding their oil production. In the far north the Soviet air bases, navy and armies are now independent of the rest of Russia for their oil and gasoline. Refinery equipment which the United States shipped to Russia under lend lease is in operation in the Arctic. Supplying two refineries in the north is the huge Taimyr-Lena basin. I helped discover this basin and explored it from 1934 to 1939. Rotary drilling was started in 1938; production now may be as high as 3,500,000 barrels per year. I also helped discover the Franz Josef Land basin; production is undoubtedly under way in this frozen land nearly 1,000 miles north of the Arctic Circle. . . .

"And so you see that Russia's 'inferior' position in oil production is much less inferior than the barrels-per-day figures seem to show. And the same is true of her steel and other heavy industries."

We leave to the military experts the decision as to the kind of war the next big conflict will be—as to what differences atomic weapons, if used, would make between past and future conflicts. We venture to say, however, that petroleum still must be ranked as a war material of highest priority. The simplest example is that atom bombs must be delivered to their targets in oil-using carriers and that all over the world airports must be guarded and supplied by oil-burning naval vessels and carriers. Military planners today must view petroleum through their World War II experience which taught certain basic and invaluable lessons. The importance of the location and control of strategic crude-oil sources, the relationship of these sources to refineries and the availability of transportation sum up the major factors to be considered.

In the last analysis, it appears that Russia has strategically located fields, refineries and stockpiles west, east, south and north. Moreover, she has a great standing army and, seemingly, a potent military striking power. In the light of these facts and in view of petroleum's role in modern warfare, nothing could be more evident than the necessity for the Free World's not only having oil in plentiful supply, but having it where it will be available for global warfare. Moreover, it should be so placed as to offset the type of warfare which conceivably can knock out with one blow a great producing area. Given a series of swift blows by Russia and China which might eliminate Middle Eastern or Indonesian supplies, the Free World's superiority becomes highly theoretical. Only when one recognizes that the threat against us involves global defense—defense not only in the West but in the Middle and Far East—only then does one fully recognize the importance of and the need for the Free Nations to continue their vigorous search for and development of petroleum throughout the world.

Under these circumstances what American oilmen have contributed, and are continuing to contribute, to Free World defense by adding new petroleum areas throughout the world comes home to us vitally. Who knows but that some day the Canada discoveries or the at-long-last strikes in New Guinea and Australia may not prove to be the deterrent to would-be aggressors or, perhaps, supply the ammunition that spells victory for the Free World?

How do we know, indeed, that the Free World's vigorous and widespread development of petroleum has not been—and is not now—making aggressors think twice before striking?

What a contrast our petroleum relations with the Free Nations make compared to those of Russia with her satellites! Generally speaking, in satellite countries Russia organized oil companies, in which she held a 50 per cent interest, to take over expropriated petroleum properties. She had advanced no risk capital, taken no long-revenue time lags. A 50-50 profit sharing at gunpoint in an enterprise to which she had contributed nothing!

Nor has there been in the Soviet bloc any development of petroleum that parallels that of the international oil companies. There has been no comparable paying of high wages or building of schools, hospitals and housing designed to advance the economy and social welfare of oil workers and their families. And "sow the petroleum" has had no application—indeed, has not yet even been stolen as a slogan by the Russian rulers.

"We must suppose that the intent of any steps to improve the lot of the Soviet-bloc consumer is to improve it just enough to rescue his productivity in the interest of the state," said Stassen in his report, "but not enough to give him such a taste of better living as would lead to a wider and wider opening of the valves and hinder the buildup of the totalitarian war economy." Then he added, "If that is a correct assumption, the world, yearning for assurance of peace, is entitled to wish that the Kremlin's calculations might be upset and the consumer might get enough to whet his appetite in a big way."

The Free World is strong in oil—it is strong in every way—as against Soviet Russia.

Chapter 23

OIL AND FREE WORLD DEFENSE

Oil for Free World defense means oil for the security of the individual and collective Free World countries, both in their efforts to strengthen their economies and to prepare for the emergencies of war. We have seen that World War I first focused attention on petroleum as a strategic material of highest priority for the military machine as well as for the industrial economy required to back up that machine. We have seen, too, that World War II was a gigantic underscoring of the lesson of the first conflict. The question of oil and effective defense is a mutual problem which all Free World countries must face. But many of its aspects revolve around the American petroleum industry in both its domestic and international phases, for the phrase, "America, the arsenal of democracy" is no empty one. That our own petroleum resources should enjoy continued development in keeping with best conservation practices and that our foreign supply sources should be adequate, strategically placed and ready are defense factors vital to our nation and to the entire Free World.

The invaluable oil resources possessed by the United States in 1939 when war began in Europe lay not merely in its oil fields, refineries and other plant facilities but also in the technical know-how and the technical manpower necessary to cope with the great world emergency. In these resources no other nation even approached the United States.

Once before, in the emergency of World War I, American oil had gained the day for democracy, and Lord Curzon was only one of many who gave credit where credit was due. "The Allies floated to victory on a sea of oil," said the statesman who was one of the four members of the British War Cabinet, in whose charge rested the details of all military and civilian operations. The American petroleum industry supplied the bulk of that oil. As great as were the requirements then, however, they were little as compared with the monumental demands of the United Nations in World War II. To meet those demands the United States supplied an estimated 69 per cent. In World War II the United States shipped overseas twice as many tons of oil and oil products as the combined total of all other cargoes— twice as many tons of oil as the weight of all the men, weapons, ammunition, food and other supplies put together! Petroleum sparked every invasion, every wave of every invasion and the complicated system of supply that grew in their wakes. Without oil no plane could fly, no tank could move, no ship could sail. Petroleum shaped the course of every battle on every beachhead. From our enemies' lack of it stemmed their inevitable and final defeat.

Oil was everywhere, and everywhere when needed. To keep the tanks, mobile guns, half tracks, trucks and jeeps of a single armored division fighting for one day required 60,000 gallons of gasoline. To operate the Air Forces 24 hours, fourteen times as much gasoline was necessary as was shipped to Europe for all purposes in World War I. Oil supplied block-buster bombs with toluene, the basic ingredient of TNT, and the asphalt for paving landing strips and military roads. Oil heated tents and billets, purified water, powered laundries, waterproofed uniforms. Oil made possible many medicines, anesthetics, bug killers. Oil moved battleships, cruisers, aircraft carriers, submarines, troop transports, cargo and hospital ships, every kind of vessel. For refueling and lubricating the war machine, oil in drums and jerry cans was stacked in supply dumps or supplied by mobile refueling units along the roads, airstrips and docks. Pipelines ran into combat areas, jerry cans littered the path of every armored force break-through. Too, oil fought on the home front. It kept farm tractors and trucks operating, heated and powered homes and factories, carried war workers to their jobs. It supplied butadiene, essential to the synthetic-rubber production that kept our motor transport going. At the beginning of hostilities Admiral Nimitz said that victory was a matter of "beans, bullets and oil." Before the war's end he had changed his emphasis. "Now," he said, "it's oil, bullets and beans."

The American oil industry helped win the war by finding more oil, by improving the techniques of exploration and production, by developing on a quantity scale such vital products as 100-octane gasoline and by improving the techniques of refining and chemical research —in short, by having the technical know-how. At its finger tips our government had skilled manpower trained in petroleum production, refining, transportation and marketing. Technical know-how was "one of America's formidable weapons in battle."

Through a large number and variety of industry committees, headed by the Petroleum Industry War Council, the Petroleum Administration for War coordinated the important contributions of the American petroleum industry to the winning of the war. Largely the PAW and industry committees were staffed by men whose services were contributed by the industry. Trained transport men worked out the coordination of tanker operations with available petroleum supplies between the War Shipping Administration and the United States Navy. The Army-Navy Petroleum Board was to a large extent staffed by American oil-industry personnel. As members of the armed services, oilmen handled petroleum transportation, laid military pipelines and served as "lieutenants in logistics." [1]

To those who during World War II guided the Petroleum Administration for War from its beginnings to its dissolution, the demonstration of the importance of oil was most impressive. "But," to quote from PAW's *History*, "war did more than give new emphasis to oil's importance. It also dispelled the prewar delusion that United States resources would be forever unlimited. Though having come out of World War II (as we did out of World War I) without the fear of 'running out of oil' there nevertheless had been some frightening experiences. New discoveries had run far behind production. The day had come when crude oil production no longer was able to supply the crude oil requirements domestically . . . [we] had to balance out with foreign oil." [2]

Barring profound changes which might possibly occur through the development of inexpensive atomic energy, we must assume that in the event of another world war the outcome will be substantially influenced by the relative availability of petroleum to the opposing forces. Faced with the duty of being ready for any emergency—up to and

[1] *The Rise of American Oil*, pp. 114, 115.
[2] *A History of the Petroleum Administration for War, 1941–1945*, U.S. Government Printing Office, Washington, D.C., 1946, pp. 293, 294.

including war—defense and other government department planners drew heavily upon the knowledge and experience of the oilmen and began to give top attention to petroleum before the smoke had cleared from the last gun fired in World War II. The chilling blasts of the "cold war" spurred them on, and in 1948 government and industry were hard at the problem. The Armed Services Petroleum Board considered immediate problems of supplying military needs. In September the National Security Resources Board received confidential recommendations from Wallace Pratt, the consulting petroleum geologist who had been its special consultant.[3] The oil industry's National Petroleum Council had its Committee on National Emergency studying measures "to safeguard and assure supplies for essential needs in time of emergency." The American Petroleum Institute's Defense Services Committee was on the job. The Interior Department's Military Petroleum Advisory Committee, of which Bruce K. Brown, vicepresident of Standard Oil Company (Indiana), was chairman—was studying ways of assisting the government to find the oil which would be needed in the event of another war.[4]

Fundamental though they are, the problems of oil for defense are not simply those of physical supply and demand—they are not confined solely to such vital questions as, "How much oil will be needed? How much additional refinery capacity will be necessary? Should military stockpiles be built up? What will be the requirements for steel and other critical materials? How should allocations be made?" If such questions were the sole consideration for defense, the knowhow of American technical manpower would solve them quickly and with relative ease. But, necessarily, in today's world, the problems of oil for defense are vitally touched by international political problems—some of them in so-called "explosive" areas—by policies of friendly as well as of unfriendly countries and definitely by Communist aggression and infiltration on a world-wide scale.

What part would Latin-American oil play should a third world war come? The First Inter-American Oil Congress—organized by Communistic labor leader Toledano and held at Mexico City on September 27, 1948—voted to refuse to send oil to the United States and Britain in case of another war. In March, 1948, Perez Alfonso,

---

[3] *The Oil and Gas Journal*, September 30, 1948.
[4] *World Petroleum*, November, 1948.

Venezuelan Minister of Development, balked at oil-defense talk and was quoted as saying that Venezuela was not interested in increasing its oil production. "Our responsibility is to future generations to transform oil resources, which are exported to other countries, into productive investments." [5] In May, however, Alfonso claimed that his remarks had been misinterpreted and that Venezuelan oil readily would be available in an emergency. Venezuela, as a member of the United Nations, he said, would put her oil resources fully at the disposal of "those who fight for freedom and democracy." His previously stated reservations, he said, applied merely to normal conditions and times.[6] Nevertheless, an attempt to have the Inter-American Economic and Social Conference, which began at Bogotá on March 30, 1948, take up the question of oil and hemispheric defense was decided against, in deference to Venezuela's wishes.[7] A large staff of trained experts, including several from the military who had been extensively briefed on oil, accompanied Secretary of State Marshall to Bogotá since, before the conference, we had officially proposed to 20 Latin-American countries, including Mexico, that they help to assure adequate oil for themselves and the Western Hemisphere by opening sources to foreign capital, technical knowledge and experience. In fact, a memorandum prepared by Paul Daniels, Chief of the State Department's Division of American Republic Affairs and a United States representative to the Inter-American Economic and Social Council, had intimated that Western Hemisphere countries with oil resources of their own might be forced to develop them to keep their own economies going and no longer could look with assurance to the United States for petroleum supplies. Though it invoked only the self-interest and security of the individual countries, the memorandum hinted at a broader purpose of hemispheric oil independence, the fulfillment of which would increase the indigenous and importable supply and thus conserve United States reserves. The note did not directly suggest that the nationalization re-strictions—which applied in Mexico, Bolivia, Brazil, Argentina and other countries which had government-owned oil-development com-panies—should be lifted. But, in effect, it did say that American and other qualified oil interests should be given access to those countries

[5] *The Oil and Gas Journal*, March 11, 1948, p. 16.
[6] *The Oil and Gas Journal*, May 20, 1948.
[7] *World Oil*, April, 1948, p. 25.

and pointed out that the development of any country with large potential oil areas required vast amounts of capital, efficient management and large numbers of trained personnel.

"It is doubtful," Daniels wrote, "whether any one company or entity, no matter how large, could be expected to develop such resources successfully and efficiently. What is required is access to adequate and large volumes of risk capital, all of which would be available fully and freely by calling upon the world petroleum industry."

But at the time when the ill-fated Bogotá conference got under way, the United States government itself may have been opposed to the raising of such a delicate question as hemispheric oil defense, for nationalistic fervor and Communist activity—both marked by virulent anti-United States propaganda—were rife in Latin America. A preliminary oil-policy report of the staff of the National Security Resources Board, submitted about this time, recommended a shift in meeting the bulk of Europe's peacetime liquid-fuel demand from the Western Hemisphere to the ample resources of the Eastern Hemisphere and, in the meantime, the pressing of the development of all Western Hemisphere sources at maximum speed. "There can be no doubt," the report asserted, "that full development of these latter sources will provide supplies ample to meet our total anticipated emergency requirements for years to come." But before this could be fully accomplished, the report pointed out, refineries would have to be further expanded in Europe and more Middle East pipeline outlets to the Mediterranean would have to be built. In previous chapters we have seen how the oil companies' Middle Eastern expansion programs in oil finding, refining and transportation together with the Marshall Plan materially advanced the Western Hemisphere oil-security thesis. Not only was there enough eastern oil for the Eastern Hemisphere, but the great reserves found in the Middle East—in Free World territory—afforded increased insurance for the West by way of imports.

During the early postwar years a threatened oil shortage in the United States in the face of greatly increased domestic consumption resulted in the first imports of Middle East oil. New discoveries in the United States, Canada and Venezuela promptly dissipated the shortage scare, but not before the flow of oil from the Middle East to the United States had become established. In 1948 the United States became for the first time, except for a brief period in the early 1920's, a net importer of petroleum. From a defense standpoint Middle East oil could be looked at in two ways: (1) when imported it relieved the drain on United States production and made possible the building up of Western Hemisphere reserves, and (2) in the Middle East it established a vast reserve, strategically placed in the event of war.

The outbreak of the Korean War in 1950, with the consequent mobilization of United States industrial resources and the development of the North Atlantic Treaty Organization, made the assurance of oil supplies a matter of emergency, and Middle East development officially was spurred. Even before the Korean War, the nod had been given to the steel allocation needed to build the huge Tapline system which extended 1,000 miles from the Saudi Arabian oil fields on the Persian Gulf to the Mediterranean Sea, and on which deliveries were started in December, 1950.

Both the strategic importance of Middle East oil and its vulnerability to attack by Russia have been much discussed. The Middle Eastern oil countries are close to Russia, but their geographical proximity is compensated for to some extent by certain factors not readily apparent from examination of an ordinary world map. One has to see the mountain chains of Iran to realize what an obstacle they are to invasion. Similarly, a firsthand look at the deserts of Iraq, Kuwait and Saudi Arabia brings home the seriousness and the magnitude of the problems with which an invading army would have to cope. Distances are greater than they appear in the conventional Mercator projection. The air-line distance from the southern end of the Caspian Sea to Kirkuk in Iraq, for example, is 425 miles, to Abadan in Iran 480, to the Burghan field of Kuwait 560 and to Darhran in Saudi Arabia 710 miles. Bounded on three sides by the Red Sea, the Indian Ocean and the Persian Gulf, the Arabian Peninsula readily is accessible to any force having control of the sea. Iraq and Kuwait lie on the Persian Gulf as also, of course, does Iran. In the sense, then, that a sea power bent on defending these areas would have very real advantages while an invading power coming down from the north would have to overcome serious obstacles, the oil fields of the Middle East are not so vulnerable as at first they might appear.

Yet history has shown that mountainous terrain, no matter how rugged, cannot always stop a determined enemy. The Mongolian invasion of this area in the mid-thirteenth century—which culminated in the destruction of Baghdad and the Abbasid Caliphate—is a classic example of that fact. On the other hand, the rugged barrier deflected the spread of militant Islam and forced the armies of Mohammed and the Omayyad Caliphs toward the south and west.

The seas which surround the entire Middle East area have been protective moats. During the Crusades the passage across the eastern Mediterranean was a major hazard to the Christian armies. Later, the same body of water curbed the ambitions of Napoleon.

In the Arabian Peninsula the most formidable natural barriers are the vast areas of soft, shifting sands and the almost complete lack of easily accessible potable water. The availability of water in the area has affected even the distribution of populations, causing the intense development of the Fertile Crescent, the Nile Valley and of northern Iran, but retarding the development of the Arabian Peninsula. In the last analysis, however, modern transportation and equipment can overcome all these barriers. Hence our concern.

But vulnerability of oil reserves, whether located in the Middle East, Latin America or elsewhere, can spring from a source other than direct military attack. Nationalization, perhaps inflamed by patriotic emotionalism, perhaps incited by cynical influences such as Communism, can cut off oil supply as effectively as an invading army. Few Americans realize that the nationalization and loss of Iranian oil in 1951 presented a serious threat to the Korean War effort, to the success of the Marshall Plan, to the defense and rearmament program of the United States and to NATO. In June, 1951, the last tanker had been loaded at Abadan; the Free World abruptly had lost 610,000 barrels a day of crude oil and products. Quickly the United States government countered by preparing a "voluntary agreement relating to the supply of petroleum to friendly foreign nations," drew up a plan of action and invited 19 American oil companies engaged in foreign operations to join a Foreign Petroleum Supply Committee. The program which the government proposed called for increases in crude-oil production, if necessary, in 11 countries and for a rise in product manufacturing in 27 nations. It outlined arrangements among the participating companies for the purchase, sale, loan or exchange of crude oil and refined products for the most efficient use, without regard to ownership, of terminal and storage facilities, tankers, pipelines and other installations. By the end of 1951 the committee's efforts had averted any setbacks to rearmament which might have resulted from lack of oil and also had replaced much of the Iranian production which Iran's huge Abadan refinery formerly had supplied to Europe and to India, Pakistan, Malaya and West African countries. By July of 1952 the Petroleum Administration for Defense had approved schedules of various transactions, involving about 19½ million barrels of crude oil and 26½ million barrels of refined products.

"I am certain—and this I say very deliberately—I am certain that the direction of those millions of barrels to points of need plus the effective expansion in Free World tanker capacity made possible by reroutings under the Plan of Action contributed heavily to the salvation of the Free World's defenses," Secretary of the Interior Oscar L. Chapman, Petroleum Administrator for Defense, declared.[8]

In January, 1951, President Truman formed the President's Materials Policy Commission with William S. Paley as chairman and George R. Brown, Arthur H. Bunker, Eric Hodgins and Edward S. Mason as members. After a year of preparation, the Paley Report was issued in June, 1952. Constituting one of the most exhaustive studies ever made of the problem of strategic materials for defense, the report predicted a doubling of United States petroleum consumption by 1975.[9]

A précis of some of the Paley findings as they relate to oil follows.

A materials problem of considerable severity affects the United States and the industrialized nations of Western Europe, and unless it is effectively met, the long-range security and economic growth of this and other Free Nations will be seriously impaired. The basic reason for the problem is soaring demand. With less than 10 per cent of Free World population, and only 8 per cent of the Free World area, the United States consumed more than half of 1950's supply of such fundamental materials as petroleum, rubber, iron ore, manganese and zinc. As for petroleum, United States consumption in 1975 will be in the neighborhood of 5 billion barrels, more than double the 1950 demand. When we reach the stage at which we must turn abroad for additional supplies of one material after another, the point may be

[8] Address before American Petroleum Institute Annual Meeting, November 12, 1952.

[9] The President's Materials Policy Commission Report, June, 1952. (See Appendix II for extracts from report.)

raised that we are endangering our security by dependence on foreign sources—on "fair-weather friends" whose supplies may not be available to us in time of war. If a war should cut off the flow of oil to Western Europe from the Middle East, the burden of fueling Western Europe would fall heavily upon the oil-producing nations of the Western Hemisphere. In that event the United States would face the problem of reconciling its own needs with those of its Allies—a problem which would transcend purely domestic considerations.

To meet these energy demands the United States is prepared in varying degrees. We have burned up more coal, oil and natural gas in the last 50 years than in all previous history. The pressure of rising demand against the limits of known reserves and known technology presents the possibility of energy shortages and of mounting real costs which could impair the nation's economic growth and security. The remaining reserves of gas and oil that are known to exist in the United States will be no match for the probable demands of the next 25 years. We shall certainly discover more in the years ahead, but real costs of discovery and extraction seem likely to rise as we are forced to drill deeper, to drill more "dry holes" for every well brought in. Possibly, too, we shall have to rely on new pools of smaller average size.

Even if oil discoveries and production keep rising for a decade or more, United States demand may far outstrip domestic production, as it already has begun to do. Demand for natural gas also may outpace supply and put further upward pressures on price. We shall not suddenly "run out" of these highly important fuels, but we could well enter a long period of dwindling supply accompanied by rising real costs. Petroleum is the great enigma of future energy supplies. No one can know how much more petroleum will be discovered in the United States during the next two decades, or how much it will be feasible—geologically and economically—to produce by 1975. But no matter how large the nation's domestic petroleum resources ultimately prove to be, one fact is now clear: eventually the resources will dwindle—progressively they will become inadequate. Already a significant warning signal has appeared—the United States became an important net importer in 1948, has been one since and no hope of resuming its export status looms on the horizon. This recent development suggests that the United States, faced with an approximate doubling of oil demand by 1975, will find it economical if not necessary to turn increasingly to foreign supplies, and eventually to liquid fuel from shale and coal.

"We can never forget that once we have passed the immediate problem of supply for the military and essential civilian needs we have come squarely against the longer-range problem: How can we assure that in case of all-out war there will be enough oil and gas to fuel the Free World's defenses?" PAW Administrator Chapman told the American Petroleum Institute in November, 1952.[10] "Since oil, unlike other materials, can't possibly be stockpiled in sufficient quantities above the ground, all that we can provide by way of an emergency reserve is a reserve of potential capacity.

"There has to be oil, known, proved, and at least partially developed, underground beyond present production to serve as a reservoir for tapping in case of need. There has to be at least a potential of transportation to move the oil from the point of production to the point of refining and then to points of need. There has to be a reserve capacity in refineries, over and above that being used to satisfy current demands, that could be pressed into use to turn out the products we would need—and need quickly—in case of war.

"It is PAD's duty to figure what reserve is needed, and the agency has done that, and continued to do it as it revises calculations to fit changing conditions. The results of the calculations are, for obvious reasons, classified as security secrets. I do not violate security, though, when I say that at present we do not begin to have the reserve we should have in order to provide, not absolute security, but just the minimum of security that would give us room for maneuver in the opening months of a war. Our only consolation can be that at the moment the Soviet and its satellites have much less oil than we do, only about one-eleventh in fact. But then that's a balance that could all too easily be disturbed almost overnight.

"How are we to get the reserve we must have? I am frank to confess that I am not sure. Certainly there's no magic formula to be applied, no simple solution that can be demonstrated on a slide rule."

PAD's program, launched immediately after the outbreak of the Korean War, called for the industry to build up an excess crude-oil

[10] Address before American Petroleum Institute Annual Meeting, November 12, 1952.

producing capacity of 1 million barrels daily. Such a reserve was considered necessary in the event that foreign sources of supply were cut off.

In May, 1954—nearly four years after the Korean conflict began—the nation's oil fields had a record shut-in production of 1,500,000 to 1,800,000 barrels daily. In the same month wells in Texas—which produces more than 40 per cent of the country's and 20 per cent of the Free World's output—were permitted to produce only 17 days. As a member of the Interstate Oil Compact, Texas adheres to a policy of proration among oil-producing states. During the same period imports of crude oil and petroleum products were averaging about 1,000,000 barrels a day. Proved crude-oil reserves at the end of 1953 had totaled 28,944,828,000 barrels, compared with 27,468,031,000 barrels at the end of 1951.[11]

When the defense authorities called for greater crude-oil producing capacity, they requested an excess refining capacity reserve of the same amount—1 million barrels a day. This goal, too, has been reached. Though PAD closed its offices early in 1954, at the present writing great activity continues in wildcat operations and in refinery expansion or rebuilding.

In a word, since Korea, discovery has followed discovery in the United States. A report of the Texas Railroad Commission showed that in one week in May, 1953, twenty new Texas oil fields were discovered, bringing the year's total in that state to 266, for an increase of 62 fields over those reported the year before.

In recent years, therefore, not only in the Middle East, Venezuela and Canada has petroleum development surged ahead, but also in the United States. In the sense that "they always find the oil," history again has repeated itself [12] to such an extent that today the problem is not a threatened world oil shortage but a threatened world oil oversupply.

As this situation has been materializing, manifestations of the complexity of, and of the numerous facets involved in, the problem of foreign oil and the Free World have shown themselves in many places. In the United States oil producers not engaged in foreign operations expressed fears that Middle East oil imports—added to South Ameri-

[11] See Appendix I, Table 23, Estimated World Oil Reserves.
[12] They Always Find the Oil, *National Petroleum News*, February 15, 1950, p. 306.

can imports and the pipelining of Canadian crude oil into the United States which began in 1953—threatened the prosperity of the domestic industry. They asked for some control on imports by a quota system or by the imposition of higher tariffs. United States coal interests, notably John L. Lewis, took up the agitation to control imports. South American oil-producing countries became alarmed. With its former large exports to Europe greatly reduced because of Middle East intrusion, Venezuela looked to the United States and to growing South American markets to offset its loss, and inasmuch as oil is Venezuela's greatest source of revenue the matter was serious to that nation's economy. On the other hand, rigid quotas and higher import tariffs in the United States could discourage the building up of the Western Hemisphere petroleum-supply facilities and reserves which would be vital to the Free World if the Middle East were cut off as a source of supply.

During the last few years the differences in viewpoint held by international companies with foreign operations on the one hand and by strictly domestic concerns and coal interests on the other have been aired before Congressional committees, notably before the House Ways and Means Committee in May, 1953, and in the press. There is no easy answer to the import question—no more so than there is to the entire question of foreign oil and the Free World.

We have pointed out in Chapter 21 that the nationalization trend in Latin America seems to have been checked, or, at any rate, several countries have shown a distinct inclination to put out the welcome mat for foreign capital. But what about Communism in Latin America? The suddenly nasty Guatemalan situation in mid-1954 makes the query most timely. In May, 1954, A. T. Steele, writing in the *New York Herald Tribune*, after returning from an extended tour of South America, reported significant Communist activities in 11 countries—Chile, Brazil, Mexico, Argentina, Bolivia, Panama, Colombia, Venezuela, Ecuador, Uruguay and Cuba. Light penetration, he said, existed in five nations—Peru, Costa Rica, Nicaragua, Paraguay and El Salvador. Only in the three countries of Haiti, Honduras and the Dominican Republic was Communist penetration insignificant. The picture gives cause for concern.

"It is only since World War II that the Communists have become a [factor in] serious hemispheric disunity, crippling strikes and sabotage of production and supply lines . . ." Steele stated. "The stakes are tremendous. Latin America accounts for close to one-third of United States foreign trade. It is an important and close-at-hand source of certain strategic materials—copper, tin, bauxite, iron, petroleum and natural nitrates, to name only a few. In some of these industries (nitrates, for example) there has been heavy Communist penetration via the labor unions. . . . Brazilian Communists are said to have authored the slogan, 'The Petroleum Is Ours,' which had a lot to do with persuading Brazilian legislators to vote against foreign participation in the development of Brazil's oil reserves." [13]

As recently as June, 1954, Assistant Secretary of State Henry A. Byroade declared before the Senate Foreign Relations Committee that Russia was stepping up the cold war in the Middle East with an eye to controlling oil supplies of that area. He said that Russia was setting herself up as the champion of the small Arab states to widen the split between them and the West. This was evidenced, he stated, by the Soviet's support of the Arab states in the case of the oil dispute between Britain and Iran and during the controversy over the Suez Canal between Britain and Egypt. This support also was apparent when Russia twice exercised her veto in the United Nations to block resolutions unfavorable to the Arab nations. Russian policy "is a very dangerous one, as we see it, in the Middle East," Byroade warned. He added that there are dangers of losing the Middle East "through this type of cold war that we are in." The committee's record showed defense officials and Congress also alarmed about the Arabian situation. Senator Wiley, chairman of the committee, reported that all military men he had talked with "sense that the big target of the Kremlin is the Middle East, because there is more oil there than at any other place in the world." If and when Russia thinks the time is ripe, "she is going in that direction," Wiley added.[14]

Any discussion of the role of oil in Free World defense must emphasize two phases of the world petroleum situation which are of the highest significance.

First, the activities of American and other companies throughout the world have given the Free World its great oil reserves. No precise information as to the oil supplies of Russia and her satellite countries

---

[13] *New York Herald Tribune,* May 24, 1954.
[14] *National Petroleum News,* July 19, p. 73.

is available, but reasonable estimates place current productibility in these areas at a little over a million barrels a day. The non-Communist world, therefore, has ten or eleven times as much oil at its disposal as has Russia. Obviously the Free World's oil superiority is a deterrent to whatever plans the Kremlin may have for World War III.

Second, oil development can build up friendly relationships between nations. Despite the Iran experience, oilmen point to a record in most Middle Eastern countries which has fostered at least the beginning of an essential understanding between West and East. This friendly, mutually profitable understanding can become an invaluable contribution to the peace and security of the Free World. The fact that the widely divergent viewpoints which brought on the Iranian break apparently have been resolved (see Chapter 25) underlines the increasing intercooperation between Free World nations.

Chapter 24

WHY NOT AN INTERNATIONAL
OIL POLICY?

The fundamental importance of petroleum to the Free World demands an international oil policy.

Government and industry alike see the gravity of the problem, but perhaps the present situation resembles the early days in the evolution of our oil conservation policy when industry did not always see eye to eye with government and was divided in its own ranks. As was the case in the preliminaries to the evolution of a domestic conservation policy, sporadic endeavors have been made to establish an international petroleum policy. Perhaps the most significant attempts took place during World War II.

Though the spheres of foreign relations and national oil policy were not among the specific wartime assignments of the Petroleum Administration for War, the Petroleum Industry War Council or the Foreign Operations Committee, nonetheless these government and industry agencies found themselves unavoidably occupied with both subjects. Before they had finished their wartime tasks, therefore, they had played major roles in the building of an Anglo-American Oil Agreement—which did not become effective—and had presented to Congress in considerable detail their views as to what the oil pattern of the future should be. The outlines of this over-all pattern may be found in the contemporary public addresses and writings of government officials, in testimony before Congressional committees, in the published statements of oil-company executives and in the pronouncements of industry groups as well as in the provisions of the proposed Anglo-American Agreement.

In the large volume of material developed on the subject, three points repeatedly stand out as epitomizing the oil industry's position:

1. that the United States petroleum industry should remain strictly a private industry, both at home and abroad;

2. that the United States government should not in any manner become an active participant in the oil business;

3. and that the United States government in the interest of the orderly development of world petroleum resources should take steps to bring the conflicting oil policies of the various nations into harmony.

If the end of the war found government and industry in substantial agreement as to many basic principles of a future oil policy for the United States, scarcely can it be said that the road traveled was altogether smooth.[1] As a matter of fact, even the Anglo-American Agreement was not enacted, and no definite international oil policy emerged.

According to *A History of the Petroleum Administration for War*, the genesis of the idea of an agreement between the United States and the United Kingdom is lost in a conflict of records and memoranda.[2] In digest form PAW's account follows: About 1944 the original idea was broached to the British by the American State Department, only to produce an "obvious lack of interest." Early in 1943, meanwhile, spokesmen for American oil interests in the Middle East had visited Petroleum Administrator Ickes and had "expressed concern as to the security of their concessions, indicating they feared certain foreign interests were working to undermine their position." Extensive discussions ensued among representatives of the State, War, Navy and Interior Departments and the Foreign Economic Administration. Out of them came instructions from President Roosevelt for the creation, under the Reconstruction Finance Corporation Act, of a Petroleum Reserves Corporation, endowed with a broad charter which empowered it to conduct virtually any type of oil activity abroad. Though it was established June 30, 1943, with Secretary Ickes as president and with its charter and plans a closely guarded secret, enough information leaked out to convince many oil men that PRC was an attempt to put the government into the oil business. In November, PAW's Foreign Oper-

[1] A Case History of Oil-shortage Scares, *Our Oil Resources*, pp. 352–364.

[2] Foreign Relations and Oil Policy, *A History of the Petroleum Administration for War, 1941–1945*, Government Printing Office, Washington, D.C., 1946, pp. 275–287.

ations Committee completed a study entitled "A Foreign Oil Policy for the United States," which included a proposal for an International Oil Compact. In January, PIWC's Special Committee on Foreign Oil Policy endorsed the report, but reserved judgment on the compact proposal.

On December 11, 1943, meanwhile, the Independent Petroleum Association of America took a stand against government in business in a resolution petitioning the government to establish and maintain a consistent oil policy (1) by giving diplomatic support to its nationals engaged in foreign oil operations, (2) by fostering the private enterprises of its nationals in foreign petroleum operations, and (3) by establishing the cardinal principle in foreign oil policy that the government itself will not directly or indirectly engage in foreign oil operations.

Since Secretary Ickes was of the opinion that numerous high-level national problems made industry advice desirable, he requested PIWC to appoint a committee on national oil policy. This was done, but before the National Oil Policy Committee was ready to report, the Ickes Petroleum Reserves Corporation project to construct a pipeline from the Persian Gulf to the Mediterranean—first announced February 6, 1944—"struck the industry by surprise and created a violently unfavorable reaction." All United States factions united to condemn the government entrance into the oil business and to warn of the dangers of direct government operations in the explosive Middle East. Ickes denied that the government intended competitive operations as PIWC condemned the project. The pipeline, described by Ickes as "only a single, and not too important, item in what we may hope will be a comprehensive national oil policy, embracing both domestic and foreign operations," was abandoned. A "greater undertaking"—the Anglo-American Oil Agreement—emerged.

Discussions between Great Britain and the United States at a cabinet as well as at a technical level began in April, 1944, extended over a long period and resulted in the formulating of two Anglo-American Oil Agreements. The first agreement, though signed by both Britain and the United States, was discarded because of the American oil industry's violent and almost unanimous opposition. The second was submitted to the Senate for enactment as a treaty and was referred to the Committee on Foreign Relations where, eventually, it was pigeonholed.

Yet certain proposals in the document are of particular current interest. At one point the State Department took the position that the agreement should be drafted in such a way as not to confine it to a two-party pledge, but instead to make it "open to immediate accession by all producing and consuming countries." Britain resisted, and the American delegation yielded to the British point of view only after insisting upon definite assurance that other countries would be invited to join in a future multilateral petroleum agreement. The British accepted the condition, and in the final draft the two nations pledged that, as soon as practicable, they would propose to all other interested countries the negotiation of an international agreement. Clear evidence exists, therefore, that the pact was not intended to freeze out other countries.

The United States and the United Kingdom took the first step toward an international policy simply because they had problems of mutual concern which called for settlement. Since their nationals controlled about 80 per cent of the world's oil, it was logical that they should initiate efforts to bring harmony and order into their respective oil spheres. But from the beginning the goal of both governments was to try to enlist the participation, in an effective world agreement which would include consuming as well as producing nations, of such countries as Russia—then a wartime ally—the Netherlands, France and other nations of both hemispheres.

The Department of Justice, however, did not like a clause in the second draft which protected the American industry from prosecution under antitrust laws in the event that the industry acted under the agreement—even upon the government-approved recommendations. Industry spokesmen asserted they could not promise that the pact would be effective unless they enjoyed this guarantee. The clause on antitrust immunity finally was deleted from the document on the understanding that PAW Administrator Ickes and Deputy Administrator Davies would support legislation toward that end before Congress.

As sent to the Senate Committee on Foreign Relations, the second Anglo-American Oil Agreement signed September 24, 1945, affirmed the principles that (1) "adequate supplies of petroleum . . . should be accessible in international trade to the nationals of both countries on a competitive and nondiscriminatory basis," and that (2) concerning the rights of weaker nations, "the interests of producing countries should be safeguarded with a view to their economic advancement."

The two governments pledged further that they would "so direct their efforts" (1) that all valid concessions, contracts and lawfully acquired rights would be respected, and there would be no interference, directly or indirectly, with such contracts or rights; (2) that, with regard to the acquisition of exploration and development rights, the principle of equal opportunity would be respected; and (3) that the exploration for and development of petroleum resources, the construction and operation of refineries and other facilities, and the distribution of petroleum would not be hampered by restrictions inconsistent with the purposes of the agreement.

Secretary Ickes interpreted these clauses (1) as ensuring that an individual or a company obtaining a concession in a country would "have considerably more assurance than heretofore that someone will not come in the following week and try to steal it from him," (2) as proclaiming the principle of equal opportunity, and (3) as moving "directly against cartels."

"This is the paragraph [3] which states, as I quoted, that there shall not be 'restrictions inconsistent with the purposes of this Agreement,'" the Secretary said. "In other words, we go on record against the tying of hands and closing of doors which have cramped the normal operation of trade in the past to the disadvantage, not only of the oil operators, but of the consumers whom they were barred from serving as efficiently and economically as might have been the case.

"To me, this paragraph means, among other things, that there will be no more hobbling of American nationals with such devices as the Red Line Agreement. This Red Line Agreement, in case any of you have forgotten, was the price that American companies had to pay in order to participate in the development of the Iraq fields. It provided, among other things, that no participating company would go after oil within a territory roughly comprising the old Ottoman Empire. Or, if any such company did go in there and find oil, then it had to share the concession with the certain favored others. Now, whatever else this Red Line Agreement may be, it certainly is not competitive. I say, therefore, that there is no place for it in the new scheme of things which our Anglo-American oil treaty contemplates. Neither is there a place for a certain type of marketing restriction, with which most of you are familiar. I mean that in which a company promises—as the price of a concession—that it will not market in places which another company has staked out as its own. I mention these as just a couple of cartel practices which we hope, and expect, to consign to oblivion through the operation of the Anglo-American Agreement."

The pact also provided for the setting up of an International Petroleum Commission, consisting of three members from each signatory country. A similar stipulation had been one of the most controversial articles of the original agreement and had been attacked on the ground that it gave too much power to the commission. Industry spokesmen expressed full satisfaction that the second agreement conferred no worrisome powers upon the commission, but limited its prerogatives to the making of studies, estimates and reports. Within a certain broad framework the commission might study anything that it cared to, might make estimates as to world supply and demand and, in the interests of efficiency and order, might report as to means for correlating those supplies and demands. Its terms of reference were broad enough, as a matter of fact, to allow the commission wide latitude in its reports and studies, so long as they related to the international petroleum trade. But, no one was obligated to act upon the reports.

Regardless of its powers, however, the commission was expected to serve an important purpose by providing a forum to which the problems of the international petroleum trade could be brought, threshed out openly and frankly and ways pointed to their *voluntary* solution. The treaty's proponents believed that if the commission and its staff were composed of able men who did their work competently, then its reports would win acceptance on the strength of their logic, supported by public opinion. On this belief was based much of the hope for the success of the agreement.

While the first Anglo-American Agreement had evoked wide industry condemnation, the second won quite general support from the oilmen. At its annual meeting October 14 to 17, 1945, the Independent Petroleum Association of America urgently recommended to the Senate of the United States "that it do give its affirmative advice and consent to the ratification of such treaty." Directors of the American Petroleum Institute, in annual session at Chicago on November 12 to 15, 1945, resolved that "the treaty recently negotiated . . . merits ratification and approval by the Senate of the United States." On November 4, 1945, the Petroleum Industry War Council issued a press release announcing support of its National Oil Policy Committee's stand that "the present Anglo-American Agreement will result in the establishment of machinery for effective and equitable solution of petroleum problems encountered in the progress of international petroleum trade." Secretary Ickes hailed it as "a document of great potentialities"; and Davies saw in it the "first step—and an all-important step—along the road of international cooperation."

"It is generally acknowledged today," said Davies, "that economic maladjustments are principal among the causes of war. Ways must be found for peacefully and intelligently removing the causes of friction as they arise. They must not be allowed to accumulate to the point where they can only be settled by death and destruction. It is this realization that has produced the Anglo-American Oil Agreement."

After a rough and troubled journey, then, government and industry came to the close of their wartime association in substantial agreement on the terms of a first step toward an international oil policy.

Yet the Senate Foreign Relations Committee never acted on the proposed treaty, and that proved to be the end of it, possibly due to Ickes' retirement from President Truman's cabinet in 1946 and the loss of a champion.

Julius A. Krug, who succeeded Ickes as Secretary of the Interior, also felt the need for some sort of a national oil policy. At his request the National Petroleum Council, an advisory body of the petroleum industry, formulated a comprehensive "national oil policy for the United States" and presented it to him on January 13, 1949.[3] The NPC document endorses conservation methods, such as those advocated by the Interstate Oil Compact, as a fundamental principle of an oil policy. As to foreign oil, NPC states that the participation of United States nationals in the development of world oil resources is in the interest of all countries and, moreover, is essential to our national security; that an effective oil policy should not only encourage access by our nationals to world oil resources on equal terms with other nationals but also stimulate stable agreements between foreign governments and private industry on a basis which will promote development by free enterprise methods; that the Federal government should encourage American nationals engaged in foreign oil development

[3] See Appendix II, full text.

with efforts directed through diplomatic channels aimed at reducing the political risks involved and by permitting United States citizens to operate abroad in conformity with the laws and customs of other countries.

As imports into the United States are of vital interest in connection with any discussion of an oil policy, the section of the report dealing with the subject is reproduced in full:

"The nation's economic welfare and security require a policy on petroleum imports which will encourage exploration and development efforts in the domestic industry and which will make available a maximum supply of domestic oil to meet the needs of this nation.

"The availability of petroleum from domestic fields produced under sound conservation practices, together with other pertinent factors, provides the means for determining if imports are necessary and the extent to which imports are desirable to supplement our oil supplies on a basis which will be sound in terms of the national economy and in terms of conservation.

"The implementation of an import policy, therefore, should be flexible so that adjustments may readily be made from time to time.

"Imports in excess of our economic needs, after taking into account domestic production in conformance with good conservation practices and within the limits of maximum efficient rates of production, will retard domestic exploration and development of new oil fields and the technological progress in all branches of the industry which is essential to the nation's economic welfare and security."

In 1953 when the controversial question of imposing quotas on imports was being debated within the industry and before Congressional committees, the executive committee of the American Petroleum Institute formally endorsed the National Petroleum Council's "National Oil Policy for the United States." The action, President Frank Porter stated, meant that the institute "concurs with the philosophy that imports of foreign oil should be used to supplement but not displace or retard domestic production." The executive committee, he said, had provided the institute "with positive policies in areas where none existed before." [4]

The large American oil companies which have immense domestic as well as foreign operations are opposed to rigid controls or quotas on

[4] *The Oil and Gas Journal,* February 16, 1953, p. 96.

imports. They, too, approve the NPC's national oil-policy principles that a vigorous domestic home industry should be maintained and that oil should be imported into this country to supplement, not to supplant, United States production and thus provide flexibility of supply. In line with these views, numerous oil companies voluntarily vary the volume of their imports from time to time as their judgment of the domestic supply-demand situation indicates. For example, J. S. Leach, chairman of the board of Texas, says,[5] "The Texas Company has no intention of flooding the country with imported oil to the detriment of domestic production, but it is only prudent practice to have sources available to cushion normal domestic fluctuations, to be ready to help with the constantly growing domestic demand and to meet great emergencies."

In 1953, Colonel Ernest O. Thompson, chairman of the Texas Railroad Commission, made an interesting move to compromise the differences between independent producers and importers. On the ground that such a measure would invite Federal control, he spoke out against the movement for a quota on imports to be set by an act of Congress as well as against a view that some government agency should be established to make forecasts of foreign oil needs by which importing companies could be guided.[6] "He and his two colleagues on the commission decided on a course that would help solve the problem." Warning the importers that the Texas conservation laws, "the most important stabilizing force in the oil industry, would be jeopardized by continuing allowable reductions and to be guided accordingly," he requested the companies to file with the Texas Railroad Commission each month an estimate of their anticipated imports. All major companies now report current imports and estimate their shipments on a monthly basis a half year in advance. The commission releases the figures to the industry through the trade press.[7]

So much for the background of attempted, offered or drafted "oil policies." The National Petroleum Council oil policy stands today as the last pronouncement toward that end. But it can be construed as no more than an important statement of principles. Oilmen believe that a policy—concrete, effective, embracing global operations and

[5] *The Texaco Star*, Spring, 1954.
[6] James A. Clark, *Three Stars for the Colonel*, 1954, pp. 235, 236.
[7] *The Oil and Gas Journal*, June 28, 1954, p. 86.

mutually satisfactory to industry and government—is badly needed. Some of them think that the old Anglo-American Oil Agreement, or some set of statements resembling it, might be desirable, though they do not look for a revival of that forgotten treaty.

It would seem, however, that events are shaping toward a showdown on the question of an oil policy. It is clearly evident that petroleum occupies a unique position in the destinies of our country and of the Free World. Further, it must be apparent that petroleum problems and pressures overlap, have an interrelationship one with the other requiring not merely national but international consideration. What Americans might look upon as a simple domestic matter—for instance, taking care of our domestic industry by raising oil tariffs or creating import quotas—is revealed as having ramifications affecting the daily bread and butter of other oil-producing nations and affecting our amicable relations abroad. What we might imagine to be a simple matter of filing an antitrust suit against American international oil companies penetrates quickly to other countries and deeply undermines United States prestige. Numerous such illustrations could be drawn from preceding chapters. Each and every one would bear directly upon the security of our nation and the Free World. This being the case, a thoroughgoing appraisal of the over-all petroleum situation would appear to be overdue.

The matter goes much further than the question of imports and is bigger than the specific problems of a single nation, company, or group of companies. Today's *vis-à-vis* situation across the Iron Curtain between the Free World and Russia heightens the pressing need for an oil policy.

What would be the primary questions offered for appraisal for possible inclusion in an international oil policy? Those which we consider as important follow:

1. The part played by business in a dynamic economy.

2. The necessity for joint operation.

3. A clarification of the factors that require the husbanding of our reserves as well as the continued expansion of the domestic industry.

4. The status of America's overseas operations not only in relation to the control of strategic reserves in case of war but also as to their contribution to the prosperity of nations and the raising of living standards in underdeveloped countries.

5. Appraisal of our imports in relation to the defense of the United States and the Free World, in relation to the economies of other nations, and in relation to world trade.

6. Realistic appraisal of big business—why it exists; its indispensable features, inherent and evolutionary, that make it a part of our dynamic economy.

7. Clarification of the status of United States companies with respect to divergent laws and customs of our own and other countries.

8. Appraisal of the principle of comity among nations—what American activities abroad more properly fall within the jurisdiction of a foreign nation than of our own.

9. Review of the consequences of the tendency to apply American antitrust laws to activities outside the United States.

10. Consideration of the question as to whether the Antitrust Division of the Department of Justice should be able to begin suit relating to foreign operations against the international oil companies without first having the approval of the National Securities Council.

11. Need for a consistent government policy.

12. Need for taking international oil out of politics.

Petroleum's vital relationship to the Free World's economy and defense increasingly demands that it be accorded a policy declaration or a treaty of its own. Recent events in Iran at once emphasize the need, and conceivably may hasten considerations, in that direction.

Chapter 25

THE IRANIAN OIL SETTLEMENT

On August 4, 1954, two men—Dr. Ali Amini, Finance Minister, representing the Iranian government, and Howard W. Page, vice president of Standard Oil (New Jersey) representing a consortium of eight international oil companies—initialed a 30-page *aide mémoire*. The simple ceremony held at Elahiyeh Villa, former official residence of the Teheran manager of the Anglo-Iranian Oil Company, ended a three-year dispute over Iran's oil. The settlement—some final details of which were still to be completed—came only after 11 months of negotiation. Under its terms the consortium will operate Iran's petroleum industry, and, in return, that country's government will receive about 400 million dollars over the next three years in addition to a large and continuous annual income thereafter. The agreement ranks as a decisive event in the fortunes of the Free World.

Officials of the Free World lost little time in voicing satisfaction at this accomplishment. President Eisenhower wrote to Shah Mohammed Riza Pahlevi of Iran expressing confidence that the agreement marked the beginning of "a new era of economic progress and stability for your country." Praising the Iranian ruler for his "valuable contribution" to the negotiations, the President declared that the "fair and equitable settlement" of the long-standing oil dispute was "indeed gratifying."

Simultaneously Secretary of State John Foster Dulles hailed the agreement as a gain for the entire Free World. The United States, he said, was extremely pleased that another significant step had been achieved toward solving a problem which, for several years, had worked hardships on Iran, Great Britain and, indeed, upon the whole Free World. "Every member of the community of Free Nations stands to gain from the settlement of this issue between two of its members," he said. "In the past the issue has operated as an irritant among countries which have so much in common and so much to gain from close friendship and collaboration."

Both the President and the Secretary of State called attention to the good that should come to Iran as a result of the oil agreement.

In his message to the Shah, the President stated: "Like myself, all Americans have a deep concern for the well-being of Iran. With them, I have watched closely your courageous efforts, your steadfastness over the past difficult years, and with them I, too, have hoped you might achieve the goals you so earnestly desire. The attainment of an oil settlement along the lines which have been announced should be a significant step in the direction of the realization of your aspirations for your people."

Referring to the oil revenues that would be restored to the Iranian economy, Secretary Dulles prophesied that, under the Shah's leadership, the Teheran government now should be able to carry out a long-range development program designed to "improve the welfare of the Iranian nation as a whole," and one which would "mark the beginning of a new era for Iran—an era of great hope and of prosperity." Both the President and the Secretary pledged the continuing friendship of the United States, a friendship, added Mr. Dulles, that will continue to be demonstrated in "practical ways."

British Foreign Secretary Anthony Eden wrote to Iranian Foreign Minister Abdullah Entezam as follows:

"I send you my warmest congratulations on the announcement that agreement in principle has been reached on all aspects of the oil problem. I am convinced that a settlement on the lines that have been negotiated will be in the interests of Persia and can bring greater benefits to her. I am particularly glad to know that it has been possible to satisfy both Persia's aspirations and the practical requirements of the oil industry. I see in this the best assurance that the agreement will endure. We have now the opportunity of restoring relations between our two countries to their traditional friendship. You know how much I have desired this and I know full well how hard [Premier] General Zahedi and you have worked for the same cause. I am sure that our two countries can now go forward together in confidence and goodwill."

Coupling the agreement with the settlement only a week previously of the seemingly endless struggle between Britain and Egypt as to the control of the Suez Canal, many commentators hailed the pact as marking a distinct diplomatic victory for the West. They foresaw amity and stabilization in an area which politically has been one of the world's most explosive and unpredictable—the Middle East.

Not the least interesting of the messages on the occasion of the settlement was Secretary Eden's cable to Secretary Dulles. "Allow me," he said, "to thank you for generous help which the United States Government have given in the negotiations and, in particular, for the unfailing cooperation of Mr. [Loy] Henderson the United States Ambassador in Teheran."

The State Department, however, prefers the agreement to be looked upon purely as a commercial transaction, and that it definitely is. Moreover, financial circles have called it the biggest business deal in history. The fact remains, nevertheless, that our State Department played a leading role in the last act—if, indeed, it is the last act—of the Iranian oil nationalization drama, and the curtain rings down on optimism rather than on stark tragedy. In fact, the Department engaged a special consultant, Herbert Hoover, Jr., for the specific purpose of trying to work out a formula which would break the long and progressively critical stalemate.[1]

The day on which the Iranian agreement was signed—it happened to be Hoover's fifty-first birthday—the President wrote him a congratulatory letter in which he stated that the conclusion of the agreement "is due in significant measure to your expert knowledge of the oil business, to your persistence and to your skillful diplomacy." Secretary Dulles wrote him in similar vein.[2]

From September, 1953, the time of his assignment as a negotiator, Hoover toiled so unremittingly at his task that he maintained apartments in Washington, London and Teheran. He started his work almost three years to the day from the breaking off of diplomatic rela-

---

[1] It will be recalled that young Hoover was one of the special American oil consultants employed by the Venezuelan government in formulating the Petroleum Law of 1943 which first advanced the 50-50 profit-sharing principle (see Chapter 9).

[2] Subsequently, on August 17, the President named Hoover Under Secretary of State to succeed General Walter Bedell Smith. The son of the former President never before has held political office.

tions between Britain and Iran and the departure of the last British employees of Anglo-Iranian Oil Company from the soil of Iran. Beginning with that rupture the production of the oil fields and the operation of the great Abadan refinery became paralyzed (see Chapter 11).

But Hoover's mission began two months after an attempt by Shah Mohammed Riza Pahlevi to dismiss Mossadegh, father of Iran's oil nationalization law, had brought on a brief, bloody revolution. At first the Shah was forced to flee, but then in a sudden shift of sentiment the army and mobs of irate Iranians turned on Mossadegh. The Shah returned to power and named General Fazlollah Zahedi as Premier. Mossadegh went to jail.

Both the Shah and his Premier sought for some method of getting the oil industry going again as a means to save the country from financial ruin and possible default to the Communists. Yet they had to exercise extreme caution since Iran's oil nationalization law had been the very symbol of fervent nationalism.

Hoover, however, found that both Iran and Britain were hoping for a solution. And his preliminary study led him to two conclusions: first, the political situation in Iran required that the oil properties would have to remain nationalized; second, so unpopular was Anglo-Iranian, because of the intensive political vilification which had been leveled at it through the years, that the company would never be permitted to operate the concession alone. Obviously, other companies would have to be brought in.

With these points as his basis, Hoover started negotiations with the Iranian government, at the same time setting in motion a series of conferences among oil companies that led to the creation of the consortium. Anglo-Iranian invited other companies to discuss the matter in London, and the conferences began in December, 1953. The conferring companies comprised the leading concerns operating in the Middle East: Anglo-Iranian, Royal Dutch–Shell and the Compagnie Française des Petroles—all part-owners of Iraq Petroleum Company—and five United States companies, Standard of Jersey, Socony-Vacuum, Standard of California, The Texas Company and Gulf Oil. Standard of Jersey and Socony-Vacuum also are represented in the international group which owns Iraq Petroleum. They also are part-owners of Aramco in Saudi Arabia. Standard of California and Texas are part-owners of

Aramco and 50-50 partners in Bahrain Petroleum. With Anglo-Iranian, Gulf is half-owner of Kuwait Oil.

For its part, the Anglo-Iranian Oil Company, in which the British government is a large owner, long since had reached the reluctant conclusion that it could never resume its old oil monopoly in Iranian oil. The company had reserved the right to claim from Iran adequate compensation for its properties. While barrel for barrel AIOC had found substitute supplies for its lost Iranian oil, the monetary loss represented by the seizure was enormous and could be permanent if conditions were allowed to go from bad to worse. Under such conditions the British were ready to accept any solution that would preserve a measure of Anglo-Iranian's interest. The arrangements that have been negotiated cover:

1. A 40 per cent interest for Anglo-Iranian in the consortium of eight companies which will operate the oil fields until 1994.

2. A reported commitment of $600,000,000, payable partly on a per barrel basis over a period of years, from the seven other companies.

3. A payment of $70,000,000 to Anglo-Iranian from Iran partly for some of the nationalized properties and partly as compensation for the company's three-year losses.

4. Full ownership by the Iranian government of Anglo-Iranian's properties, under the nationalization law which created the government-owned National Iranian Oil Company, and 50 per cent of the profits from the operation of the properties by the consortium, realized from both royalties and income taxes.

5. A 40 per cent interest, or 8 per cent each, for the five American companies in the consortium—Standard of New Jersey, Socony-Vacuum, Standard of California, Texas and Gulf—giving them access to Iran's rich oil fields for the first time.

6. A 14 per cent interest for Royal Dutch–Shell and a 6 per cent interest for the Compagnie Française des Petroles (30 per cent owned by the French government) in the consortium, also giving each access to Iran for the first time.

If the report that $600,000,000 is to be paid is correct, the American companies are committed to pay $80,000,000 each, and the total sum involved in the Iranian settlement and in the organization of the consortium marks the entire transaction as the biggest in the history of private business. Considering the 40 per cent interest Anglo-Iranian will retain, a total valuation of the concession properties and rights in excess of a billion dollars is indicated.[3]

The difficulties involved in reaching an agreement cannot be over-emphasized. On the one hand was a flaming national political issue and on the other the issue of the inviolability of a legal contract, the basis of doing business in Western World civilization. Moreover, the oil companies were chary of any agreement that would set a new precedent in the Middle East or elsewhere. And under the Iranian nationalization law, vesting outright ownership in the consortium or any other private group was prohibited. The wonder is that any agreement was reached.

In an interview head consortium negotiator Page dismissed fears held in some circles that the agreement to operate the nationalized Iranian installations for 25 to 40 years without the ownership rights which hitherto have been inherent in a concession would set a "dangerous precedent." He conceded that the members of the oil consortium "would have preferred to have obtained the more familiar lease or concession arrangement" which would have given them outright ownership of the properties for a specified period. But under the Iranian nationalization law, this procedure was impossible of attainment.

Careful study of the agreed-upon arrangements, Page said, will reveal to oilmen that the consortium is provided with rights that are "just as effective" as ownership. "Instead of a contract giving us ownership of the properties for a long period of time," he explained, "we have a contract giving us full rights to exclusive use and complete management of those properties for the same period of time and on the same financial terms."

The chief consortium negotiator observed that "the difference is about the same as whether someone sells you a car, or sells you full rights to its use for the life of the car. It's a fine legal distinction that even top-notch lawyers will argue themselves silly about." [4]

Iran's oil industry will be handled by two operating companies wholly owned by the consortium. In accordance with the agreement

[3] For full text of the Iranian Oil Agreement, see Special Supplement, *Platt's Oilgram*, October 6, 1954.

[4] W. M. Jablonski, *N.Y. Journal of Commerce*, August 9, 1954.

these new companies, Iranian Oil Refining Company and Iranian Oil Exploration & Producing Company, were incorporated in the Netherlands and registered in Teheran. They will control the operations, and the oil produced will be acquired by subsidiaries of the individual consortium companies at cost plus a nominal fee. At this writing, all consortium companies, except Compagnie Française des Petroles, have formed their Iranian subsidiaries. The French company intends to use a branch—not a separate company—in Iran.

Many provisions of the Iranian settlement closely resemble the agreement which Iraq Petroleum Company made in 1952 with the Iraq government (see Chapter 11). Actually, the period during which the agreement will be in effect can easily work out to be slightly longer than the old AIOC concession. The area, while differing somewhat from the old concession area as far as metes and bounds are concerned, is not, in fact, greatly different and is considered as promising, if not more promising. The provisions for surrender of acreage in connection with renewals are not more onerous than those in effect, say, in Saudi Arabia.

The pact provides 50-50 profit sharing between government and companies, now practically a basic financial provision in Middle East oil concessions. And as previously pointed out, the rights of management control and the right to exclusive use of property stipulated in the Iranian agreement are on a par with those of other Middle East concessions. In short, leaving aside differences in language and what on the surface seem to be differences in form, the new arrangement is quite comparable to those of other areas and, in fact, contains many protective provisions not found in existing concessions.

Under the terms, for instance, Iran is barred from making "Onassis-type" tanker deals. This refers to such activities as those of Aristotle Socrates Onassis, a Greek-born shipowner who concluded an agreement for certain oil-hauling rights with the Saudi Arabian government effective April 9, 1954. Approaching other Middle East producing countries as well as Saudi Arabia, Onassis caught the international oil companies by surprise and his activities have brought protests of concession violation in which the companies are backed by both the American and British governments.[5]

---

[5] *National Petroleum News*, June 16, 1954; *The Oil and Gas Journal*, June 28, 1954. "Quite recently another [Middle East] problem developed, in this case in-

A significant feature of the Iranian agreement relates to labor and social obligations. The government's National Iranian Oil Company will take over such functions as industrial training, public transport and road maintenance together with such non-basic facilities as housing, medical care and social welfare. While the operating companies, "with whom close cooperation will be maintained," will reimburse NIOC for most of the cost of the facilities and services, clearly the step is designed to give the government a new sense of responsibility in training and caring for Iranian oil workers. Thus the foreign oil companies will be relieved of the paternalistic activities which so often are thrust upon them in operating in underdeveloped countries, which so often lead to increased demands upon them and which, oddly enough, so often boomerang against them. In this respect, also, the agreement may be precedent-making.

---

volving Saudi Arabia. . . . A. S. Onassis, controlling a large number of tankers, made an arrangement with the Saudi Arabian Government whereby he is in effect given a preferential call on any cargoes seeking transportation from Arabia to other countries when ships previously owned by the Aramco companies and having previously traded in that commerce were not available. As a practical matter, the number of ships available to all of the Aramco partners together which would qualify under these conditions would suffice to carry only a small percentage of the total volume moving out of Saudi Arabia and therefore the remainder would have to move in the Onassis ships under the arrangement contemplated.

"Another feature of the scheme is that the minimum rates under which the Onassis ships would operate are approximately 50 per cent higher than the freight rates currently available in the world tanker markets. The proposal has extraordinarily far-reaching dangers. It is completely contrary to the specific terms of the Aramco concession, but even that is perhaps less important than what it could do to world trade. Obviously, if a given country with an exportable commodity could require that all of that export be carried in its own ships, an importing country could with equal logic require that all its imports be carried in its own ships. Thus, if all countries were to follow the Onassis plan, there would be no international trade at all.

"Adoption of this plan by just those countries which are primarily exporters would bring about a complete change in the pattern of ownership of the world's merchant marine. For example—Norway with a big merchant fleet and no sizeable exports would be virtually displaced from the seas and a principal earning power of that country eliminated. The effect on Britain's merchant marine would be only slightly less pronounced and the repercussions of that discombobulation in an essential element in the world balance of payments are almost incalculable. I am still hopeful that the world will be spared a demonstration of the consequences of the Onassis proposal, but the problem unfortunately is not yet solved." Address by B. Brewster Jennings, President of Socony-Vacuum, "Oil in World Affairs," before The Los Angeles World Affairs Council, September 29, 1954.

In September, 1954, representatives of the Iranian government and the consortium signed a detailed 56-page agreement, which became the substance of a bill introduced in the Iranian Parliament. This procedure was in line with a stipulation by the consortium companies that the agreement override all previous agreements and become part of the law of the land. The bill's passage was facilitated since the measure was given prior consideration by the combined finance and budget committees of the Senate and of the Lower House rather than by a special group such as that which came under Mossadegh's control as a prelude to nationalization. Incidentally, in a handwritten brief addressed to the Shah and the Supreme Court, Dr. Mossadegh stated that in his opinion the pact meant "enslavement of my country for 40 years." He further alleged that Anglo-Iranian wholly controlled the consortium. Mossadegh wrote while in the second year of a three-year sentence for attempting to overthrow the Shah.[6]

Favorably reported by the joint committee, the Iranian Oil Settlement Agreement was approved by Parliament and, having received the assent of the Shah, it became effective on October 29, 1954.[7]

Plans to "sow the petroleum" already are under way in Iran. At the proposed level of operations the government will receive an income equivalent to 400 million dollars over the next three years, plus further large annual sums as production continues. In a dramatic appearance before the Majlis, August 12, 1954, Premier Zahedi disclosed that the nation soon will embark on a $500,000,000 five-year program embracing land reclamation, increased agricultural and mineral production and improvements in communications and transportation. The plan will be financed by effected oil revenues and by further credits which the government seeks from the International Bank for Reconstruction and Development. "The oil agreement is the key to the rehabilitation of our economy," General Zahedi declared, "but the oil income alone will not be sufficient to generate the comprehensive economic expansion we envisage."

According to the Premier the government would distribute 5,000,-000 hectares (12,350,000 acres) of potentially productive farmland in the southwestern province of Khuzistan among landless peasants from all parts of the country. The Karkheh Dam, being completed with the

[6] *The New York Times*, September 10, 1954.
[7] *New York Herald Tribune*, October 30, 1954. Also for payments to Anglo-Iranian.

help of Point Four funds, will irrigate part of this land, the Premier indicated, and the Agricultural Bank will provide the money for other improvements. The Sefid Rud Dam project in the Caspian province of Gilan and the Durud project in the southwestern province of Luristan also will reclaim large areas for cultivation, Zahedi announced, and the entire undertaking will receive high priority under the five-year plan.

To eradicate what he termed admitted corruption in government, the Premier has ordered that severe measures shall be taken against corrupt civil servants, and that honest government employees shall receive monetary rewards equivalent to the amount of graft they discover and report. Bitterly General Zahedi remarked that Iran had become so impoverished in the last three years that "there is hardly anything for anyone to steal nowadays, but we trust that the situation will change for the better once the oil revenues begin flowing into our treasury."

Immediately after the war foreign consultants studied Iran's economy and mapped out a far-reaching development program, known as the Seven Year Plan (see Chapter 14). Abolhassan Ebtehaj, the new chief of the government's planning organization, has stated that, although the nationalization law provides for all of the oil revenues to go to the planning agency, for as much as five years, probably, a part of the revenues will be applied to the nation's operating budget to meet deficits. Projects now on the books will be revised in favor of a comprehensive plan that will give top priority to highway and railroad repair and construction.

In striking highlights the Iranian oil crisis and settlement point up many aspects of the foreign oil and Free World picture as painted in preceding chapters.

Extreme nationalism brought on the crisis, and the Communists lent a hand to it. Indeed, Soviet Russia finally overplayed her cards. Her threats in an attempt to wreck the negotiations had much to do with swinging the people to support the government in making the pact.

Again, the settlement is reminiscent of the first international oil agreement in Iraq, concluded back in 1928 (see Chapter 5). Then as now the State Department played a prominent role. At that time it acted in the interest of the "open door," and, until the 1954 agreement, Iran may be said to have represented the last bulwark of Britain's "closed door" petroleum policy.

But the Iranian oil settlement has modern and pressing significance in its exemplification of the Free World's need not only for oil but also for an international oil policy. Injected into the Iranian scene are four nationalities where formerly there had been only one. The Free World could not afford to let Iran go by default. Though all-important as giving Americans their first foothold in the Middle East, the Iraq oil agreement of 1928 was not designed with any particular concern for the Iraqi nation. In the case of the Iranian pact, however, it is no accident that the participants are called a consortium which Webster defines as: "Any business or banking agreement or combination to *assist* another nation."

In 1954, in effect, the State Department, through Hoover, called upon certain American oil companies to go to the rescue of Iran. Since Premier Zahedi succeeded Mossadegh on August 19, 1953, United States aid to Iran has totaled $79,000,000. Further demands of Premier Zahedi for additional funds to support the new five-year plan were granted—a total of about $120,000,000 for the fiscal year of 1954–1955. In other words, simple recognition was made of the fact that the only way to save Iran—and its strategic oil supply—for the Free World was to work out a solution of the oil stalemate.

Along this line it must be noted that our government, in effect, invited the very oil companies—Standard of New Jersey, Socony-Vacuum, Standard of California, Texas and Gulf—against which it had filed a suit, still pending, charging violation of United States anti-trust laws—to become participants in a joint operation which is almost identical in character with that alleged by the Department of Justice in its antitrust suit. These are the concerns which are accused of constituting, along with Anglo-Iranian and Royal Dutch–Shell, two other prominent members of the consortium, a gigantic cartel in restraint of competitive trade (see Chapter 20).

Obviously, the State Department could not expect the officers of the accused American concerns to commit their companies to acts which might bring another indictment against them. At the suggestion of the State Department, therefore, the Justice Department drew up in writing a clearance which, with certain qualifications, agreed in principle to the American companies' joining the consortium. But, while approving United States company participation in the consortium to produce and refine Iranian oil, the Justice Department's clearance did not include marketing arrangements and was "very specific in its non-applicability to the cartel case."

This little-publicized phase of the negotiations underlines certain points previously referred to as worthy of consideration in formulating an international oil policy (see Chapter 24). And the simple fact that clearance was necessary demonstrates the urgent need for a policy.

To say the least, an amazing inconsistency exists in our government when it calls upon the very companies accused of violating the law to step into the breach of an international crisis the solution of which is of the utmost importance to the Free World—when, seemingly, it asks them to do the very thing which caused them to be accused of breaking the law. Does the fact that this is a consortium—an action to assist, perhaps to save, a country—alter the legal questions involved? Any argument that the Iranian oil agreement is fundamentally different from the joint operations of American companies in Iraq and Saudi Arabia must stand on so shaky a foundation as to be specious. Is it not time realistically to appraise the world petroleum situation and to act accordingly?

Government officials may find some alleviation of the cartel side of the picture in that, under the terms of the agreement, participation in the 40 per cent consortium share owned by the American group can be offered—up to 5 per cent—to other United States companies with the consent of the Iranian government. Certainly the offering—or, better still, the actual sale—of part of their group holdings to other companies would have the sympathy of the State Department since it would serve to appease the strong antitrust lobby and thus, to a certain extent, bring in line the obvious inconsistency between the State Department's encouragement and acceptance of consortium membership and the Department of Justice's cartel suit.

How can Iran be fitted into a world market already oversupplied? Just before the seizure of the Anglo-Iranian Oil Company's facilities, in mid-1951, Iran's production was running approximately 700,000 barrels a day. The Abadan refinery was processing crude oil at the rate of 500,000 barrels daily. Not only do all areas have an excess productive capacity, but many countries—notably those of the Middle East—depend almost entirely on oil to pay the expenses of government.

Any material decrease in production to make room for Iranian oil would result in serious objections from such countries.

Under the settlement agreement, the minimum amount of oil to be taken from Iran for the first full year of operation would be 302,000 barrels daily, stepped up to a minimum of 474,000 barrels daily the second year and to 600,000 barrels daily in the third year. In so far as possible the companies belonging to the consortium individually plan to fit Iranian oil into the Eastern Hemisphere markets to which it was almost entirely restricted before the shutdown.

The indications are, then, that some time will elapse before Iran again attains its former place as the largest producer in the Middle East. The Abadan refinery was running only 20,000 barrels daily at the time of the settlement. No improvements of importance have been made for four years. Certain improvements and innovations are planned, but for the next two years the refinery's output is expected to be held at 100,000 to 200,000 barrels daily and by the third year may hit 258,000 barrels daily. Additional evidence that the Abadan refinery will not reach its former capacity for years is seen in the fact that it has forfeited its position to other refineries, several of which were built or enlarged to meet the emergency caused by its closing. Of these the largest is Anglo-Iranian's 120,000-barrel-a-day Aden refinery. Standard-Vacuum—which before the shutdown bought products f.o.b. the Persian Gulf under contract with Anglo-Iranian and moved them into its markets in India, South Africa and other areas—put on stream its 25,000-barrel-per-day Bombay refinery in August, 1954, six months before schedule. Early in the year the company also completed a new 15,600-barrel plant at Durban, South Africa. Still to be finished at this writing were Burmah-Shell's 40,000-barrel plant at Bombay; Caltex's 22,000-barrel refinery in Australia, its 13,000-barrel plant in the Philippines and its 10,000-barrel refinery on India's East Coast, and Anglo-Iranian's 62,000-barrel plant in Western Australia (see also Chapter 18).

To appreciate fully the magnitude and the significance of the Iranian oil settlement one must weigh the essential problem that confronted—that still confronts—the consortium members. It cannot be supposed that the countries where oil has been found in quantity—or will be discovered in great volume in the future—will be satisfied unless they have their share in the world's markets. Iran's return to production brought visions of at least some cutbacks in Saudi Arabia, Kuwait and Iraq, cutbacks which are not out of the question. Lower production in Venezuela and the United States as well as the retarding of Canada's development also was feared. Serious though the problem is, its solution is far from impossible as is indicated by the willingness of the parties to the Iranian agreement individually to tackle it step by step to meet practical considerations.

For oversupply is, basically, a temporary situation. The present danger is that the problem might cause politicians to overlook this fact, this truism, and apply measures which might do incalculable harm. Panic legislation throwing up barriers to the natural development and movement of Free World oil conceivably could divorce us from our friends and allies, bankrupt their economies and break down our Free World oil defense insurance. Moreover, hasty and ill-advised measures could halt in its tracks the promise inherent in the continued development of Free World oil—the promise of making available greater energy resources with which underdeveloped nations can hope for a better living. If ever a need existed for a broad view of world petroleum that day is now. Politically and morally, economically and socially, the Free World climate calls for the utmost in statesmanship both on the part of government and industry.

Chapter 26

NEW FRONTIERS

It has been said that new frontiers in foreign oil are no more, that the "pioneers" of industry have departed with a vanished generation of venturesome Americans. Yet since World War II, the record of the oil industry is one of a succession of bursting frontiers.

"Some people prefer to call this the Age of Anxiety or the Era of the Cold War," says Augustus C. Long, president of The Texas Company. "Within the limitations of their concepts, they are right. It seems to me, however, that we should accent the affirmative qualities of our times and refer to this as the Age of Energy. Certainly, never before in history have enterprising men by trial and error and hard-won experience applied themselves so effectively to what well may be remembered as the outstanding characteristic of our age—the seeking and finding, releasing and harnessing of vast amounts of energy that for aeons have lain locked in the fastness of the earth.

"At a time when the entire world turns more and more to petroleum as a source of energy, and at a time when the center of world petroleum reserves has shifted from the Western Hemisphere to the Eastern Hemisphere, we can count ourselves blessed that some American oil companies had foresight and persistence over the years. Now, when the Free World so desperately needs it, we have extensive participation in the development of foreign oil resources. The contribution of American oil companies to the vast growth of the foreign petroleum industry since the start of World War II has been one of the great achievements of private enterprise and has important bearing on the maintenance of our standards of living and on the present and future security of the United States." [1]

[1] The American Petroleum Industry Abroad, *Yale Scientific Magazine*, May, 1953.

In summary, what does the record of our preceding chapters show? The story makes clear that economically foreign oil operations have meant many things to the United States. Large numbers of Americans share as stockholders in the profits of petroleum activities abroad. The American oil company direct petroleum overseas investment of $4,291,000,000 represents one of the largest of our foreign enterprises—29 per cent of the grand total. Moreover, purchases in the United States by American oil companies for foreign operations, and business stimulated by foreign petroleum operations among allied home industries, including agriculture, account for further huge benefits to our economy. As a result of oil development abroad, reciprocal benefits accrue to the United States through dollar purchases originating in the foreign countries where main operations are carried on as well as in other nations where similar purchases have stemmed from such activities. Venezuela, where it is estimated that over three-quarters of all the dollars available for foreign purchase are provided by the operations of the oil industry, is a big customer of ours. In 1952, while exporting to us oil valued at $334,000,000 she imported from our country goods valued at over $500,000,000 and services worth $350,000,000. Not the least important is the affirmative contribution to our economy embraced in petroleum's contribution to stabilizing and strengthening the economies of other nations. And, more directly, the development by American companies of oil resources abroad serves our country by providing sources of supply for supplementing domestic oil production. Since the United States is not self-sufficient, this supply is invaluable to the American economy. Moreover, the United States government collects a considerable tax income from oil operations abroad.

Foreign countries derive notable benefits from developing petroleum resources through private enterprise and encouraging outside investment. Witness the effect of the Canada oil boom on the whole Canadian economy.

The logbook reveals, too, that foreign oil operations have been an economic boon to underdeveloped countries. Development of foreign petroleum reserves has transformed life in certain countries, by increasing their national incomes over and over again and by making possible substantial rises in living standards. In Venezuela, where 60 per cent of the government's revenue comes from oil, a large percentage of the income has been used to improve highways and ports, to build schools and hospitals and to improve agriculture. In Iraq, 70 per cent of all oil revenue received by the government must, by law, be turned over to the Iraq Development Board, which uses the money for such purposes as irrigation, drainage projects, road construction, mechanization of agriculture and the extension of electrification. In Saudi Arabia— the only Middle East country with substantial production in which the concession is owned and operated entirely by American interests— Aramco, at the government's request, has assisted materially in the building of a port, a railroad and substantial agricultural projects. In addition, the company has a realistic and going program for setting up Arabs in independent businesses to furnish the various goods and services needed by the country. Using revenues from oil royalties, the Saudi Arabian government finances the many projects which are raising the country's standard of living. Similarly petroleum is being sowed in Bahrain and Kuwait with notable results.

The record also shows that company operations have meant much in social progress. The operations of American companies have resulted in employment, vocational training, general education, modern housing and health facilities—all on a substantial scale—for the local residents in a number of countries. In Latin America, for example, the medical and health programs made possible by oil revenues have cut deeply into the incidence of malaria and other diseases which formerly were widespread. Hospitals and clinics have brought modern medical care to great numbers of people. Children who previously never even hoped for a smattering of formal education now accept daily schooling as commonplace. Venezuela's highway-building programs in the past 15 years have more than trebled the mileage of all-weather roads linking once-isolated communities.

In the Middle East, in a relatively few years, revenue from oil investment has brought to a desert people standards of living which normally represent the progress of centuries. Health standards have been transformed. Water supplies have been created by drilling wells which make it possible for once barren areas to produce more of their own food. Oil-company employees have been taught not only the skills essential to their jobs at the drilling rigs or refineries, but also the "three R's," typing, bookkeeping, nursing and other subjects. Particularly promising employees have been sent to universities. Doctors, engineers, and teachers do and will continue to come from these programs, and they will enable the countries to press forward with increasing vigor and speed, for such policies have a cumulative benefit.

The evolution of "sowing the petroleum" seems to depict the oil companies as spearheading the movement toward better living in underdeveloped countries. Certainly, an objective view points to them as having introduced the economic, social, medical and educational advancement which justifies an expressed evaluation of their efforts in terms of a private Point Four Program. Realistically, we have assessed this activity on the part of the oil people as a movement of enlightened self-interest—an enlightenment derived from an appreciation that a social change of profound depth and inexorability is abroad in the world. Whether the oil companies' policy is based on enlightenment may or may not be overly important. The simple fact is that it exists and is doing infinite good. In some cases the companies' adoption or acceptance of change unquestionably has been in advance of "advanced" legislation. Often their programs have exceeded the minimum requirements of such legislation and, indeed, often they still do.

On the other hand, time has disclosed that by no means have the foreign governments been backward in so-called social advances in so far as legislation is concerned and also that they are making progress. Slowly but surely, they are applying their oil revenues beneficially. And wisely so, for, in the last analysis, the governments of the countries—not the companies—will be judged as to the final success or failure of the application of the philosophy of "sowing the petroleum." It is the governments rather than the companies which must see that great revenues from oil are spent wisely for the benefit of all the people.

A phase of the world oil picture not generally recognized is the positions and problems of oil-producing countries with an unbalanced oil economy. Oilmen operating in nations which have attained high production in the last two decades—countries in South America and the Middle East—point to the evidence of vested authority in the governmental departments charged with running the oil industry. In their eagerness to build up a national industry employing nationals and in their pride in the task, they are at once aggressive, resourceful, alert and watchful. The departments are well informed on world oil affairs. Along with the policy makers, they run the oil industry in their countries. They are "in the driver's seat."

In this connection, the following extract from the *Report for the Year 1953*, issued by the Venezuelan Minister of Mines and Hydrocarbons, is of interest: [2] "Naturally, the Bureau of Economics handles all economic matters. Considering the importance of the oil and mining industries and the tremendous influence these industries have on the life, development and over-all economy of the nation, the importance of this bureau, not only to the department but to the entire nation, becomes evident. The Bureau of Economics is in a position to take the economic pulse and to diagnose the financial status of the Republic at any time. The lamentable fact that no such organism existed prior to 1951 is all the more reason to applaud its creation.

"Exploration, drilling, production, storage, transportation, exportation and selling are the classical divisions that comprise the integrated industry. They are without doubt active components of the whole but inert within their own boundaries, non-expandable, isolated from the surrounding fervid national activity, whose collective action, or end result, seems achieved by a strange and invisible hand. Industry such as this does not satisfy national pride.

"Watching over, inspecting and prosecuting have likewise been classic chapters, stagnant and monotonous, of government action. This acquiescent sort of action does not satisfy national pride either.

"Just as methods of government inspection, which improve day by day, have evolved towards the dynamics of conservation—the magic-eye of the State—thus have the methods and disciplines of the Bureau of Economics substituted for that strange and invisible hand, and are combining at will, and interrelating, the phases of industry and conscientiously achieving common goals and interpreting these goals separately, together and in relation to the other productive forces of the nation.

"This, though it is much, is not enough. The action of the State would still be limited, secondary to the intrinsic actions of the industry. Because of this, the Government, through the bureau, and the bureau through the board, has introduced action which is aggressive because of its creativity, substantive because of its independent nature, originality and national desire for its existence. Official action anticipates, advises, criticizes, prohibits, excites, corrects, controls, and definitely administers."

[2] *Memoria y Cuento Año 1953*, Ministerio de Minas y Hidrocarburos, p. xxix.

In Venezuela and other rich oil-producing countries, the petroleum industry represents a challenge to national pride and aspirations. A cut in production, in price—any severe displacement—can have a violent reaction upon the economy of any country so dependent on oil revenues and on the welfare of the people who, in turn, are so dependent upon the "sowing of petroleum." This aspect in the world oil picture constitutes a new force which affects the oil industry everywhere.

Past events also have proved that foreign oil operations have had appreciable political meanings. That the maintenance of a vigorous and prosperous oil business abroad which contributes immeasurably to the raising of living standards has served as a bulwark against the spread of Communism cannot be doubted. Furthermore, company policies which are based upon the premise that *what is good for the country is good for the company*, which see to it that nationals are given maximum employment, which require full compliance with local laws and customs, all serve to promote amity among nations. The promotion of confidence and friendship between the people of Saudi Arabia and of America has been and still is one of the most important objectives of Aramco management. Without question American oil operations in the Middle East have advanced understanding between the West and the East. On the whole, American oil operations abroad have been of a character and on a plane to serve the Free World well in these times of tension.

Without doubt the record shows that foreign oil operations have a potent military meaning. To the United States, the role of foreign oil development in national security is indicated by the fact that not only did such sources provide fuel to the armed forces of our Allies during World War II as well as to essential industries in our own and in Allied countries, but the American armed forces also received large deliveries of fuel from these points of supply. In any future emergency, the ability of our armed forces to conduct widespread operations would depend on the Free World's capacity to supply fuel at far-flung points. Our country's chances to keep an aggressor far from our shores would be gravely handicapped if our land, sea and air units were obliged to depend for fuel only upon sources within our own borders.

If the Free World is to meet the Communist threat, the factor of petroleum, simply and starkly, is the security of the United States and the Free World. In this connection, two incidents must be recalled. The first was Russia's delay in withdrawing its troops from Iran in accordance with its treaty commitment after World War II. The appearance of armed force and possible aggression in an area containing the world's greatest oil reserves constituted a threat to world peace and became the first crisis which the newly formed United Nations had to face. Only after being confronted with a strong attitude by the Iranian government firmly supported by the Free Nations did Russia withdraw its troops.

The second incident was Premier Mossadegh's "nationalization" of Iranian oil in 1951. Not only did this act result in the paralyzing of Iran's economy, but also it created a political vacuum which Russia practically was invited to fill either by direct action or by the now fully recognized methods by which Communists take advantage of a people's distress to seize power from within. Moreover, this second threat to the Free World in Iran came at a time when the Korean War was in a crucial stage and when Middle East crude oil and the products of Abadan's great refinery constituted a strategic supply for the armed forces of the United Nations.

To amplify the security factor, in today's divided world the oil resources outside the Iron Curtain must be searched for, developed and then guarded (1) for the survival of the Free World in case of war and (2) for the survival of the Free World in this time of uncertain peace, when the essential uses of petroleum products peculiarly are tied into daily life and can be the key to rising living standards for millions of people in many countries.

As related to the importance of the United States fostering the development and having control of petroleum abroad, the security factor is readily recognized. Less understood, however, is the relation of this security to the building up of the big American companies engaged in foreign activities. To put the matter simply, in connection with available strategic oil sources, what would America's position be today had not oil companies gone out and established themselves? How else could the companies establish themselves except by long-term evolutionary processes? How else except by having the financial resources and the courage to take risks? How else could they have made the gains that they have without exercising business prudence in dividing the risks in so far as possible? Moreover, how could they have accomplished what they have without the active support of their own government? For, as a matter of fact, our government has been an *ex officio* party to jointly owned companies engaging in specific operations. In rightfully espousing the cause of the "open door" in the interest of our economic and military security and of fair play, our government has, at the same time, encouraged the evolutionary trend that produced a few big American international oil concerns. The government actively encouraged American oil investment abroad, and to be successful American oil investment abroad had to be done in full measure and on a large scale.

Militarily, foreign oil operations have meant insurance against war for the Free World. Another world conflict might bring a new type of warfare, but new or old it would call for vast quantities of petroleum. Perhaps it would be conducted from distant and widely separated bases which could be more readily supplied from sources abroad than from domestic sources. Certainly without foreign sources, warfare must be waged largely from domestic bases, thus exposing the United States to greater potential damage.

Obviously the best way to assure the availability of overseas supplies is for American oil companies to continue their participation in the discovery and development of overseas sources. The "cold war," the Korean War, the Indo-Chinese War and the building up by Russia and Communist China of armies and armaments give the Free World no choice but to combat Communist aggression. Preparedness is the overriding, inescapable consideration facing the United States and the Free World in connection with foreign oil operations. And the paramount point in that preparation is to ensure the widest possible development of foreign oil in the interest of stronger economies, higher living standards and mutual security.

Experience makes clear the great cost and risks entailed in foreign operations. One risk the industry regards as inherent and takes for granted—that money expended in mapping, exploration and drilling activities may not result in finding oil. If oil is discovered, however, there is likely to be a considerable time lag between the development of the field and the first commercial shipments. Pipelines, separators, stabilizers, storage tanks, docks and many other facilities have to be provided. It seems as if foreign oil generally is found in relatively inaccessible areas, thus making it necessary to provide electricity and water-supply systems, schools and hospitals; to train local labor; and to make expenditures which normally are made by other industries or by municipalities. Also, in investing large sums abroad, oil companies sometimes are forced to take the chance of not being allowed to repatriate their capital or to remit profits because of exchange difficulties. Since the outlay of the vast sums required often is beyond the resources of single companies—and also because of the necessity to lessen the risks involved—joint ownership and operation of development has evolved as a solution.

Past events also indicate clearly that one of the great risks is that the enormous investments made in foreign petroleum can be placed in jeopardy at any time by people who raise the cry of "nationalization" as a politically convenient means to popularity and power. Iran, of course, stands as an example. Early in 1953 the oil people were exercised over a resolution, adopted by the Economic and Financial Committee of the United Nations General Assembly, that seemed to favor the principle of nationalization of resource industries in the less developed countries. The resolution provided no adequate protection for the rights of foreign investors in the nationalized properties, and coming at the time of the Iranian seizure the measure had the flavor of a scarcely disguised program of expropriation and confiscation. An amendment offered by the United States, but rejected by the committee, would have assured foreign investors of their full rights under international law.

Despite its happy resolution, the Iran episode points up the essential difficulty which must always exist when a commercial company operates under a contract the other party to which is a sovereign government. We have seen that several countries—including certain ones with nationalized petroleum companies and which excluded foreign participation—have passed new petroleum laws to encourage foreign, as well as home, investment. Nonetheless, increased nationalism continues to be a major deterrent or threat to Free World petroleum development. Viewed as a manifestation of a desire to improve the lot of one's fellow citizens, nationalism has the sympathetic understanding of the oil people. But when nationalists permit themselves to be misled by Communists, they work against their own aspirations—political, as well as social and economic. Also, through excessive nationalism, a government may aspire to accomplishment in the realm of petroleum development without adequate experience and without comprehension of the costs, risks and world trade processes involved—thus defeating the very objectives of its planning.

Unquestionably, the record proves that petroleum development under nationalized government monopoly is far less effective than under private auspices. Russia, which in 1901 outranked the United States as world's foremost oil producer with 51 per cent of total production, accounted for only 8.0 per cent in 1953. In the same years Mexico produced 25.4 per cent against only 1.4 per cent. Argentina, with 1.2 per cent of total world output in 1942, yielded only six-tenths of 1 per cent in 1953. Iran, which in 1950 accounted for 6.4 per cent—about the same as Russia that year—was without production in 1953. By way of contrast, Venezuela, which has welcomed foreign investment, has climbed from an insignificant production in 1922, to 9.7 per cent of the world's oil in 1930, to 12.5 per cent in 1940, and to 13.4 per cent in 1953. With oil companies and government alike spending millions of dollars on social and economic advancement as this growth occurred, what better argument exists for free enterprise?

To put the crux of the matter as simply as possible, the facts indicate that the growth of the petroleum industry abroad has been made possible and practicable by the existence of favorable investment conditions. When such conditions do not exist, growth and progress have slowed. And the record reveals, of course, that while American companies are eager to extend their operations they cannot do so—they even will withdraw—under adverse conditions, as has been the case in Egypt before the recent legal changes and, more recently, in Standard of Jersey's withdrawal from the Po Valley development after 17 years because of an Italian law favoring state-controlled companies.[3]

The record reveals, too, that the growth of world consumption has been the stimulating force behind postwar expansion. Substantially increased industrial activity, gains in the number and use of automotive vehicles, increased consumption of liquid fuels for home heating and for industry, and the large volumes required to supplement coal supplies in Western Europe and Great Britain, all may be pointed out as contributing factors. Even if there had been no need for rearming, many authorities feel that the world use of energy resources would

[3] *The Oil and Gas Journal*, July 12, 1954, p. 86.

be very high for two reasons: (1) the greatly expanding world population, and (2) the upsurge among all peoples toward better living standards.

In this connection, the record is most illuminating in that consumption of fuel—coal, oil, natural gas and hydroelectric power—seems to be an index of a nation's standard of living. We in the United States use fuel at the rate of 229 million British thermal units annually per person. Canada, with an annual consumption of 207 million BTU's per person, is in the same classification with us. These are the highest national per capita rates of fuel-energy consumption in the world. By comparison, the Western European nations use about 66 million BTU's per capita; Russia—so far as we know—about 45 million; and Asia only 6 million per capita. The conclusion is drawn that added energy use by peoples is a self-multiplying force. Where the utilization of energy increases, there seems also to be an increase in the effectiveness of its use to the benefit of a nation and its people.

On this agreeable note, let us turn to the future—to the new frontiers.

The oilmen—suppliers of liquid energy, as they call themselves—are completely confident that, so long as they have the freedom to inquire and explore, they will obtain the petroleum to supply their customers. Their confidence is justified by the record: "They always find the oil." If demand should mount to a level where they could not satisfy it from petroleum, they add that they would expand the manufacture of liquid fuels from coal, tar sands and other sources.

How pleasing and relatively uncomplicated it would be to consider the situation of liquid fuel supply and demand in a world at peace—in a world which would permit the suppliers of energy normally to expand their markets in the low-consuming countries with resulting dynamic rises in the living standards of those nations! The hope that energy consumption holds out for the world is all-important. Here lie the new frontiers.

New frontiers always exist where there are adventurous spirits. From such spirits may be traced the great advances made in many fields since the beginning of civilization. To our knowledge the human story of American overseas oil exploration remains untold. An attempt to present some record of exploratory expeditions and to gather together accounts of some of the pioneers was made in the *Report of*

American Petroleum Interests in Foreign Countries.[4] Here the names and exploits of more than a few American geologists and geophysicists who have roamed the globe as consultants or as staff employees of companies have been preserved for posterity. Yet, admittedly, the coverage is incomplete, the tale of hardships endured no more than indicated. One reads piecemeal of Ralph Arnold's early work in Venezuela. On the strength of his explorations, General Asphalt acquired its huge concession. One learns that Edward E. de Golyer—now of De Golyer and MacNaughton, perhaps one of the best known firms of American geologists in the international field today—was the "boy discoverer" for Pearson (later Lord Cowdray) of Potrero del Llano No. 2. In an accompanying album of photographs—field shots garnered from the cooperating pioneers and reproduced from old trade journals —one sees the cherubic De Golyer pensively sitting on the concrete cap built over the well during a revolution. That well was to share fame with Doheny's Casiano No. 7 and Cerro Azul No. 4 as one of the top single producers of the world. Potrero del Llano No. 2 yielded over 100 million barrels—perhaps more oil than has ever been recovered from a single well. Too, one follows Chester Naramore and J. P. McCullough into icy arctic wastes of Siberia and Sakhalin and, subsequently treks with the former into the sweltering, tsetse fly infested tropical land of Angola, Africa, or with the latter into the sweltering, debilitating, malarial country of Panama and Costa Rica.

What hardships did they suffer? What ingenuity did they display? We have asked many pioneer geologists and geophysicists about their foreign experiences. They admit hardships and obstacles only as discomforts. One senses that the privations and obstacles were but the *pièce de résistance*, which rendered the fare more palatable. For these men were and are scientist-adventurers. The "discomforts" mean nothing against the challenge of the search, the opportunity to exercise their trained skill in any part of the world however remote.

Oil exploratory pioneering is neither dated nor dead. As anomalous as it may sound, it continues today and continues intensively. Modern expeditions may boast far better equipment, but the hardships endured, the obstacles encountered by geologists and geophysicists, in-

---

[4] Report on *American Petroleum Interests in Foreign Countries*, Chapter 8, Parts 3 and 4, Government Printing Office, Washington, D.C., 1946.

deed, the challenge to their skill and intelligence have never been more pronounced than in today's world.

The pioneer spirit, the adventurer is as active today as ever he was, and in a sense, probably more so. For the field worker but reflects the adventurous spirit in the home office, in the board room where the big decisions are made. And, simply to see the oil men at their work with the tools they use is to bring home sharply the fact that the greater the knowledge and the more modern the devices that are brought into play, the wider becomes the range of the field man's work, the larger grows his horizon of rejection or discovery.

Riding in a company plane from Caracas to San Tome in eastern Venezuela one runs into two young geologists. Somewhere deep in the *llanos* country they are doing a structural job. A few months before one encountered them in a field camp in Kuwait, Arabia. With distance annihilated by plane travel, the range of today's operations is world-wide. So the adventure heightens, and the adventures compound themselves. The frontiers become limitless.

Summing up, as to the probability of opening new frontiers, one sees as contributing factors the American oilman's drive, his ability to make snap decisions as well as carefully weighed and evaluated ones, his confidence in his own ability, his ingenuity—the American flare for taking 65 pieces of nothing and making something sorely needed with them—and his frequent accomplishment of the impossible in logistics and long-range planning. (During World War II, the popular expression was: "The difficult we do immediately; the impossible takes a little longer.") [5] One sees, too, that larger urge that possesses man—the unfathomable desire to accomplish—in this case, a desire which finds fulfillment through free enterprise.

Then there is the American ability to make friends abroad when he sets his mind to it. A Middle Easterner favorably compares the landing of the Standard of California geologists on the sands of Saudi Arabia in 1933 to Christopher Columbus discovering America. Their landing resulted in great oil discoveries. But he was referring not only to their finds. He knew the part that they played as ambassadors of good will among the proud, isolated Bedouin tribesmen of Saudi Arabia. What promise for the future this vista of amity among peoples opens up!

[5] *A History of the Petroleum Administration for War, 1941-1945,* Government Printing Office, Washington, D.C., 1946, p. 1.

As discoveries establishing great new oil-producing areas have occurred, the fundamental interrelationship of the oil fields of the world, wherever they may be located, is wiping out natural boundaries from the supply-and-demand picture and making national interdependence, rather than national independence, more marked. The narrow view of an isolated, domestic industry is as untenable as a United States itself isolated from the Free World.

The very geographical noncoincidence of producing and consuming areas makes it clear why the oil business tends to be a global one. There is no relation between the places where oil is found and where it is used. Oil is found where nature put it. It is consumed where populations have concentrated and industry flourishes. Only in a few cases do the two coincide geographically. But the far-flung, efficient system that has been built up to transport oil permits producing and consuming areas to be brought together with relative ease and economy. "If such barriers as international politics, currency restrictions, and similar impediments did not exist," the international oilmen say, "there would be no problems, relatively speaking, in supplying all parts of the world with all the oil they need for as far as we can see into the future."

New frontiers? Who can doubt it?

APPENDIX I

STATISTICAL SECTION

BIBLIOGRAPHY OF MORE IMPORTANT SOURCES OF INTERNATIONAL STATISTICS ON PETROLEUM

United Nations
Statistical Yearbook
New York
(Annually, since 1948)
   Contains a wide range of annual statistical data on economic and social developments throughout the world, in most cases covering the past 20 years. The petroleum data given include production of crude shale oil, natural gasoline, natural gas, manufactured gasoline, kerosene, fuel oils and lubricants.

United Nations
Monthly Bulletin of Statistics
New York
(Monthly, since January, 1947)
   Contains annual and monthly data similar to those of the *Yearbook,* but less comprehensive in coverage. Petroleum data deal only with production of crude oil and natural gas.

United Nations
Yearbook of International Trade Statistics
New York
(Annually, since 1950)
   Contains annual data on the principal imports and exports of about 70 countries.

United Nations
World Energy Supplies in Selected Years, 1929–1950
New York
(September, 1952)
   Statistics on production, trade and consumption of fuel and power in the years 1929, 1937, 1949 and 1950, by country and region, with world totals.

International Labor Organization, Petroleum Committee
General Report
Second Session, Geneva, 1948
Third Session, Geneva, 1950
Fourth Session, The Hague, 1952
Includes world reviews of recent developments in the petroleum indus-
try, as well as reviews of social conditions and of actions taken by various
groups in response to Petroleum Committee resolutions.

World Power Conference
Transactions
(Third World Power Conference, Washington, 1936)
(Fourth World Power Conference, London, 1950)
A wide variety of data on the fuel and power situation in many coun-
tries. Petroleum was especially well covered in the Transactions of the
Third World Power Conference.

World Power Conference
Statistical Yearbook, Numbers 1 to 6
London
Annual data on production, trade and consumption of fuel and power in
many countries.

Office of European Economic Committee
(*Annual*) *Report on Coordination of Oil Refinery Expansion in the OEEC
Countries*
Paris
October 1, 1949; August 2, 1951; June 3, 1953
An excellent source of data on supplies, refining and utilization of oil in
Western Europe.

U.S. Bureau of Mines
World Petroleum Statistics
Washington
(Monthly)
Current statistics on production, processing, trade and consumption of
petroleum and products throughout the world.

International Petroleum Trade
Washington
(Monthly)
Petroleum and products statistics issued by U.S. Bureau of Mines.

American Petroleum Institute
Petroleum Facts and Figures
New York
(Annually)
Deals primarily with the United States industry, but contains useful
tables on production, refinery capacity and consumption in the world.

Regul, Dr. Rudolf
Energiequellen der Welt
in Schriften des Instituts für Konjuncturforschung
Berlin, 1937
A first-class study of the energy industries up to 1936. Contains excellent statistics on production processing and trade in each of the energy sources.

U.K. Colonial Geological Surveys
Statistical Summary of the Mineral Industry
London
(Annually)
Production, processing and trade data on minerals and derivatives, including refining products. For world coverage, this is probably the most complete of all sources of data for the period beginning about 1930.

Petroleum Press Service
London
(Monthly, since 1933)
One of the best sources of up-to-date information and discussion of world-wide developments in petroleum and related industries.

Petroleum Times
London
(Fortnightly, since 1919)
An excellent source of current information on developments in the world petroleum industry.

Erdöl und Kohle
Hamburg
(Monthly)
Contains brief reviews of recent developments in the petroleum industry throughout the world, with more complete data on the industry in Germany.

Glückauf
Essen
(Fortnightly)
Deals largely with coal, but occasionally includes excellent studies on oil and energy.

La Revue petrolière
Paris
(Monthly)
Deals chiefly with petroleum in France, but includes a summary of world developments and articles on subjects of special interest to the petroleum industry.

Moniteur du pétrole Roumain
Bucharest
(Monthly)
Prewar issues contain a considerable volume of current and historical statistics on the world petroleum industry.

Oil and Gas Journal (The)
Tulsa
(Weekly)
Covers international petroleum news, and includes an annual "International" number with much useful detail on foreign countries.

World Oil
Houston
(Monthly)
Deals largely with technical and economic developments in various countries, and includes an annual "International Operations Issue."

Petróleo Interamericano
Tulsa
(Monthly)
South American edition of *The Oil and Gas Journal.*

World Petroleum
New York
(Monthly)
Specializes in articles on foreign oil developments in all fields of activity.

Oil Forum
New York
(Monthly)
Selected news and feature articles on international as well as national subjects.

National Petroleum News
New York
(Monthly)
Formerly a weekly news magazine including international reports; changed to a monthly dealing with the marketing field, beginning November, 1954.

TABLE 1. WORLD CRUDE-OIL PRODUCTION

(In thousands of barrels daily)

Area	1947	1948	1949	1950	1951	1952	1953
Canada......................	20.0	32.5	57.6	78.4	130.5	167.2	221.6
Mexico......................	153.8	159.5	166.4	197.6	211.2	210.6	198.4
Colombia....................	68.1	64.9	81.2	93.1	105.7	105.8	108.1
Trinidad....................	55.7	54.9	55.1	55.4	57.1	58.1	61.2
Venezuela...................	1,190.8	1,338.8	1,321.5	1,497.9	1,704.6	1,804.7	1,765.9
Total Caribbean..............	1,314.6	1,458.6	1,457.8	1,646.4	1,867.4	1,968.6	1,935.2
Argentina....................	59.9	64.8	61.9	64.3	66.9	67.8	78.0
Bolivia......................	1.3	1.3	1.9	1.7	1.4	1.5	1.6
Brazil.......................	0.3	0.4	0.3	0.9	1.9	2.4	2.5
Chile........................	...	...	0.4	1.6	1.8	2.4	3.4
Cuba........................	0.7	0.3	0.4	0.3	0.2	0.1	0.1
Ecuador.....................	6.6	7.1	7.2	7.4	7.6	7.7	8.1
Peru........................	35.0	38.5	40.5	41.2	44.1	44.8	43.8
Total Other Latin America....	103.8	112.4	112.6	117.4	123.9	126.7	137.5
Total Western Hemisphere (except U.S.)..............	1,592.2	1,763.0	1,794.4	2,039.8	2,333.0	2,473.1	2,492.7
France.......................	1.0	1.1	1.1	2.5	5.4	6.5	6.9
Germany (Western)............	11.1	12.1	15.6	20.7	25.9	33.6	42.0
Italy........................	0.2	0.2	0.2	0.2	0.4	1.4	1.9
Netherlands..................	4.0	9.4	11.8	13.4	13.6	13.6	15.6
United Kingdom...............	1.0	0.9	0.9	0.9	0.9	1.1	1.1
Yugoslavia...................	1.0	1.1	2.5	3.0	3.2	3.1	3.4
Total Free Europe...........	18.3	24.8	32.1	40.7	49.4	59.3	70.9
Albania......................	1.0	1.0	2.5	3.5	3.0	3.0	3.0
Austria......................	16.0	17.0	17.8	26.0	45.0	55.0	60.0
Czechoslovakia................	0.6	0.4	0.5	0.5	1.9	2.5	2.5
Hungary.....................	11.9	10.0	10.0	10.0	10.0	11.0	14.0
Poland......................	2.6	2.7	2.8	2.8	4.0	4.5	4.0
Rumania.....................	78.0	78.0	84.5	89.0	85.5	85.0	125.0
Total Eastern Europe........	110.1	109.1	118.1	131.8	149.4	161.0	208.5
Total Europe..............	128.4	133.9	150.2	172.5	198.8	220.3	279.4
Algeria......................	...	...	...	...	...	0.8	1.7
Egypt.......................	25.5	36.0	43.2	44.5	44.6	44.9	46.1
French Morocco...............	...	...	0.3	0.8	1.6	2.1	2.1
Total North Africa...........	25.5	36.0	43.5	45.3	46.2	47.8	49.9

TABLE 1. WORLD CRUDE-OIL PRODUCTION (*Continued*)

(In thousands of barrels daily)

Area	1947	1948	1949	1950	1951	1952	1953
Bahrain..................	25.8	29.8	30.1	30.2	30.1	30.1	30.1
Iran....................	422.1	518.5	560.4	663.7	349.6	27.6	26.2
Iraq....................	99.2	72.2	86.3	136.2	176.3	385.1	576.0
Kuwait..................	44.5	127.2	247.0	345.1	561.4	747.1	861.7
Qatar...................	...	...	2.1	33.8	48.8	68.8	85.2
Saudi Arabia.............	246.2	390.3	476.7	546.7	761.5	824.8	844.6
Turkey..................	...	...	0.3	0.7	0.3	0.4	0.5
Total Middle East.......	837.8	1,138.0	1,402.9	1,756.4	1,928.0	2,083.9	2,424.3
British Borneo............	36.1	55.0	69.2	84.9	102.7	104.5	101.0
Indonesia and Netherlands New Guinea.................	22.0	87.1	120.6	135.7	156.5	175.7	212.7
Total Oceania...........	58.1	142.1	189.8	220.6	259.2	280.2	313.7
Burma..................	0.5	0.5	0.5	1.0	1.2	2.0	2.3
China...................	1.1	1.8	1.4	1.5	2.0	2.0	3.0
India...................	6.1	6.3	5.2	5.1	5.3	5.7	5.5
Japan...................	3.4	3.1	3.8	5.7	6.4	5.8	5.8
Pakistan.................	*	*	2.0	2.9	3.2	2.7	4.1
Total South and East Asia.....	11.1	11.7	12.9	16.2	18.1	18.2	20.7
Total Eastern Hemisphere (except Russia)...........	1,060.9	1,461.7	1,799.3	2,211.0	2,450.3	2,650.4	3,088.0
Total foreign (except Russia)....	2,653.1	3,224.7	3,593.7	4,250.8	4,783.3	5,123.5	5,580.7
United States.............	5,087.7	5,519.6	5,046.4	5,407.1	6,158.1	6,262.3	6,465.8
Total world (except Russia)......	7,740.8	8,744.3	8,640.1	9,657.9	10,941.4	11,385.8	12,046.5
Russia..................	543.0	600.0	685.0	752.0	842.0	935.0	1,050.0
Total world..............	8,283.8	9,344.3	9,325.1	10,409.9	11,783.4	12,320.8	13,096.5

* Included in India.

Source: Compiled from U.S. Bureau of Mines and other sources. For comparable table, years 1857 to 1948, see *Our Oil Resources*, 1950, pp. 28–31

TABLE 2. ESTIMATED WORLD CRUDE-OIL RESERVES

(In thousands of barrels, as of January 1)

Area	1952	1953 *	1954 *
North America except United States and Alaska............	2,780,000	4,202,000	3,701,500
South America			
Caribbean area..............	10,650,000	10,178,600	10,580,000
Other South America.........	570,000	578,000	616,000
Total Western Hemisphere except United States.....	14,000,000	14,958,600	14,897,500
Europe except USSR...........	875,800	1,061,700	1,191,000
Near and Middle East..........	51,825,000	61,625,000	79,075,000
Other Eastern Hemisphere......	1,902,650	2,304,600	2,841,500
Total Eastern Hemisphere except USSR and Sakhalin	54,603,450	64,991,300	83,107,500
Total except United States and USSR and Sakhalin..	68,603,450	79,949,900	98,005,000
USSR and Sakhalin...........	5,565,000	6,600,000	9,865,000
Total except United States....	74,168,450	86,549,900	107,870,000
United States................	27,468,000	27,966,100	29,007,482
World total.................	101,636,450	114,516,000	136,877,482

* Source: *World Oil.*

Sources: For United States, American Petroleum Institute; for other countries, private sources.

TABLE SERIES 3. INVESTMENTS THAT HAVE NOT PAID OUT

Many leases and concessions upon which considerable money is expended for exploration and development do not pay out, as illustrated in the following typical examples submitted by American oil companies operating in foreign countries. (For other examples, see *American Petroleum Interests in Foreign Countries*, Government Printing Office, Washington, D.C., 1946, pp. 230, 231, 232, 233.)

CANADA

Company name withheld
Amount expended:

1. For concessions or lease....	$16,533,078
2. For exploration...........	9,722,750
3. For drilling..............	13,980,051
4. For other purposes........	18,128,069
5. Total.................	$58,363,948
Amount taken out............	23,629,484
Loss........................	$34,734,464

COLOMBIA

Company name withheld
Amount expended:

1. For concessions or lease....	$ 4,900,000
2. For exploration...........	8,666,000
3. For drilling..............	16,625,000
4. For other purposes........	4,695,000
5. Total.................	$34,886,000
Amount taken out............	2,339,000
Loss........................	$32,547,000 *

Approximate period of time covered—1934 to June 30, 1953.

* After eight years of exploration and unproductive drilling by the company, its affiliates and partners in various areas of Colombia, a discovery well was drilled on one concession in 1942. After producing about 1½ million barrels of heavy crude, this concession was sold in 1951. Presently, exploration and wildcat drilling are being conducted on a relatively small scale.

TABLE SERIES 3. INVESTMENTS THAT HAVE NOT PAID OUT (*Continued*)

COLOMBIA

Company name withheld; field, Southern Llanos
area
Amount expended:
1. For concessions or lease..... $ 57,000
2. For exploration............ 5,810,000
3. For drilling...............   546,000
4. For other purposes......... 1,240,000

5.   Total................... $7,653,000
Amount taken out.............   —
Loss......................... $7,653,000

Approximate period of time covered—10 years.

COLOMBIA

Company name withheld
Amount expended:
1. For concessions or lease..... $ 339,000
2. For exploration............ 5,543,000
3. For drilling............... 1,351,000
4. For other purposes.........   —

5.   Total................... $7,233,000
Amount taken out.............   —
Loss......................... $7,233,000 *

Approximate period of time covered—1944 to 1952.

* During the period 1944 through 1952 of this company's latest venture in Colombia, in addition to intensive field exploration work, five wells were drilled, all of which were dry holes. The exploration work in that country has now been terminated.

TABLE SERIES 3. INVESTMENTS THAT HAVE NOT PAID OUT (*Continued*)

CUBA

Company name withheld
Amount expended:
1. For concessions or lease..... $ 271,000
2. For exploration............   2,919,000
3. For drilling...............   1,337,000
4. For other purposes.........   —

5.   Total.................. $4,527,000
Amount taken out.............   —
Loss......................... $4,527,000 *

Approximate period of time covered—1946 to 1952.
* Exploratory efforts in Cuba largely occurred after 1946, and, to date, two unsuccessful wildcat tests have been drilled. Large blocks of acreage, concessions and privileges have been renounced, but some additional acreage is presently being acquired.

ECUADOR

International Ecuadorean Petroleum Co.*
Amount expended:
1. For concessions or lease.... $ 1,138,000
2. For exploration...........   4,201,200
3. For drilling..............   4,877,200
4. For other purposes........   1,942,000

5.   Total................. $12,158,400
Amount taken out............   —
Loss........................   —

Approximate period of time covered—1937 to 1949.
* Subsidiary of Standard Oil Company (New Jersey).

TABLE SERIES 3. INVESTMENTS THAT HAVE NOT PAID OUT (*Continued*)

ECUADOR

Esso Standard Oil Co. (Ecuador) S.A.*
Amount expended:
1. For concessions or lease..... (Not available)
2. For exploration............. $ 779,000
3. For drilling............... 1,216,000
4. For other purposes......... 3,000,000

5. Total.................. $4,995,000 †
Amount taken out.............. —
Loss.......................... —

Approximate period of time covered—1948 to 1950.
* Owned 50 per cent Standard Oil (New Jersey), 50 per cent Shell.
† Shell spent like amount in 1948 to 1950 and $24,842,000 before 1948.

EGYPT

Standard Oil Company of Egypt.*
Amount expended:
1. For concessions or lease.... —
2. For exploration........... $ 6,836,500
3. For drilling.............. 2,584,800
4. For other purposes........ 2,905,700

5. Total.................. $12,327,000
Amount taken out............. —
Loss......................... $12,327,000

Approximate period of time covered—1937 to 1949.
* Subsidiary of Standard Oil Company (New Jersey).

TABLE SERIES 3. INVESTMENTS THAT HAVE NOT PAID OUT (*Continued*)

EGYPT

Company name withheld
Amount expended:
  1. For concessions or lease....   —
  2. For exploration............ $ 4,117,000
  3. For drilling............... 11,534,000
  4. For other purposes......... 6,367,000

  5. Total.................. $22,018,000
  Amount taken out............. 19,320,000

  Loss......................... $ 2,698,000 *

Approximate period of time covered—1936 to June 30, 1953.
* Several dry holes were drilled prior to World War II. Operations were suspended from 1942 to 1945. Production was found in 1946. Drilling in proved areas has been completed, and exploratory efforts have been suspended because of restrictive legislation and regulations. The company's share of gross production, which averaged 11,100 barrels per day in 1950, was (December, 1953) averaging 6,500 barrels per day and is continuing to decline.

EGYPT

Company name withheld
Amount expended:
  1. For concessions or lease.....   —
  2. For exploration............   —
  3. For drilling...............   —
  4. For other purposes.........   —

  5. Total.................. $1,674,801
  Amount taken out............. 71,541

  Loss......................... $1,603,260

Approximate period of time covered—seven years.

TABLE SERIES 3. INVESTMENTS THAT HAVE NOT PAID OUT (*Continued*)

EUROPEAN COUNTRY

Company name withheld
Amount expended:

1. For concessions or lease..... $ 642,000
2. For exploration............ 5,785,000
3. For drilling................ 2,071,000
4. For other purposes..........   —

5.   Total.................. $8,498,000
Amount taken out..............   —
Loss.......................... $8,498,000

Approximate period of time covered—1938 to 1952.
NOTE: At the termination of the war in Europe in 1945, field investigation and exploratory work were resumed as soon as conditions permitted, and have been continued to date. By the end of 1952, 14 wells had been drilled without success.

VENEZUELA

Creole Petroleum Corporation; * field, Barbacoas/
Tamanaco concessions in Guarico
Amount expended:

1. For concessions or lease.... $ 1,730,000
2. For exploration............ 5,035,000
3. For drilling.............. 9,565,000
4. For other purposes........ 5,700,000

5.   Total.................. $22,030,000
Amount taken out.............   —
Loss.......................... $22,030,000 †

Approximate period of time covered—1944 to 1948.
* Subsidiary of Standard Oil Company (New Jersey).
† Exploration was carried out over an area of 317,000 hectares in the northern part of the state of Guarico. Because of the remoteness of this area, Creole built a camp with modern living accommodations for its workers, schools, a hospital and an airport. Also the company contributed a large part toward the construction of a 200-mile highway from the concession to the seaport at Puerto la Cruz. Drilling activities were unsuccessful. Not one well produced oil.

TABLE SERIES 3. INVESTMENTS THAT HAVE NOT PAID OUT (*Continued*)

VENEZUELA

Company name withheld
Amount expended:
    1. For concessions or lease....   —
    2. For exploration............   —
    3. For drilling...............   —
    4. For other purposes.........   —

    5.   Total................. $96,000,000
Amount taken out.............   35,000,000

    Loss......................... $61,000,000

Approximate period of time covered—1926 to December 31, 1952.

TABLE SERIES 4. LARGE INITIAL INVESTMENT AND LONG TIME LAG

Between the date of first investment, the date of first discovery and the date that oil*is first commercially marketed, large amounts may be expended on exploration, development and facilities for gathering, storage and transportation. This time lag before there is any return whatsoever from the investment is illustrated by the following typical examples submitted by American oil companies operating in foreign countries. (For other examples, see *American Petroleum Interests in Foreign Countries*, Government Printing Office, Washington, D.C., 1946, pp. 226, 227, 228.)

CANADA

Company name withheld
    A. Date of first investment............................ February, 1948
    B. Date of first discovery.............................. May, 1951
    Total investment between *A* and *B* periods............... $14,488,985
    C. Date of first oil commercially marketed............... May 24, 1951
    Total investment between *A* and *C* periods............... $14,488,985

TABLE SERIES 4. LARGE INITIAL INVESTMENT AND LONG TIME LAG (*Continued*)

CANADA

Company name withheld
  A. Date of first investment....................... July, 1941
  B. Date of first discovery......................... September 22, 1948
  Total investment between *A* and *B* periods............ $5,445,000
  C. Date of first oil commercially marketed............ June, 1949
  Total investment between *A* and *C* periods............ $8,269,000 *

* After considerable geological and geophysical effort, particularly in 1946 to 1948, this company's first discovery well was completed in September, 1948, as a gas-distillate producer. Although this well has not yet produced commercially because of lack of outlets for gas, it acted as a spur to further drilling of a number of wildcats in early 1949, with the result that commercial production was available for sale by June of that year from four producing wells in one field and one oil producer in another field.

CANADA

Company name withheld
  A. Date of first investment........................... 1944
  B. Date of first discovery............................ October 6, 1950
  Total investment between *A* and *B* periods.............. $6,800,000
  C. Date of first oil commercially marketed.............. January 2, 1951
  Total investment between *A* and *C* periods.............. $7,915,000 *

* Extensive exploration and drilling operations were conducted in Alberta, British Columbia and the Northwest Territories from 1944 to 1951. Small production was found in Alberta in 1950. Exploration was begun in Saskatchewan in 1951, and in 1952 several discovery wells were drilled on jointly held properties. For the year 1952, the company's share of gross production was 958 barrels per day. Production was (December, 1953) averaging 2,100 barrels per day and is increasing.

CANADA

Imperial Oil Limited; * field, Prairie Provinces †
  A. Date of first investment........................... 1937
  B. Date of first discovery............................ February, 1947
  Total investment between *A* and *B* periods.............. $23,000,000
  C. Date of first oil commercially marketed.............. Late 1947
  Total investment between *A* and *C* periods.............. $30,000,000

* Subsidiary of Standard Oil Company (New Jersey).
† Prairie Provinces, after Turner Valley.

TABLE SERIES 4. LARGE INITIAL INVESTMENT AND LONG TIME LAG (*Continued*)

COLOMBIA

Company name withheld; field, Puerto Boyaca area
- *A.* Date of first investment............................ 1926
- *B.* Date of first discovery.............................. November, 1946
- Total investment between *A* and *B* periods.............. $7,252,000
- *C.* Date of first oil commercially marketed............... February, 1949
- Total investment between *A* and *C* periods*............. $14,926,000

* Including all facilities for gathering, storage and transportation.
See also Chapter 4.

EGYPT

Company name withheld
- *A.* Date of first investment............................ 1936
- *B.* Date of first discovery............................. May 24, 1946
- Total investment between *A* and *B* periods............. $3,900,000
- *C.* Date of first oil commercially marketed............. December 9, 1947
- Total investment between *A* and *C* periods............. $7,400,000

NOTE: Several dry holes were drilled prior to World War II. Operations were suspended from 1942 to 1945. Production was found in 1946. Drilling in proved areas has been completed, and exploratory efforts have been suspended because of restrictive legislation and regulations. The company's share of gross production, which averaged 11,100 barrels per day in 1950, was (December, 1953) averaging 6,500 barrels per day and is continuing to decline.

INDONESIA

Company name withheld
- *A.* Date of first investment............................. 1936
- *B.* Date of first discovery.............................. 1950
- Total investment between *A* and *B* periods................. $8,917,538
- *C.* Date of first oil commercially marketed................. 1952
- Total investment between *A* and *C* periods................. $27,692,483

NOTE: Operations were suspended from 1942 to 1948 because of World War II and subsequent political disturbances.
For Mexico, see Chapter 3.

TABLE SERIES 4. LARGE INITIAL INVESTMENT AND LONG TIME LAG (*Continued*)

SAUDI ARABIA

Arabian American Oil Company *
  A. Date of first investment........................... August, 1933
  B. Date of first discovery............................ March, 1938
  Total investment between *A* and *B* periods.............. $5,000,000
  C. Date of first oil commercially marketed.............. September, 1938
  Total investment between *A* and *C* periods.............. $8,000,000

* Subsidiary of Standard Oil Company of California, The Texas Company, Standard Oil Company (New Jersey), Socony-Vacuum Oil Co., Inc.

VENEZUELA

Company name withheld
  A. Date of first investment.............................. 1926
  B. Date of first discovery............................... 1945
  Total investment between *A* and *B* periods................. $19,000,000
  C. Date of first oil commercially marketed................. 1945
  Total investment between *A* and *C* periods................. $19,000,000

TABLE 5. DIRECT PAYMENTS, BENEFITS AND WELFARE AND SUPPLEMENTARY
CONTRIBUTIONS—DAILY BOLÍVAR EMPLOYEE

Comparison of 1945 and 1952 corrected for collective contract revision

	Dollars per working day			Per cent increase (decrease)
	1945	1952 *	Increase (decrease)	
Direct payments:				
Regular wages, including overtime, travel time and night bonus..................	4.92	9.51	4.59	93
Vacation and holiday pay................	0.16	0.92	0.76	475
Paid day of rest........................	....	1.28	1.28	0
Housing allowance......................	0.14	0.84	0.70	500
Subtotal payroll.....................	5.22	12.55	7.33	140
Utilidades............................	0.87	1.95	1.08	124
Subtotal direct payments.............	6.09	14.50	8.41	138
Benefits and welfare:				
Thrift plan...........................	0.15	0.55	0.40	267
Death benefits........................	0.01	0.03	0.02	200
Education expense.....................	0.09	0.32	0.23	256
Medical and hospital expenses...........				
Sickness and accident benefits...........	0.58	0.89	0.31	53
Recreation and athletic expense..........	0.14	0.29	0.15	107
Housing facilities......................	0.65	1.61	0.96	148
Employees stores expense................	0.29	0.29		
Miscellaneous.........................	0.07	0.05	(0.02)	(29)
Subtotal benefits and welfare...........	1.98	4.03	2.05	104
Subtotal direct payments, benefits and welfare.........................	8.07	18.53	10.46	130
Supplementary contributions:				
Pensions and dismissal pay costs..........	0.03	1.59	1.56	
Industrial illness and accident indemnity..	....	0.05	0.05	0
Subtotal supplementary contributions...	0.03	1.64	1.61	
Grand total.........................	8.10	20.17	12.07	149

* This is actual 1952 data corrected for the present collective contract. It is therefore a "representative post contract year" but is not one particular year such as 1953.

NOTE: Average number of Bolívar employees, 6,490; average number of working days, 286; exchange rate, Bs 3.09 = $1.00.

Source: Creole Petroleum Corporation.

TABLE 6. ESTIMATED CRUDE RUNS TO STILLS AT REFINERIES OUTSIDE THE
UNITED STATES

(In barrels of 42 U.S. gallons daily)

Year	Foreign	Foreign except Russia	American	Per cent of foreign	American per cent of foreign except Russia
1927	757,100	613,300	142,800	18.9	23.3
1928	871,500	682,500	141,300	16.2	20.7
1929	1,064,500	840,000	219,600	20.6	26.1
1930	1,253,700	933,200	254,000	20.5	27.2
1931	1,314,900	916,700	268,200	18.9	27.1
1932	1,335,200	931,400	242,500	18.2	26.0
1933	1,369,700	1,032,800	286,400	20.6	28.0
1934	1,580,300	1,173,600	359,400	22.7	30.6
1935	1,726,900	1,304,700	405,800	23.5	31.1
1936	1,892,900	1,400,000	446,700	23.6	31.9
1937	2,078,500	1,563,200	307,400	24.4	32.5
1938	2,165,300	1,627,900	504,300	23.3	30.9
1939	2,242,500	1,669,000	524,800	23.4	31.4
1946	2,594,000	2,156,000	831,000	32.0	38.5
1947	3,001,000	2,484,000	948,000	31.6	38.2
1948	3,450,000	2,880,000	1,077,000	31.2	37.4
1949	3,841,000	3,189,000	1,156,000	30.1	36.2
1950	4,496,000	3,781,000	1,378,000	30.6	36.4
1951	5,086,000	4,288,000	1,666,000	32.8	38.9
1952	5,404,000	4,518,000	1,830,000	32.9	40.5
1953	5,903,000	4,704,000	2,021,000	34.2	43.0

Sources: U.S. Bureau of Mines and private sources.

TABLE 7. TOTAL FOREIGN PETROLEUM DEMAND VERSUS U.S. EXPORTS

(In thousands of barrels of 42 U.S. gallons)

Period, years	Years	Average annual total foreign demand	Average annual U.S. exports	Per cent total demand
10	1865–1874	3,417	2,887	84.5
10	1875–1884	14,125	9,706	68.7
10	1885–1894	45,684	16,289	35.7
10	1895–1904	101,413	23,319	23.0
10	1905–1914	150,142	40,555	27.0
5	1915–1919 (World War I)	192,640	63,054	32.7
10	1920–1929	352,706	115,021	32.6
10	1930–1939	726,901	142,190	19.6
6	1940–1945 (World War II)	917,441	149,460	16.3
8	1946–1953	1,582,133	142,682	9.0

Source: U.S. Bureau of Mines.

TABLE 8. EXPORTS AND IMPORTS OF CRUDE AND PRODUCTS BY THE UNITED STATES

(In thousands of barrels of 42 U.S. gallons)

Year	United States exports	United States imports	Per cent United States exports to foreign demand
1913	52,251	18,231	29.8
1914	54,359	17,247	30.6
1915	56,449	18,192	29.7
1916	62,459	21,244	31.1
1917	64,503	31,563	32.1
1918	68,012	38,963	38.5
1919	63,848	54,198	32.9
1920	79,576	108,822	35.2
1921	71,652	128,792	29.1
1922	74,344	135,973	30.2
1923	101,981	99,653	35.1
1924	117,144	94,581	35.6
1925	113,834	78,200	33.3
1926	131,950	81,320	33.6
1927	141,649	71,736	33.1
1928	154,957	91,557	31.8
1929	163,120	108,710	30.3
1930	156,499	105,618	27.3
1931	124,394	86,087	22.1
1932	103,275	74,494	18.1
1933	106,727	45,394	17.5
1934	114,507	50,494	16.9
1935	128,987	52,635	17.8
1936	131,994	57,104	16.6
1937	172,834	57,157	19.6
1938	193,728	54,308	21.1
1939	188,959	59,060	19.8
1940	130,466	83,751	14.4
1941	108,830	97,142	11.8
1942	116,907	35,966	14.0
1943	149,957	63,412	17.2
1944	207,616	92,311	21.1
1945	182,983	113,619	18.7
1946	153,123	137,676	15.1
1947	164,477	159,389	13.8
1948	134,674	188,144	10.3
1949	119,376	235,559	8.2
1950	111,306	310,261	6.8
1951	154,052	308,194	8.3
1952	158,188	348,507	7.8
1953	146,258	383,157	6.7

TABLE 9. COMPARISON OF DOLLAR VALUE OF UNITED STATES EXPORTS AND IMPORTS OF CRUDE PETROLEUM AND PETROLEUM PRODUCTS (IN THOUSANDS OF DOLLARS); ALSO, PER CENT OF PETROLEUM IMPORTS AND EXPORTS TO TOTAL UNITED STATES IMPORTS AND EXPORTS

Year	Value of total United States exports	Value of total petroleum exports	Per cent petroleum to total	Value of total United States imports	Value of total petroleum imports	Per cent petroleum to total
1913	2,448,288	160,584	6.6	1,813,008	12,997	0.7
1914	2,071,056	149,040	7.2	1,893,926	11,501	0.6
1915	3,493,236	159,792	4.6	1,674,170	10,564	0.6
1916	5,422,644	221,136	4.1	2,197,884	13,887	0.6
1917	6,169,620	275,148	4.5	2,659,355	20,605	0.8
1918	6,047,880	371,184	6.1	2,945,655	25,670	0.9
1919	7,749,816	377,124	4.9	3,904,365	31,441	0.8
1920	8,080,476	592,872	7.3	5,278,481	65,903	1.3
1921	4,378,932	401,232	9.2	2,509,148	78,844	3.1
1922	3,765,096	345,504	9.2	3,112,747	88,485	2.8
1923	4,090,716	366,792	9.0	3,792,066	78,713	2.1
1924	4,497,648	443,784	9.9	3,609,963	101,357	2.8
1925	4,818,720	474,024	9.8	4,226,589	107,694	2.6
1926	4,711,716	555,432	11.8	4,430,888	124,556	2.8
1927	4,758,864	486,768	10.2	4,184,742	113,434	2.7
1928	5,030,100	526,740	10.5	4,091,444	132,842	3.3
1929	5,157,084	562,116	10.9	4,399,361	143,557	3.3
1930	3,781,176	495,264	13.1	3,060,908	145,116	4.7
1931	2,377,980	271,284	11.4	2,090,635	92,741	4.4
1932	1,576,152	208,992	13.3	1,325,093	60,630	4.6
1933	1,647,216	200,688	12.2	1,449,559	25,693	1.8
1934	2,100,132	228,312	10.9	1,636,003	36,521	2.2
1935	2,243,076	251,124	11.2	2,038,905	37,346	1.8
1936	2,418,972	264,540	10.9	2,423,977	40,570	1.7
1937	3,298,932	378,132	11.5	3,009,852	44,586	1.5
1938	3,057,170	390,216	12.8	1,949,624	39,461	2.0
1939	3,123,343	385,068	12.3	2,276,099	43,541	1.9
1940	3,934,182	310,140	7.9	2,540,656	70,110	2.8
1941	5,019,877	284,653	5.7	3,221,954	82,455	2.6
1942	8,003,113	350,122	4.4	2,769,285	36,918	1.3
1943	12,841,542	516,762	4.0	3,389,951	85,223	2.5
1944	14,162,000	959,608	6.8	3,887,000	113,352	2.9
1945	9,585,000	753,084	7.9	4,098,000	151,958	3.7
1946	9,503,000	436,000	4.6	4,816,000	157,623	3.3
1947	15,162,000	641,000	4.2	5,666,000	250,459	4.4
1948	12,532,000	657,000	5.2	7,092,000	416,000	5.9
1949	11,936,124	561,852	4.7	6,591,636	477,792	7.2
1950	10,142,424	499,476	4.9	8,743,080	592,452	6.8
1951	14,879,496	783,012	5.3	10,817,340	601,260	5.6
1952	15,025,656	799,908	5.3	10,744,620	691,044	6.4
1953	15,624,000	690,875	4.4	10,777,583	761,550	7.1

Sources: *Survey of Current Business* and *Foreign Commerce and Navigation Statistical Abstract of United States.*

TABLE 10. WORLD TANK-SHIP FLEET, 1953

(Ocean-going vessels of 2,000 gross tons and over)

Flag	No.	Gross tons	Dead-weight tons	Average Dead-weight tons	Speed in knots
Western Hemisphere·					
United States.............	550	5,475,800	8,639,800	15,700	14.8
Government..............	122	1,122,600	1,709,600	14,000	16.0
U.S.M.A...............	4	29,100	46,600	11,600	11.0
Military...............	118	1,093,500	1,663,000	14,100	16.1
Private..................	428	4,353,200	6,930,200	16,200	14.5
Oil companies...........	282	2,917,700	4,644,200	16,500	14.6
Non-oil companies.......	146	1,435,500	2,286,000	15,700	14.3
Panama....................	220	2,221,700	3,457,800	15,700	13.8
U.S. citizen..............	127	1,353,800	2,120,500	16,700	14.5
Canada....................	17	136,700	207,800	12,200	14.3
Others:					
Argentina................	46	342,900	462,700	10,100	12.9
Brazil....................	14	148,900	221,800	15,800	14.4
Chile.....................	3	19,200	26,400	8,800	13.3
Colombia.................	1	29,000	4,300	4,300	10.0
Costa Rica...............	4	23,700	36,100	9,000	9.9
Dominican Republic.......	1	2,400	3,200	3,200	10.5
Honduras.................	11	140,600	220,700	20,100	14.4
Mexico...................	19	121,700	180,600	9,500	10.7
Peru.....................	1	2,800	4,300	4,300	10.0
Uruguay.................	2	20,600	33,200	16,600	15.0
Venezuela................	36	128,700	176,000	4,900	9.6
Subtotal others........	138	980,500	1,369,300	9,900	12.6
Total Western Hemisphere...	295	8,814,700	13,674,700	14,800	14.3
Europe:					
Belgium...................	6	51,400	76,300	12,700	12.6
Denmark..................	38	376,300	582,500	15,300	13.5
Finland...................	10	84,200	124,300	12,400	11.8
France....................	100	933,300	1,396,600	14,000	13.2
Germany..................	21	164,800	244,200	11,600	11.4
Greece....................	14	119,400	188,400	13,500	13.5
Italy.....................	106	919,800	1,408,800	13,300	13.1
Netherlands..............	102	642,700	915,500	9,000	12.3
Norway..................	355	3,546,000	5,389,600	15,200	13.3
Poland...................	3	21,100	30,200	10,100	11.2

TABLE 10. WORLD TANK-SHIP FLEET, 1953 (*Continued*)

(Ocean-going vessels of 2,000 gross tons and over)

Flag	No.	Gross tons	Dead-weight tons	Average Dead-weight tons	Average Speed in knots
Portugal..................	7	60,400	89,900	12,800	13.1
Spain.....................	26	165,500	226,300	8,700	11.6
Sweden...................	76	786,700	1,188,700	15,600	14.0
Switzerland...............	2	14,400	22,300	11,200	11.6
Turkey...................	6	45,100	69,300	11,600	11.7
United Kingdom...........	512	4,637,800	6,828,000	13,300	12.8
USSR....................	23	149,600	213,400	9,300	11.2
Yugoslavia...............	3	17,500	25,700	8,600	11.3
Total Europe.............	1,410	12,736,000	19,020,000	13,500	13.0
China.....................	5	42,600	59,800	12,000	9.8
Indonesia.................	1	2,900	3,800	3,800	10.0
Japan.....................	57	582,600	889,500	15,600	13.6
Korea.....................	3	9,800	12,900	4,300	11.7
Liberia...................	97	1,262,000	2,037,900	21,000	15.0
Morocco..................	1	10,600	15,400	15,400	11.3
New Zealand..............	1	3,100	3,300	3,300	11.0
Pakistan..................	2	9,600	15,000	7,500	9.3
Total world...............	2,502	23,473,900	35,732,300	14,300	13.6
Total United States control, all flags.................	834	8,386,200	13,189,400	15,800	14.6

NOTE: For many analytical purposes, the flag of registry is of less significance than the country of effective control. Differences between flag and control arise from the fairly common practice of placing tankers under the registry of a friendly foreign flag, or through corporate ownership of a foreign subsidiary, which in turn owns tankers. As of December 31, 1953, the United States controlled, either through ownership by citizens of this country or through registry, 834 tank ships of 8,386,200 gross tons and 13,189,400 dead-weight tons. Positionally, this is a decrease. As recently as September 1, 1949, this country controlled 52.1 per cent of the tanker carrying capacity of the world.

Dead-weight Tonnage and Speed. The world tanker fleet at the end of 1953 was the largest and fastest on record. The average dead weight of 14,300 tons was approximately 14½ per cent over the world average of 12,500 tons at the close of the war. Measured from the prewar fleet of September 1, 1939, in the interval of slightly more than 14 years, the average dead weight has increased more than one-third from the 10,700 tons at the earlier date. The average speed of the December 31, 1953, world fleet, computed by weighting the speed of each vessel by its dead-weight tonnage, was 13.6 knots. In 1939, the average speed was 11.1 knots.

Source: Sun Oil Company, Statistical Research Division.

TABLE 11. ESTIMATED FOREIGN FREE WORLD REFINERY RUNS BY AREA

(In thousands of barrels)

Western Hemisphere

	1939	1946	1947	1948	1949	1950	1951	1952
Canada:								
Total...............	123	195	214	239	265	299	349	379
American companies...	*	138	150	172	191	210	236	241
Other North and Central America:								
Total...............	82	116	133	130	139	141	155	170
American companies...	*							
Caribbean:								
Total...............	481	774	847	883	916	1,095	1,272	1,292
American companies...	*	411	433	454	462	565	640	653
Other South America:								
Total...............	94	122	129	152	163	182	198	205
American companies...	*	50	51	58	56	60	68	68
Western Hemisphere:								
Total...............	780	1,207	1,323	1,404	1,483	1,717	1,974	2,046
American companies...	*	599	634	684	709	835	944	962

Eastern Hemisphere

	1939	1946	1947	1948	1949	1950	1951	1952
Free Europe:								
Total...............	264	145	235	373	534	803	1,141	1,452
American companies...	*	29	46	71	93	177	165	379
Middle East:								
Total...............	220	640	718	745	787	829	669	455
American companies...	*	196	255	278	283	277	355	381
Other Eastern Hemisphere:								
Total...............	257	51	102	229	263	299	354	404
American companies...	*	...	4	40	62	78	111	108
Eastern Hemisphere:								
Total...............	741	836	1,055	1,347	1,584	1,931	2,164	2,311
American companies...	*	225	305	389	438	532	731	868

Total Foreign Free World

	1939	1946	1947	1948	1949	1950	1951	1952
Foreign Free World:								
Total...............	1,521	2,043	2,378	2,751	3,067	3,648	4,138	4,357
American companies...	*	824	939	1,073	1,147	1,367	1,675	1,830

* Not available.
NOTE: Total runs include those shown for American companies.
Sources: Compiled from U.S. Bureau of Mines and private sources.

TABLE 12. PER CAPITA PETROLEUM DEMAND BY PRINCIPAL COUNTRIES

(Local demand in millions of barrels; population in millions)

Country	1952			1947			Per cent 1952 vs. 1947		
	Local demand	Population	Barrels per capita	Local demand	Population	Barrels per capita	Local demand	Population	Barrels per capita
Canada	165.5	14.4	11.5	98.2	12.9	7.6	68.5	11.6	51.3
Mexico	70.0	26.9	2.6	48.3	23.4	2.1	44.9	15.0	23.8
Argentina	65.7	18.1	3.6	49.2	15.9	3.1	33.5	13.8	16.1
Brazil	46.3	54.5	0.8	20.6	48.4	0.4	124.8	12.6	100.0
Other foreign Western Hemisphere	191.5	69.1	2.8	123.2	63.8	1.9	55.4	8.3	47.4
Total foreign Western Hemisphere	539.0	183.0	2.9	339.5	164.4	2.1	58.8	11.3	38.1
Belgium	25.3	8.7	2.9	12.1	8.5	1.4	109.1	2.4	107.1
France	107.9	42.6	2.5	47.6	40.7	1.2	126.7	4.7	108.3
Western Germany (incl. West Berlin)	48.6	50.6	1.0	12.2	47.3	0.3	298.4	7.0	233.3
Italy	55.1	46.9	1.2	24.0	45.4	0.5	129.6	3.3	140.0
Scandinavia and Finland	70.8	18.9	3.7	43.0	18.0	2.4	64.7	5.0	54.2
United Kingdom	160.1	50.8	3.2	110.6	49.6	2.2	44.8	2.4	45.5
Other free Europe	130.8	80.8	1.6	83.4	77.3	1.1	56.8	4.5	45.5
Union of South Africa	23.0	12.9	1.8	13.9	11.7	1.2	65.5	10.3	50.0
Australia	43.0	8.6	5.0	24.8	7.6	3.3	73.4	13.2	51.5
New Zealand	9.8	2.0	4.9	5.3	1.8	2.9	84.9	11.1	69.0
India and Pakistan	39.8	443.0	0.09	23.5	412.1	0.06	69.4	7.5	50.0
Japan	37.0	85.5	0.4	8.3	78.0	0.1	345.8	9.6	300.0
Other Eastern Hemisphere	308.0	502.5	0.61	190.2	442.0	0.43	61.9	13.7	41.9
Total Eastern Hemisphere	1,059.2	1,353.8	0.78	598.9	1,240.0	0.48	73.8	9.2	62.5
Total free foreign	1,598.2	1,536.8	1.0	938.4	1,414.4	0.7	70.3	8.7	42.9
United States	2,665.0	157.0	17.0	1,989.8	144.1	13.8	33.9	9.0	23.2
Total Free World	4,263.2	1,693.8	2.5	2,928.2	1,558.5	1.9	45.6	8.7	31.6
USSR	347.0	201.1	1.7	211.0	193.0	1.1	64.5	4.2	54.5
Eastern Europe (incl. Austria)	67.8	97.6	0.7	32.1	94.5	0.3	111.2	3.3	133.3
China	0.8*	463.5	...	10.7	463.1	0.02	...	0.1	
Total Communist area	415.6	762.2	0.55	253.8	750.6	0.34	63.8	1.5	61.8

* Excludes unknown receipts from USSR, etc.
Sources: U.S. Bureau of Census and U.S. Bureau of Mines

TABLE 13. SUMMARY OF RELATIVE DIRECT OIL INVESTMENT ABROAD

(In millions of dollars)

1929

	Total all enterprises		Petroleum industry		
	Amount	% total foreign	Amount	% total foreign	% all enterprises
Canada	2,010	26.7	55	4.9	2.7
Latin-American Republics	3,519	46.7	617	55.2	17.5
Western Europe	1,353	18.0	231	20.7	17.1
All other countries	646	8.6	214	19.2	33.1
Total	7,528	100.0	1,117	100.0	14.8

1940

	Total all enterprises		Petroleum industry		
	Amount	% total foreign	Amount	% total foreign	% all enterprises
Canada	2,103	30.1	120	9.3	5.7
Latin-American Republics	2,771	39.6	572	44.8	20.6
Western Europe	1,420	20.3	306	24.0	21.5
All other countries	706	10.0	280	21.9	39.7
Total	7,000	100.0	1,277	100.0	18.2

1936

	Total all enterprises		Petroleum industry		
	Amount	% total foreign	Amount	% total foreign	% all enterprises
Canada	1,952	29.2	108	10.1	5.5
Latin-American Republics	2,847	42.5	453	42.2	15.9
Western Europe	1,245	18.6	275	25.6	22.1
All other countries	647	9.7	238	22.1	36.8
Total	6,691	100.0	1,074	100.0	16.1

1950

	Total all enterprises		Petroleum industry		
	Amount	% total foreign	Amount	% total foreign	% all enterprises
Canada	3,579	30.4	418	12.3	11.7
Latin-American Republics	4,735	40.2	1,408	41.5	29.7
Western Europe	1,720	14.6	424	12.5	24.7
All other countries	1,753	14.8	1,140	33.7	65.0
Total	11,787	100.0	3,390	100.0	28.8

1943

	Total all enterprises		Petroleum industry		
	Amount	% total foreign	Amount	% total foreign	% all enterprises
Canada	2,378	30.2	161	11.5	6.8
Latin-American Republics	2,798	35.6	618	44.4	22.1
Western Europe	2,025	25.8	370	26.6	18.3
All other countries	661	8.4	244	17.5	36.9
Total	7,862	100.0	1,393	100.0	17.7

1952

	Total all enterprises		Petroleum industry		
	Amount	% total foreign	Amount	% total foreign	% all enterprises
Canada	4,593	31.0	715	16.7	15.6
Latin-American Republics	5,758	38.8	1,577	36.7	27.4
Western Europe	2,145	14.5	532	12.4	24.8
All other countries	2,321	15.7	1,467	34.2	63.2
Total	14,817	100.0	4,291	100.0	29.0

Source: All enterprises: 1929, 1936, 1943, 1950—U.S. Department of Commerce, *Direct Private Foreign Investments of the United States* (*Census of 1950*), Table 13, p. 49. 1940—Derived from *American Oil Operations Abroad*, Appendix Table 29.
Petroleum industry: All years shown—U.S. Department of Commerce, *Direct Private Foreign Investments of the United States* (*Census of 1950*), Table 9, p. 13.
1952 data: *Survey of Current Business*, January, 1954, Table 1, p. 6.

TABLE 14. GROSS AND NET INVESTMENT OF 35 AMERICAN OIL COMPANIES, DECEMBER 31, 1953

By Departments and Segregated between Domestic and Foreign

(In thousands of dollars)

Department	Gross			Net		
	United States	Foreign countries	Domestic and foreign	United States	Foreign countries	Domestic and foreign
Leases, wells, equipment—gasoline and cycling plants.........	12,620,840	1,889,457	14,510,297	5,999,226	972,625	6,971,851
Natural gas............	240,666	10,740	251,406	179,524	10,535	190,059
Total production......	12,861,506	1,900,197	14,761,703	6,178,750	983,160	7,161,910
Pipelines..............	1,891,121	210,474	2,101,595	1,104,747	139,802	1,244,549
Marine................	632,405	231,529	863,934	351,165	146,959	498,124
Tank cars..............	42,599	292	42,891	13,277	15	13,292
Motor transport........	47,107	1,154	48,261	26,846	612	27,458
Total transportation...	2,613,232	443,449	3,056,681	1,496,035	287,388	1,783,423
Refineries and chemical plants..............	5,217,584	528,376	5,745,960	2,681,950	294,019	2,975,969
Marketing..............	2,772,052	343,044	3,115,096	1,696,171	196,682	1,892,853
Others................	578,735	32,248	610,983	359,247	18,797	378,044
Total all departments..	24,043,109	3,247,314	27,290,423	12,412,153	1,780,046	14,192,199

Distribution by Departments

(Per cent)

Department	Gross			Net		
	United States	Foreign countries	Domestic and foreign	United States	Foreign countries	Domestic and foreign
Production.............	53.5	58.5	54.1	49.8	55.2	50.5
Transportation.........	10.9	13.6	11.2	12.0	16.1	12.6
Refining..............	21.7	16.3	21.1	21.6	16.5	21.0
Marketing.............	11.5	10.6	11.4	13.7	11.1	13.3
Others................	2.4	1.0	2.2	2.9	1.1	2.6
Total...............	100.0	100.0	100.0	100.0	100.0	100.0

Source: *Financial Analysis of the Petroleum Industry for* 1953, Chase National Bank, Petroleum Department.

TABLE 15. DISTRIBUTION OF OPERATIONS OF SEVEN INTERNATIONAL OIL
COMPANIES BY PRINCIPAL FREE WORLD AREAS, 1952

(In millions of barrels)

Company	Gross crude-oil production					
	North America	South America	Middle East	Far East	Other areas	Combined
Standard Oil New Jersey.....	199	332	110	12	3	656
Royal Dutch–Shell..........	110	251	51	72	4	488
Gulf Oil...................	98	50	137	0	0	285
Texas Company.............	135	19	96	3	0	253
Standard Oil California......	107	7	96	3	0	213
Socony-Vacuum.............	92	26	53	12	2	185
Anglo-Iranian..............	0	0	179	0	1	180

Company	Crude runs to stills					
	North America	South America	U.K. and Continental Europe	Middle East	Other areas	Combined
Standard Oil New Jersey.....	358	232	77	19	15	701
Royal Dutch–Shell..........	153	216	155	18	65	607
Texas Company.............	186	10	9	54	2	261
Socony-Vacuum.............	186	0	37	11	15	249
Standard Oil California......	150	0	9	54	2	215
Gulf Oil...................	166	11	0	5	0	182
Anglo-Iranian..............	0	0	97	9	1	107

NOTE: Figures include operations of company and consolidated subsidiaries and portion
of nonconsolidated companies based on percentage of ownership.
Source: Private source.

TABLE 16. COMPARATIVE WORLD OIL PRODUCTION, 1923–1953

(In millions of barrels daily)

Year	Total world	Total United States	Per cent of world	Countries outside the United States					
				Total for-eign	Rus-sia	Total foreign except Russia	Amer-ican-owned foreign	Per cent of total for-eign	Per cent of total foreign except Russia
1923	2.79	2.01	72	0.78	0.11	0.67	0.31	40	46
1926	3.01	2.11	70	0.90	0.17	0.73	0.28	31	38
1929	4.08	2.76	68	1.32	0.28	1.04	0.39	30	38
1932	3.58	2.15	60	1.43	0.42	1.01	0.33	23	33
1935	4.52	2.73	60	1.79	0.50	1.29	0.46	26	36
1938	5.46	3.33	61	2.13	0.58	1.55	0.51	24	33
1941	6.05	3.84	63	2.21	0.64	1.57	0.61	28	39
1942	5.62	3.80	68	1.82	0.53	1.29	0.36	20	28
1943	6.10	4.12	68	1.97	0.48	1.49	0.44	22	30
1944	6.76	4.58	68	2.18	0.45	1.73	0.66	30	38
1945	7.08	4.69	66	2.38	0.41	1.97	0.82	34	42
1946	7.53	4.75	63	2.78	0.46	2.32	1.04	38	45
1947	8.28	5.08	61	3.20	0.54	2.66	1.21	38	46
1948	9.34	5.52	59	3.82	0.60	3.22	1.51	40	47
1949	9.33	5.05	54	4.28	0.69	3.59	1.68	39	47
1950	10.41	5.41	52	5.00	0.75	4.25	1.95	39	46
1951	11.78	6.16	52	5.62	0.84	4.78	2.46	44	51
1952	12.32	6.26	51	6.06	0.94	5.12	2.75	45	54
1953	13.10	6.47	49	6.63	1.05	5.58	2.96	45	53

Source: Private source.

TABLE 17. FOREIGN CRUDE-OIL PRODUCTION—MAJOR NATIONALITIES *
(In barrels of 42 U.S. gallons daily)

Year	American companies	British and Dutch companies	Russian government†	All others	Subtotal (except Russia)	Total foreign companies
1912	29,908	103,825	......	222,268	....	356,001
1913	46,772	126,635	......	213,859	....	387,266
1914	49,480	148,020	......	187,315	....	384,815
1915	63,068	151,829	......	201,632	....	416,529
1916	69,551	162,966	......	204,207	....	436,724
1917	104,464	173,522	......	182,780	....	460,766
1918	129,944	163,178	......	111,277	....	404,399
1919	195,596	179,994	88,233	39,889	....	503,712
1920	330,347	246,497	75,842	42,562	....	695,248
1921	415,214	278,181	79,364	53,972	....	826,731
1922	421,858	263,285	97,786	54,409	....	837,338
1923	311,415	312,902	107,252	54,956	....	786,525
1924	328,657	306,649	123,921	66,352	....	825,579
1925	304,936	316,662	143,359	76,468	....	841,425
1926	276,446	352,939	174,958	91,545	....	895,888
1927	293,033	391,645	208,943	92,140	....	985,761
1928	354,119	470,582	239,571	97,661	....	1,161,933
1929	392,103	541,211	282,194	104,132	....	1,319,640
1930	368,285	573,625	372,587	117,319	....	1,431,816
1931	332,550	522,542	449,147	129,030	....	1,433,269
1932	328,326	550,177	425,290	129,610	....	1,433,403
1933	340,127	567,448	424,216	137,199	....	1,468,990
1934	417,079	632,914	475,494	137,694	....	1,663,181
1935	461,977	665,512	502,732	163,787	....	1,794,008
1936	484,273	707,553	538,189	178,438	....	1,908,453
1937	562,869	810,807	562,022	161,267	1,534,943	2,096,965
1938	506,978	810,051	585,969	225,779	1,542,808	2,128,777
1939	554,899	795,393	609,656	268,888	1,619,180	2,228,836
1940	528,406	708,742	638,675	296,900	1,534,048	2,172,723
1941	610,640	656,071	644,465	296,437	1,563,148	2,207,613
1942	358,750	554,452	533,600	372,916	1,286,118	1,819,718
1943	438,424	596,032	483,500	453,705	1,488,161	1,971,661
1944	655,335	707,783	450,000	365,886	1,729,004	2,179,004
1945	818,243	812,956	406,000	344,651	1,975,850	2,381,850
1946	1,034,500	927,000	457,100	359,000	2,320,500	2,777,600
1947	1,205,700	1,085,100	543,000	362,700	2,653,500	3,196,500
1948	1,513,200	1,340,300	600,000	371,300	3,224,800	3,824,800
1949	1,681,100	1,517,800	685,000	394,800	3,593,700	4,278,700
1950	1,953,900	1,827,400	752,000	469,100	4,250,400	5,002,400
1951	2,464,800	1,716,800	842,000	601,700	4,783,300	5,625,300
1952	2,763,100	1,674,200	935,000	685,200	5,122,500	6,057,500
1953	2,961,400	1,818,400	1,050,000	800,900	5,580,700	6,630,700

* Partly estimated.
† Includes Russia and Sakhalin. Also satellite countries from years they were taken over.
Source: Private source.

(In thousands of barrels daily)

Year	British-Dutch			American			Russian government	
	Production	Per cent total foreign	Per cent foreign excluding Russia	Production	Per cent total foreign	Per cent foreign excluding Russia	Production	Per cent total foreign
1927	391.6	39.7	50.4	293.0	29.7	37.7	208.9	21.2
1928	470.5	40.5	51.0	354.1	30.5	38.4	239.5	20.6
1929	541.2	41.0	52.2	392.1	29.7	37.8	282.1	21.4
1930	573.6	40.1	54.2	368.1	25.7	34.8	372.5	26.0
1931	522.5	36.5	53.1	332.5	23.2	33.8	449.1	31.3
1932	550.1	38.4	54.6	328.3	23.0	32.6	425.2	29.6
1933	567.4	38.6	54.3	340.1	23.2	32.6	424.2	28.9
1934	632.9	38.0	53.3	417.0	25.1	35.1	475.4	28.6
1935	665.5	37.1	51.5	461.9	25.8	35.8	502.7	28.0
1936	707.5	37.1	51.6	484.2	25.4	35.3	538.1	28.2
1937	810.8	38.7	52.8	562.8	26.8	36.7	562.0	26.8
1938	810.0	38.1	52.5	506.9	23.8	32.9	585.9	27.5
1939	795.3	35.7	49.1	554.8	24.9	34.3	609.6	27.4
1940	708.7	32.6	46.2	528.4	24.3	34.4	638.7	29.4
1941	656.1	29.7	42.0	610.6	27.7	39.1	644.5	29.2
1942	554.5	30.5	43.1	358.8	19.7	27.9	533.6	29.3
1943	596.0	30.2	40.0	438.4	22.2	29.5	483.5	24.5
1944	707.8	32.5	40.9	655.3	30.1	37.9	450.0	20.7
1945	813.0	34.1	41.1	818.2	34.4	41.4	406.0	17.0
1946	927.0	33.4	39.9	1,034.5	37.2	44.6	457.1	16.5
1947	1,085.1	33.9	40.9	1,205.7	37.7	45.4	543.0	17.0
1948	1,340.3	35.0	41.6	1,513.2	39.6	46.9	600.0	15.7
1949	1,517.8	35.5	42.2	1,681.1	39.3	46.8	685.0	16.0
1950	1,827.4	36.5	43.0	1,953.9	39.1	46.0	752.0	15.0
1951	1,716.8	30.5	35.9	2,464.8	43.8	51.5	842.0	15.0
1952	1,674.2	27.6	32.7	2,763.1	45.6	53.9	935.0	15.4
1953	1,818.4	27.4	32.6	2,961.4	44.7	53.1	1,050.0	15.8

Source: Private source.

TABLE 19. SHARE OF OIL PRODUCTION IN EUROPE AND AFRICA

(In thousands of barrels daily)

Year	British-Dutch		American		Russian		Area per cent of total foreign production
	Production	Per cent of area	Production	Per cent of area	Production	Per cent of area	
1914	48.3	20.5	8.3	3.5	148.1	62.8	61.3
1919	9.6	7.4	2.5	2.1	88.2	68.1	25.7
1926	26.1	10.0	5.3	2.0	174.9	66.5	29.4
1930	43.1	8.4	10.4	2.0	370.7	72.2	35.9
1935	59.3	8.6	19.7	2.9	497.5	71.8	38.6
1940	30.1	3.8	21.1	2.6	630.0	78.2	37.1
1944	27.7	3.2	....	...	700.0	80.4	35.5
1950	42.3	4.4	20.9	2.2	752.0	77.5	19.4
1951	42.8	3.9	21.7	2.0	842.0	77.5	19.3
1952	43.0	3.6	24.1	2.0	935.0	77.7	19.9
1953	46.5	3.4	25.9	1.9	1,050.0	76.1	20.8

Source: Private source.

TABLE 20. SHARE OF OIL PRODUCTION OF MIDDLE EAST COUNTRIES

(In thousands of barrels daily)

Year	British-Dutch		American		Others		Area per cent of total foreign production
	Production	Per cent of area	Production	Per cent of area	Production	Per cent of area	
1912							
1913	5.1	100.0	...	...	....	...	1.3
1921	45.7	100.0	...	...	....	...	5.5
1933	150.6	99.9	0.1	0.1	....	...	10.2
1939	247.5	78.3	49.8	15.7	19.0	6.0	14.2
1941	167.1	83.2	33.7	16.8	....	...	9.0
1943	278.4	87.7	39.0	12.3	....	...	14.4
1944	353.4	87.2	51.8	12.8	....	...	16.5
1946	461.5	65.9	214.3	30.6	24.3	3.5	25.2
1947	504.8	60.2	313.7	37.5	19.4	2.3	26.2
1948	627.5	55.1	497.1	43.7	13.4	1.2	29.8
1949	741.9	52.9	645.2	46.0	15.8	1.1	32.8
1950	939.1	53.5	782.7	44.5	34.5	2.0	35.1
1951	697.2	36.2	1,121.7	58.2	109.1	5.6	34.3
1952	606.0	29.1	1,328.7	63.8	149.2	7.1	34.4
1953	760.2	31.4	1,456.8	60.1	207.3	8.5	36.6

Source: Private source.

TABLE 21. SHARE OF OIL PRODUCTION OF WESTERN HEMISPHERE FOREIGN
COUNTRIES

(In thousands of barrels daily)

Year	British-Dutch		American		Others		Western Hemisphere
	Production	Per cent area	Production	Per cent area	Production	Per cent area	Per cent total foreign production
1900	3.3	100.0	....	....	...	...	1.4
1912	25.3	48.5	25.9	49.8	0.8	1.7	14.6
1921	145.7	25.2	409.8	71.1	21.3	3.7	69.8
1930	266.6	42.3	345.8	54.8	18.3	2.9	44.1
1939	328.8	36.0	441.6	48.3	143.7	15.7	41.0
1941	327.0	32.9	512.5	51.5	154.8	15.6	44.5
1943	284.3	34.4	399.4	48.4	142.1	17.2	40.1
1944	316.6	29.6	601.5	56.3	150.2	14.1	42.8
1945	324.0	25.8	705.2	56.1	226.8	18.1	52.7
1946	420.8	29.4	819.5	57.1	193.9	13.5	51.6
1947	490.6	30.8	886.2	55.7	215.4	13.5	49.8
1948	570.3	32.4	963.3	54.6	229.4	13.0	46.1
1949	600.5	33.5	957.8	53.4	236.1	13.1	41.9
1950	677.6	33.2	1,089.0	53.4	273.3	13.4	40.8
1951	778.1	33.4	1,251.2	53.6	303.7	13.0	41.5
1952	817.4	33.1	1,328.5	53.7	327.4	13.2	40.8
1953	796.7	32.0	1,368.1	54.9	327.9	13.1	37.6

Source: Private source.

TABLE 22. VENEZUELA—TOTAL AND AMERICAN-OWNED CRUDE-OIL PRODUCTION

(In barrels daily)

Year	Total production	American- owned production	Per cent American- owned
1921	4,100		
1922	6,600	36	0.5
1923	13,000	200	1.5
1924	25,000	1,200	4.8
1925	55,900	17,500	31.5
1926	101,200	37,400	37.0
1927	175,100	83,400	47.6
1929	376,800	206,300	54.8
1932	322,700	171,600	53.2
1936	426,000	256,300	60.2
1939	562,800	335,100	59.5
1940	508,600	312,200	61.4
1941	625,000	403,500	64.6
1942	405,500	247,000	60.9
1943	491,500	317,500	64.6
1944	702,300	496,400	70.7
1945	885,900	622,300	70.2
1946	1,064,500	730,800	64.5
1947	1,190,800	794,200	66.7
1948	1,338,800	868,400	64.9
1949	1,321,500	836,700	63.3
1950	1,497,900	952,400	63.6
1951	1,704,600	1,082,600	63.5
1952	1,804,700	1,156,000	64.1
1953	1,765,900	1,158,200	65.6

Sources: Private sources.

TABLE 23. ESTIMATED WORLD OIL RESERVES

(In millions of barrels)

	Jan. 1, 1945	Jan. 1, 1953	Jan. 1, 1954
Western Hemisphere:			
United States..........	20,000.0	27,966.1	29,007.5
Outside United States...	8,885.5	14,958.6	14,897.5
Total...............	28,885.5	42,924.7	43,905.0
Eastern Hemisphere......	34,434.3	71,591.3	92,972.5
World total...........	63,319.8	114,516.0	136,877.5

Sources: 1945, De Golyer and MacNaughton; 1953 and 1954, *World Oil.*

TABLE 24. ESTIMATED FOREIGN OIL RESERVES

(In millions of barrels)

	Jan. 1, 1945	Jan. 1, 1953	Jan. 1, 1954
Total foreign excluding Russia and Sakhalin.............................	37,554.8	79,949.9	98,005.0
Total foreign including Russia and Sakhalin.............................	43,319.8	86,549.9	107,870.0

Sources: 1945, De Golyer and MacNaughton; 1953 and 1954, *World Oil.*

TABLE 25. ESTIMATED FOREIGN OIL RESERVES OF WESTERN HEMISPHERE BY AREAS

(In millions of barrels)

Area	Jan. 1, 1945	Jan. 1, 1953	Jan. 1, 1954
Caribbean....................	7,739.6	178.6	10,580.0
Other Western Hemisphere......	1,145.9	780.0	4,317.5
Total Western Hemisphere.....	8,885.5	958.6	14,897.5

Sources: 1945, De Golyer and MacNaughton; 1953 and 1954, *World Oil*.

TABLE 26. ESTIMATED OIL RESERVES OF EASTERN HEMISPHERE BY AREAS

(In millions of barrels)

Area	Jan. 1, 1945	Jan. 1, 1953	Jan. 1, 1954
Europe excluding Russia................	629.9	1,061.7	1,191.0
Africa...............................	86.0	214.0	142.0
Near and Middle East..................	26,800.0	61,625.0	79,075.0
Far East (excluding Sakhalin)...........	203.4	140.5	198.5
Oceania..............................	950.0	1,950.1	2,501.0
Total Eastern Hemisphere excluding Russia.................................	28,669.3	64,991.3	83,107.5
Russia in Europe and Asia...............	5,765.0	6,600.0	9,865.0
Total Eastern Hemisphere including Russia.................................	34,434.3	71,591.3	92,972.5

Sources: 1945, De Golyer and MacNaughton; 1953 and 1954, *World Oil*.

TABLE 27. ESTIMATED CONTROL OF PROVED CRUDE-OIL RESERVES IN COUNTRIES OUTSIDE THE UNITED STATES

(In thousands of barrels)

January 1	Total foreign	American companies	Per cent American of total foreign	Total foreign except Russia	Per cent American of total foreign except Russia
1928	12,597,189	2,080,216	16.51	9,175,179	22.7
1929	13,036,445	2,592,961	19.89	9,702,118	26.7
1930	12,664,932	2,519,227	19.89	9,433,606	26.7
1931	12,190,353	2,423,225	19.88	9,094,362	26.6
1932	11,709,744	2,505,456	21.40	8,776,793	28.5
1933	11,284,668	2,497,868	22.14	8,506,002	29.4
1934	11,003,560	2,447,836	22.52	8,177,978	30.3
1935	11,203,574	3,054,363	27.26	8,796,160	34.7
1936	11,428,860	3,180,649	27.83	9,692,972	32.8
1937	11,727,218	3,290,692	28.06	9,968,757	33.0
1938	14,278,582	4,329,367	30.32	12,375,308	35.0
1939	21,822,424	4,820,785	22.09	19,698,999	24.5
1940	21,801,986	4,727,819	21.69	19,684,160	24.0
1941	22,440,983	5,637,909	25.12	20,299,757	27.8
1942	24,058,823	6,572,646	27.32	21,553,752	30.5
1943	23,920,743	6,690,608	27.97	21,528,797	31.1
1944	31,431,522	10,233,468	32.56	25,769,924	39.7
1945	43,419,800	17,371,700	40.1	37,554,800 *	46.3 †
1946	38,085,000	13,465,900	35.4	30,023,000 *	44.9 †
1947	47,636,000	19,099,300	40.1	38,074,300 *	50.2 †
1948	49,695,350	21,086,400	42.4	42,105,350 *	50.1 †
1949	50,322,000	22,060,680	43.8	46,047,000 *	47.9 †
1950	52,371,250	22,948,610	43.8	47,996,250 *	47.8 †
1951	68,989,900	30,775,850	44.6	63,419,900 *	48.5 †
1952	74,168,450	34,189,758	46.1	68,603,450 *	49.8 †
1953	86,549,900	‡	....	79,949,900 *	
1954	107,870,000	‡	....	98,005,000 *	

* Total foreign except Russia and Sakhalin.
† Per cent American of total foreign except Russia and Sakhalin.
‡ Not available.
Sources: January 1, 1928, to January 1, 1943—private sources. January 1, 1944, Russia— PAW, January, 1944. January 1, 1944, Iran, Iraq, Kuwait, Bahrain, Arabia, and Qatar— De Golyer, March, 1944, 1945—presented to Special Senate Committee Investigating Petroleum Resources. 1945–1946, 1946–1952—De Golyer and MacNaughton, 20th Century Petroleum Statistics. 1953–1954—World Oil.

TABLE 28. ESTIMATED OIL PRODUCTION OF USSR AND SATELLITES

(In thousands of barrels daily)

	1953			1948			1953 vs. 1948	
	Crude	Other	Total	Crude	Other	Total	Vol. increase (total)	Per cent increase (total)
Russia.........	1,050.0	30.0	1,080.0	600.0	12.0	612.0	+468.0	+ 76.5
Rumania.......	110.0	2.5	112.5	78.0	2.5	80.5	+ 32.0	+ 39.8
Austria........	58.0	....	58.0	17.0	....	17.0	+ 41.0	+241.2
Hungary.......	14.0	0.5	14.5	10.0	0.4	10.4	+ 4.1	+ 39.4
Poland.........	4.0	2.7	6.7	2.7	1.0	3.7	+ 3.0	+ 81.1
Czechoslovakia	2.5	7.0	9.5	0.4	3.0	3.4	+ 6.1	+179.4
East Germany..	...	27.3	27.3	...	12.0	12.0	+ 15.3	+127.5
Albania........	3.0	....	3.0	1.0	....	1.0	+ 2.0	+200.0
China.........	2.0	....	2.0	1.8	....	1.8	+ 0.2	+ 11.1
Total........	1,243.5	70.0	1,313.5	710.9	30.9	741.8	+571.7	+ 77.1

Source: Private source.

TABLE 29. ESTIMATE OF POSSIBLE OIL EXPORTS FROM SOVIET-CONTROLLED AREAS *

(In thousands of barrels daily)

	Crude	Gasoline	Distillate, residual and others	Total
France.............	8.0	...	0.8	8.8
Netherlands.........	...	...	0.1	0.1
Belgium.............	...	...	0.8	0.8
West Germany.......	...	1.2	3.1	4.3
Switzerland.........	...	...	2.1	2.1
Italy...............	5.0	2.0	6.0	13.0
Norway.............	...	...	7.9	7.9
Sweden.............	...	...	5.0	5.0
Finland.............	...	7.9	10.0	17.9
Iceland.............	...	0.7	3.3	4.0
Argentine...........	10.0	...	...	10.0
India..............	?	?	?	0.8
Egypt..............	...	1.5	7.2	8.7
Total.............	23.0	13.3	46.3	83.4

* An estimate based on volumes included in trade agreements, commercial transactions and import data, subject to further adjustments.

Source: Private source.

TABLE 30. EXPORTS OF CRUDE AND PRODUCTS BY RUSSIA, RUMANIA AND
POLAND, 1926–1938

(In thousands of barrels daily)

Year	Rumania	Russia	Poland	Total	Estimated per cent of total foreign demand (incl. Russia)
1926	31.2	31.4	9.4	72.0	6.7
1927	39.5	43.1	5.6	88.2	7.5
1928	46.1	59.2	5.4	110.7	8.3
1929	55.0	76.2	5.0	136.2	9.2
1930	73.5	94.7	3.9	172.1	11.0
1931	91.8	106.6	4.6	203.0	13.2
1932	98.9	122.5	4.7	226.1	14.5
1933	111.6	98.0	4.7	214.3	12.8
1934	124.7	85.1	4.3	214.1	11.6
1935	128.8	66.2	3.3	198.3	10.0
1936	135.2	52.0	3.0	190.2	8.7
1937	110.3	38.6	2.5	151.4	6.3
1938	88.5	21.0	0.8	110.3	4.4

Source: Private source.

APPENDIX II

GENERAL

1. CONCESSIONS IN THE MIDDLE EAST *

OWNERSHIP—TERM—AREA

IRAQ PETROLEUM COMPANY, LTD.

Concession:

Term—75 years from March 14, 1925
Area—Provinces of Baghdad and Mosul east of the Tigris River (approx. 32,000 square miles) except for Khanaqin concession
Expires 2000

Ownership:

Anglo-Saxon Petroleum Co., Ltd.	23.75%
(subsidiary of the Shell group)	
D'Arcy Exploration Co.	23.75
(subsidiary of Anglo-Iranian Oil Co., Ltd.)	
Cie. Française des Pétroles (French govt.)	23.75
Near East Development Corp.	23.75
(Standard Oil Co., N.J.—50%)	
(Socony-Vacuum Oil Co., Inc.—50%)	
Participations and Investments, Ltd.	5.00
(C. I. Gulbenkian)	
	100.00%

BASRAH PETROLEUM COMPANY, LTD.

Concession:

Term—75 years from November 30, 1938
Area—All of Iraq not covered by I.P.C., Mosul and Khanaqin concessions
Expires 2013

Ownership:

Same as Iraq Petroleum Co.

* As of 1952.
Source: *Graphic Summary, Middle East,* Arabian American Oil Company.

Mosul Petroleum Company, Ltd.

Concession:
Term—75 years from May 25, 1932
 Area—All of Iraq west of the Tigris River and No. of 33° latitude (approx. 40,000 square miles)
 Expires 2007
Ownership:
 Same as Iraq Petroleum Co.

Petroleum Concessions, Ltd.

(Hadhramaut & Aden)

 Exploration permit only
Ownership:
 Same as Iraq Petroleum Co.

Transjordan Petroleum Co., Ltd.

 Term—75 years from May 10, 1947
 Subsidiary of Petroleum Concessions, Ltd.

Petroleum Development (Trucial Coast), Ltd.

 Concessions and one exploration permit
 Subsidiary of Petroleum Concessions, Ltd.

Petroleum Development (Oman), Ltd.

 Sudsidiary of Petroleum Concessions, Ltd.

Petroleum Development (Qatar), Ltd.

Concession:
 Term—75 years from May 17, 1935
 Area—All of Qatar (approx. 4,100 square miles)
 Expires 2010
 Sudsidiary of Petroleum Concessions, Ltd.

* * *

ANGLO-IRANIAN OIL COMPANY, LTD.

Concession: *
  Term—60 years from May 29, 1933, but status of concession at present
    in dispute [See Chapter 25, The Iranian Oil Settlement, 1954]
  Area—(100,000 square miles)
Ownership:
  British government 56%
  Burmah Oil Co. 22
  Other (individuals) 22
                                                             _____
                                                              100%

* (Nationalization in dispute since 1951)

KHANAQIN PETROLEUM CO., LTD.

Ownership: Anglo-Iranian Oil Co., Ltd.

* * *

ARABIAN AMERICAN OIL COMPANY

Concession:
  Term—Original area—66 years from July 15, 1933
        Additional area—66 years from July 21, 1939
  Area—Original area approx. 440,000 square miles
  Expires 1999
Ownership:
  Standard Oil Company of California 30%
  The Texas Company 30
  Standard Oil Company (New Jersey) 30
  Socony-Vacuum Oil Company, Inc. 10
                                                             _____
                                                              100%

BAHRAIN PETROLEUM COMPANY, LTD.

Concession:
  Area—All Bahrain and territorial waters
  Expires 2024
Ownership:
  Standard Oil Company of California 50%
  The Texas Company 50
                                                             _____
                                                              100%

* * *

Kuwait Oil Company, Ltd.

Concession:
Term—75 years from December 31, 1951
Area—All of Kuwait (approx. 6,500 square miles)
Expires 2026
Ownership:
D'Arcy Kuwait Co., Ltd. 50%
  (subsidiary of Anglo-Iranian Oil Co., Ltd.)
Gulf Kuwait Company 50
  (subsidiary of Gulf Oil Corp.)

  100%

* * *

Sinclair Petroleum Company

Concession: All Ethiopia
Ownership: Sinclair Oil Corp.

* * *

American Independent Oil Company

Concession:
Term—60 years from June 28, 1948
Area—All of Sheik of Kuwait's undivided half interest in Saudi Arab–
  Kuwait neutral zone including islands and territorial waters (approx.
  1,950 square miles)
Expires 2008
Ownership:
Phillips Petroleum Co.
Hancock Oil Co.
Signal Oil and Gas Co.
Ashland Oil and Refining Co.
Ralph K. Davies
J. S. Abercrombie
Sunray Oil Corp.
Deep Rock Oil Corp.
Globe Oil and Refining Co.
Lario Oil and Gas Co.

PACIFIC WESTERN OIL CORP.

Concession:
  Term—60 years from February 20, 1949
  Area—All of the King of Saudi Arabia's undivided half interest in Saudi
    Arab–Kuwait neutral zone including islands and territorial waters
  Expires 2009
Ownership:
  J. Paul Getty Interests

* * *

ANGLO-SAXON PETROLEUM CO., LTD.

Concession:
  Term—75 years from 1952 (approx.)
  Area—Offshore around Qatar Peninsula (approx. 10,200 square miles)
Ownership:
  Anglo-Saxon Petroleum Co., Ltd.
    (subsidiary of the Shell group)

2. TREATIES WITH MIDDLE EASTERN COUNTRIES AND SHEIKDOMS

Extracts from *Graphic Summary, Middle East*, Arabian American Oil Company, 1954

1. Protectorate Treaty with the Irka—1902

Art. III. The aforesaid Sheik Ahmed-bin-Awadth-bin-Muhammad-ba-Das hereby binds himself, his relations, heirs and successors and the whole tribe forever that he or they will not cede, sell or mortgage, lease, hire or give or otherwise dispose of the Irka territory or any part of the same at any time, to any power other than the British Government. Atchison, p. 111, Vol. XI.

Exactly similar clauses included in following treaties:
2. Protectorate Treaty—Haura—1902—Art. III. Atchison, p. 115, Vol. XI.
3. Protectorate Treaty—Lower Yafi—1895—Art. III. Atchison, p. 120, Vol. XI.

4. Treaty with Dthubi Section of the Yaffai-as-Saffal—1903—Art. IV. Atchison, p. 121, Vol. XI.

5. Treaty with Mausatta Section of the Yaffai-as-Saffal—1903—Art. III. Atchison, p. 123, Vol. XI.

6. Treaty with Sharif Ahmad-Am-Mohsin of Behan-al-Kasab—1903—Art. III. Atchison, p. 116, Vol. XI.

7. Treaty with the Muflahai Section of the Yaffai-as-Saffal—1903—Art. IV. Atchison, p. 125, Vol. XI.

8. Treaty with Sultan Kahtan-bin-Omer Har-Hara of Yaffai-as-Saffal—1903—Art. IV. Atchison, p. 127, Vol. XI.

9. Treaty with the Hadthrami Section of the Yaffai-as-Saffal—1903—Art. IV. Atchison, p. 129, Vol. IX.

10. Treaty with the Shaibi Tribe of the Yaffai-as-Saffal—1903—Art. IV. Atchison, p. 133, Vol. XI.

11. In 1914 the following clauses appear in the Protectorate Treaty with Audali Sultan—1914—Art. III.

The said Sultan Kasim bin Ahmed, the Audali, hereby agrees and promises on behalf of himself, his heirs and successors, and the whole of the tribesmen, subjects and dependents, under his jurisdiction to refrain from entering into any correspondence, agreements, treaty or dealings with any foreign person, nation or power, except with the knowledge and sanction of the British Government and further promises to give immediate notice to the Resident at Aden or other British Officer of the attempt of any other power to interfere with the territory of the Audali or any of its dependencies.

Art. IV. The said Sultan Kasim bin Ahmed, the Audali, hereby binds himself, and his heirs and successors forever that they will not cede, sell, mortgage, lease, hire or give, or otherwise dispose of the territory of the Audali and its dependencies, or any part of the same, at any time to any Power or to the subjects of any Power other than the British Government. Atchison, p. 133, Vol. XI.

12. Protectorate Treaty with the Haushabi—1895—Art. III. Same as Art. III Treaty with Irka. Atchison, p. 139, Vol. XI.

13. Protectorate Treaty with the Alwi—1895—Art. III. Same as above. Atchison, p. 142, Vol. XI.

14. Treaty with the Amir of D'Thala—1904—Art. III. Same as Treaty with Irka—1902. Atchison, p. 146, Vol. XI.

15. Protectorate Treaty with the Wahidi (Balahaf)—1895—Art. III. Same as in Treaty with Irka. Atchison, p. 153, Vol. XI.

16. Protectorate Treaty with Wahidi (Bir Ali)—1896—Art. III. Same as in Treaty with Irka—1902. Atchison, p. 155, Vol. XI.

17. Treaty between the British Government and the Ruler of Nejd, El Hassa and Qatif, etc.—1915—Art. IV.

Bin Sa'ud hereby undertakes that he will absolutely not cede, sell, mortgage, lease, or otherwise dispose of the above territories or any part of them, or grant concessions within those territories to any Power, or to the subjects of any foreign Power, without the consent of the British Government.

And that he will follow her advice unreservedly providing it be not damaging to his interest. Atchison, p. 207, Vol. XI.

18. Treaty of Jeddah—1927—Treaty between the British Government and his Majesty the King of the Hejaz and of Nejd and its Dependencies.

Art. I. His Britannic Majesty recognizes the complete and absolute independence of the dominions of his Majesty the King of the Hejaz and of Nejd and its dependencies. Atchison, p. 227, Vol. XI.

19. Translation of a letter dated the 18th Jamadi II 1332 (14th May 1914) from Shaikh Isa Bin 'Ali Al Khalifah, Chief of Bahrain, to Major A. P. Trevor, C.I.E., Political Agent, Bahrain.

"I have received your letter No. 531, dated the 18th Jamadi II 1332 (14th May 1914), on the possibility of obtaining kerosene oil in Bahrein. Just as I informed your honour in my letter dated 17th Jamadi-us-Sani 1332, that when the time comes for obtaining that I will certainly consult the Political Agency, I do hereby repeat to you that if there is any prospect of obtaining kerosene oil in my territory of Bahrein, I will not embark upon the exploitation of that myself and will not entertain overtures from any quarter, regarding that without consulting the political agent in Bahrein and without the approval of the High Government. This is what had to be said. May you be preserved and salams. Atchison, p. 239, Vol. XI.

20. Treaty between the British Government and the Shaikh of Qatar—1916—Art. IV.

I, Shaikh 'Abdullah bin Jasim bin Thani, further undertake that I will not have relations nor correspondence with, not receive the agent of, any other power without the consent of the High British Government; neither will I, without such consent, cede to any other power, or its subjects, land either on lease, sale, transfer, gift or in any other way whatsoever.

Art. V. I also declare that, without the consent of the High British Government, I will not grant pearl-fishery concessions or any other monopolies, concessions, or cable landing rights, to anyone whomsoever. Atchison, p. 259, Vol. XI.

21. Undertaking by the Shaikh of Shargah, regarding oil, 1922. Letter from Sheikh Khaled ben Ahmed, Chief of Shargah, to the Honorable Lieutenant Colonel A. P. Trevor, C.S.I., C.I.E., Political Resident, Persian Gulf, Bushire, dated 18th Jamadi-us-Sani 1340 (17th February 1922).

After Compliments—

My object in writing this letter of friendship is to convey my compliments to you and to enquire after your health.

Secondly, let it not be hidden from you that I write this letter with my free will and give undertaking to Your Honour that if it is hoped that an oil mine will be found in my territory I will not give a concession for it to foreigners except to the person appointed by the High British Government.

This is what is necessary to be stated.

(Note a similar undertaking was given by the Chief of Ras-al-Khaima, on the 22nd February 1922.) Atchison, p. 261, Vol. XI.

22. Undertaking by the Shaikh of Dibai, regarding Oil—1922. Letter from Shaikh Saeed ben Maktoom, Chief of Dibai, to Lieutenant-Colonel A. P. Trevor, C.S.I., C.I.E., Political Resident, Persian Gulf, dated 4th Ramazan 1340 (2nd May 1922).

After Compliments—

Let it not be hidden from you that we agree if oil is expected to be found in our territory, not to grant any concession in this connection to any one except to the person appointed by the High British Government.

Note—Undertakings similar in substance were given by the following Shaikhs on the dates mentioned:

23. Shaikh of Abu Dhabi, 3rd May 1922.
24. Shaikh of Ajman, 4th May 1922.
25. Shaikh of Umm-al-Qaiwain, 8th May 1922. Atchison, p. 261, Vol. XI.
26. Agreement by the Ruler of Kuwait, regarding oil—1913. Translation of a letter from Shaikh Sir Mubarak-as-Subah, Ruler of Kuwait, to the Political Resident in the Persian Gulf, dated the 26th Zu-al-Kada 1331 (27th October 1913).

After Compliments—

With the hand of friendship we received your esteemed letter dated the 26th Zu-al-Kada 1331, and in it you stated with reference to the conversation which passed between us yesterday if we saw no objection therein it would be desirable for Your Honour to inform the British Government that we are agreeable to the arrival of His Excellency the Admiral. We are agreeable to everything which you regard advantageous and if the Admiral honors our (side) country we will associate with him one of our sons to be in his service, to show the place of bitumen in Burgan and elsewhere and if in their view there seems hope of obtaining oil therefrom, we shall never give a concession in this matter to any except a person appointed from the British Government.

This is what is necessary and I pray the continuance of your high regard and may you be preserved.

Dated 26th Zu-al-Kada 1331. Atchison, p. 265, Vol. XI.

27. Undertaking by the Sultan of Muscat regarding Oil—1923. Translation of a letter, dated the 21st Jamadi I 1341, i.e., 10th January 1923, from Taimur bin Faisal (His Highness the Sultan) to Major Rae, His Britannic Majesty's Consul, Muscat.

After Compliments—We inform Your Honour in reply to your letter No. 1751, dated 16th December 1922, that we agree that we will not exploit any petroleum which may be found anywhere within our territories and will not grant permission for its exploitation without consulting the Political Agent at Muscat and without the approval of the High Government of India. What we hear about the existence of the mineral oil in our territory at Masirah is not still certain. We are beginning to enquire into the existence of the mineral oil and after we know about it there will be a discussion between your Honour and us regarding its exploitation, taking measures, arrangement of works and necessary conditions. It will, of course, be a monopoly. We believe in the complete assistance of the High Government of India in this important matter as it has always assisted us for which we are grateful. Atchison, p. 319, Vol. XI.

3. EXTRACT FROM THE PRESIDENT'S MATERIALS POLICY REPORT, "RESOURCES FOR FREEDOM," VOL. III, June, 1952, pp. 9, 10

The rest of the free world consumed in 1950 only a little more than half as much oil as did the United States. Oil consumption can be expected to increase much more rapidly abroad than in the United States as the pattern of consumption overseas comes more closely to resemble that of this country. In particular, automobiles and trucks are much less commonly used, but an increase paralleling the growth of motor vehicles in the United States over the past 25 years is in prospect. Furthermore, coal will probably continue to be much more expensive or less freely available in many countries abroad than in the United States. Some important industrial countries will find it necessary to import large amounts of energy fuels, and petroleum from the Middle East is likely to be the most economical form. Consequently, the oil demand of the rest of the free world can be expected to increase even more rapidly than in the United States, possibly increasing between three- and four-fold as indicated in table X.

Adequate supplies should be available to meet even this growth. Not only can the present great exporting areas—the Middle East and to a lesser extent Venezuela—greatly increase their production, but some countries

TABLE X. FREE WORLD DEMAND FOR CRUDE OIL AND PRODUCTS

(Thousands of barrels per day)

Region	1929	1950	Projected 1975	Per cent increase 1950–1975
United States.................	2,580	6,510	13,700	110
Other North America..........	210	590	2,300	290
South America................	170	600	2,300	283
Total Western Hemisphere...	2,960	7,700	18,300	138
Europe......................	460	1,200	4,000	233
Africa, Asia, and Oceania.......	300	1,100	4,500	309
Total Eastern Hemisphere....	760	2,300	8,500	270
Free world excluding United States...................	1,140	3,490	13,100	275
Total free world.............	3,720	10,000	26,800	168

Sources: 1929 and 1950, Bureau of Mines estimates. 1975 for United States, vol. II, Projection of 1975 Materials Demand.

formerly net importers can be expected to increase their output as well. As techniques of finding oil improve, areas previously deemed unfavorable come to have important production possibilities. Canadian production is already growing rapidly and may soon support net exports from that country. Other discoveries may be made in countries not now producing significant amounts of oil. Even in the absence of these new sources of production the Middle East and other major exporting countries appear to have the resources for meeting the projected vigorous growth in demand.

The physical basis accordingly exists for an adequate peacetime oil supply at real costs substantially unchanged from those of the present. In the Middle East these potentialities can be realized by drilling more wells and by providing tankers, pipelines and refineries to transport and process the oil. In other areas the geological prospects for success in further exploration are promising.

The future balance sheet of world petroleum supplies might look something like the hypothetical pattern in table XI, in which projections are compared with actual 1950 figures.

TABLE XI. HYPOTHETICAL PATTERN OF FREE WORLD OIL SUPPLIES AND DEMAND IN 1975 COMPARED WITH 1950

(Thousands of barrels per day)

Region	Production		Apparent consumption		Net imports − Net exports +	
	1950	1975	1950	1975	1950	1975
United States....................	5,910	11,200 *	6,450	13,700	−540	−2,500
Other Western Hemisphere........	2,040	5,900	1,190	4,600	+850	+1,300
Total Western Hemisphere......	7,950	17,100	7,640	18,300	+310	−1,200
Europe.........................	60	300	1,200	4,000	−1,140	−3,700
Middle East and other Eastern Hemisphere.................	2,040	9,400	1,100	4,500	+940	+4,900
Total Eastern Hemisphere.......	2,100	9,700	2,300	8,500	−200	+1,200
Free world excluding United States.	4,140	15,600	3,490	13,100	+650	+2,500
Total free world................	10,050	26,800	9,940	26,800	+110	

* Crude oil, natural gas liquids, shale oil and other synthetics.
Sources: 1950, Bureau of Mines. Illustrative 1975, PMPC.

This picture is merely one possible shape that the future pattern may take, but it does emphasize the prospective developments that set the background for the future oil problems of the free world. Those developments are a tremendously increased level of consumption and correspondingly increased dependence on production in the Middle East and in the Western Hemisphere outside the United States.

It is quite possible that production in the United States by 1975 may differ considerably from the 11.2 million barrels per day suggested in table XI. If it should be much below, free world dependence on the Middle East and possibly on Western Hemisphere production outside the United States would be correspondingly greater. In view of the wartime essentiality of oil, and the hazards to the Middle East in particular and to world oil supplies and transport in general, the future pattern poses a serious problem of free world security and offers a strong challenge to public policy to encourage the growth of production capacity in the United States and the rest of the Western Hemisphere.

4. A NATIONAL OIL POLICY FOR THE UNITED STATES

Formulated by THE NATIONAL PETROLEUM COUNCIL *at the Request of the Secretary of the Interior* *

INTRODUCTION

An adequate supply of oil is essential to the American standard of living. Oil in increasing quantities will be required in the future to meet the needs of our expanding economy. A prime weapon of victory in two world wars, it is a bulwark of our national security.

Favorable conditions have existed for the growth of the American oil industry—conditions which have made possible its achievements and its many contributions to the nation. The methods and procedures and the regulations and laws relating to oil which have evolved over the years have constituted a national oil policy, the success of which would indicate that its key elements should continue to guide us.

The industry has expressed its position on past occasions. It would now seem in the public interest that the principles of a sound national oil policy should be reappraised and restated. The National Petroleum Council, by virtue of its broad representation, the experience of its members in the oil industry, its realization of the great importance of oil and natural gas, and its deep interest in the welfare and security of this country, is pleased to respond to the request of the Secretary of the Interior and present its views as to the aims and essentials of such a policy.

THE AIMS OF A NATIONAL OIL POLICY

To be effective, a national oil policy should have the following objectives:

1. It should result in a maximum contribution by the oil industry to an expanding American economy and to a rising standard of living, including stable employment at fair wages within the industry.

2. It should maintain conditions most likely to assure adequate supplies of petroleum in both peace and war.

3. It should maintain conditions, within the free-enterprise system, most likely to assure adequate supplies of essential materials equitably available to all units in the industry in both peace and war.

* Presented January 13, 1949.

4. It should contribute to the expansion of trade and of industrial activity at home and abroad by encouraging American nationals in the development of both domestic and foreign oil resources.

5. It should operate to strengthen our free institutions by demonstrating that the issues which periodically arise in an industrial democracy, involving the relations of government and private industry, of state and individual, can be successfully resolved within our existing institutional framework.

To attain these ends, a national oil policy should establish the broad terms under which there will be sufficient flexibility to meet new conditions resulting from technological progress, economic change, and the possible requirements of national emergencies.

The oil industry has been progressive in its support and application of scientific research and in its readiness to meet new demands. A national oil policy must anticipate and provide for the certainty that further progress will create new problems. It should encourage flexibility in the functioning of the industry itself and continued adaptability to new circumstances in time of peace or crisis, which is one of its outstanding characteristics.

Fundamental Principles

The following general principles are fundamental to a sound national oil policy:

1. The national security and welfare require a healthy domestic oil industry.

Continuing supply to meet our national oil needs depends primarily on availability from domestic sources. Due consideration should be given to the development of foreign oil resources, but the paramount objective should be to maintain conditions best suited to a healthy domestic industry, which is essential to national security and welfare. To this end, adequate and equitable availability of essential materials is a fundamental requisite.

2. The public interest can best be served by a vigorous, competitive oil industry operating under the incentives of private enterprise.

The very nature of oil is such that multiple efforts on a very wide scale and initiative in high degree are required in all phases of industry operations from finding to distribution.

The participation by many in the far-flung and diverse activities of the industry provides those multiple sources of initiative, imagination, and responsibilty, out of which spring a great variety of discoveries and inventions, new ideas, and tremendous productivity.

The competitive form of economic organization, by offering the promise of reward commensurate with contribution and efficiency, utilizes a motivating force for which no adequate substitute has been found. Other nations have tried other methods, but it is the American oil industry operating under the American system which sets the highest standards of achievement and service.

3. The appropriate functions of Federal and state governments in relation to the industry and the principles underlying their present relationships should be maintained.

Under the concepts of the American economy the functions of government with respect to industry are primarily to provide the conditions under which industry may operate with maximum efficiency and to assure that the public interest is safeguarded.

The functions of the oil industry are to discover, produce, and transport oil and to refine and distribute its products. Participation in such operations is not a proper function of government.

In the exercise of their powers a clear line of demarcation should continue to exist between Federal and state governments.

The operation of the American petroleum industry is grounded on state regulations of oil and gas production in the interest of conservation. State regulation under our constitutional system evolved as the legal and most effective answer to the problem of a widely dispersed natural resource. State authorities have proved effective in their protection of the public welfare, and the decentralized approach has been highly successful in meeting the wide variety of conditions that prevail in different areas.

When oil-conservation problems have arisen involving coordination among states, instrumentalities have been developed to deal with them effectively, such as the Interstate Oil Compact to Conserve Oil and Gas, operating with the sanction and aid of the Federal government.

4. No government actions specifically affecting the oil industry should be taken without proper regard for the long-term effect and without consultation with the industry.

Mainly because of restrictions brought about by the war, temporary difficulties developed in supplying the sharply increased postwar demand. Some, in both public and governmental circles, gained the false impression that this country was faced with a permanent oil shortage requiring special measures.

Situations of this kind invite the consideration of dangerous expedients. Such measures directed at a single, passing phase of a cycle are not only unnecessary but can be destructive of sound long-range policy.

The oil economy is acutely sensitive to governmental interferences with the free market. As long as a free market prevails, price functions effectively as a regulator of supply and demand and as an allocator of supply to the channels of greatest need. It also provides the necessary incentives for exploration, increased efficiency, and technological improvement and permits the capital formation necessary to continued progress.

These conditions assure a vigorous industry prepared to meet a real emergency if it arises. In the two world wars, the industry's readiness was a decisive factor in our victories.

The Elements of a National Oil Policy

The general principles which have been outlined constitute the broad base of a sound national oil policy. In the formulation of that policy consideration should be given to a number of elements, which are outlined herewith under five headings, Domestic Oil, Natural Gas, Foreign Oil, Imports, and National Security.

I. DOMESTIC OIL

1. The key industry function of oil exploration and discovery presents extraordinary difficulties and risks. It is best promoted by competitive effort and by the incentive of commensurate reward.

Undiscovered oil is a present asset to no one.

The natural petroleum potentialities of the United States are very large, and oil exists outside the United States in great abundance. When conditions justify, these natural supplies can be supplemented by the vast resources available through synthesis of coal, shale, and natural gas. There will be liquid fuels enough for many generations to come.

Details of policy relating to production, refining, distribution, and utilization of oil become academic, however, unless provision is made to assure that this oil will be found and brought to the surface. The promotion of new discoveries, therefore, must be the primary consideration of national policy. This involves continuing encouragement of private exploration efforts at home and abroad, so that ample sources of oil will be under development at all times for peace or emergency needs.

Finding oil calls for the efforts of a great many people of different characteristics. Despite the development of scientific methods, a major factor in discovery is still the willingness of many individuals and competing industry units, exercising independent judgments, to take risks. The chances of finding oil are increased as more people are encouraged to accumulate and venture their capital on their own initiative.

Many government policies have a bearing on exploration efforts, including actions with respect to public lands, tidelands, and tax provisions. These policies should operate to accelerate and not retard exploration.

2. Conservation of our petroleum resources will best be furthered by facilitating continued industry efforts to reduce waste and promote maximum recovery of oil through optimum-rate production, unit operation, secondary recovery, and other methods.

True conservation of our oil resources cannot be achieved by hoarding them in idleness. It is only by active development that the earth's potential wealth is converted into real wealth useful to man. The resulting gain is not only in products. Through the exercise of its human resources society acquires skilled workers and technicians and a vast storehouse of knowledge with which to make further progress.

Optimum-rate Production. Over the past twenty years the industry has developed engineering methods designed to eliminate waste and to increase the recovery from oil fields. This procedure is based on the discovery that the total recovery is greatly augmented when the flow from oil wells is not permitted to exceed maximum efficient rates. Most of the information on which maximum efficient rates are determined has been developed through industry research on the nature of oil-bearing structures and underground movements of oil.

The economic operations of oil fields within the limits of maximum efficient rates are referred to as "optimum-rate production." The public interest and the private interests of oil operators are equally served by the application of this principle. On the one hand, it assures the consumer of a greater supply of fuel in the long run, and on the other it enables the producer to obtain the maximum yield from his properties.

The system of optimum-rate production has been very effectively developed in those states having conservation statutes. Efficient production rates are periodically fixed and revised after public hearings by state regulatory bodies upon the basis of engineering studies and actual operating conditions. Support and extension of this system by the states should be encouraged.

Unit Operation. In oil fields in which more than one operator have interests and where unit operation would result in greater ultimate recovery, appropriate action should be taken by the states to encourage such operations.

The establishment and operation of unitized pools, which satisfactorily protect the correlative rights of the various operators and royalty owners against the improper and inequitable drainage of their respective reserves by adjacent operators, should be favored. Considerable progress in this direction has been made by voluntary unitization and cooperative agreements.

Where legal obstacles to such arrangements exist, the state laws should be clarified to encourage voluntary cooperative unit plans.

The development of our oil resources can be further encouraged by clarifying Federal tax laws with respect to unit operations. Voluntary unit operation of a single reservoir by several operators is clearly in the interest of conservation. Such undertakings should not be taxed as separate business entities, because the effect would be double taxation. The elimination of uncertainties on this score will give further impetus to oil and gas conservation.

Secondary Recovery. Vast amounts of oil still remain in so-called "depleted" fields which were developed and produced before modern methods of optimum-rate production became general.

The industry has developed scientific and economic methods of secondary recovery which provide the means of adding vast quantities of oil to our recoverable reserves. Continued research and improvement in techniques are desirable.

Utilization. The efficient utilization of oil products by fuel-burning mechanisms of all kinds and in other applications is important to conservation. The oil industry should continue to cooperate with other industries in seeking the maximum development of oil-saving improvements.

3. Technology is a creative force of major importance in expanding our petroleum resources and in providing adequate supplies of oil at reasonable prices. The competitive conditions under which the industry's great technological advances have been made should be maintained.

The oil industry is a conspicuous example of the extraordinary achievements of American research and technology. In all phases of the petroleum industry they have operated to multiply our resources and lessen costs to the consumer.

Scientific advances in exploration have augmented our ability to locate oil fields. Technology and engineering have increased the quantity of oil which can be recovered from new and old fields. Research has improved the efficiency of refining processes, increasing flexibility in yield and quality and diversity of products. Losses in oil handling and transportation have been greatly reduced. Continual improvements in oil-burning devices of all kinds have the net effect of increasing the quantity of oil available for future use.

Computing barrels of recoverable oil in proven fields is not an adequate measure of the ultimate volume of oil or oil products obtainable. Calculations made in one period are likely to be invalidated later by advances in production, refining, or utilization techniques. In the period between the First World War and the Second World War, research was a major factor in the multiplication of reserves and in the industry's ability to produce aviation fuels, special lubricants, synthetic rubber, toluol, and many other products.

Science and technology can flourish only in a society in which there are intellectual freedom and freedom of expression. Our competitive economy not only provides these conditions, but it stimulates the best efforts of thousands of individuals to pursue independent paths of inquiry unhampered by centralized control.

In the United States, both private and public agencies have provided unexampled research facilities. To the unrestricted individual pursuit of knowledge, American organizational genius has added another factor—the coordination of research, engineering, and development within a company—which reduces duplication of effort and speeds the solution of problems by directed teamwork of scientific workers.

Our patent laws have also played a vital part in encouraging technological progress. They are based on the fundamental principle of disclosure. By offering exclusive rights for a limited time, our patent system provides inducements for the prompt disclosure of new advances and discoveries which, when known to others, become in turn the foundation for new improvements.

4. The economic and efficient development of synthetic fuels to supplement natural petroleum as needed can best be achieved by private industry.

The oil industry through extensive research has provided the technological basis on which a synthetic-fuel industry can be established when conditions require. The furtherance of research and process development by the industry is desirable. Research by governmental agencies should be limited to fundamental studies and to surveys of raw-material reserves. The construction of synthetic-fuel plants by government intervention would defeat the objectives of an adequate oil supply by impeding the normal functioning of the industry. Synthetic fuels will attain an orderly and economic development by private industry, if normal incentives are free to operate.

5. Oil and gas are only a part of our nation's energy resources. All these resources combined are adequate to meet energy needs; the relative use of each will be determined most effectively by the operation of price in a free market.

A continuance of favorable conditions for private competitive enterprise will provide American consumers with sufficient energy and power for an expanding economy. There are ample energy resources—coal, crude oil, gas, and water power—to meet our needs for a long time; and price adjustments will regulate the relative use of these resources so that over an extended period the demand and supply of each will be balanced. Present technology makes it possible to convert coal and gas into liquid fuels, thereby appropriately supplementing petroleum for the uses in which liquid fuels are superior. The degree to which this conversion will take place will best be determined by economic considerations which include consumers' evaluation of the relative convenience of liquid fuels.

6. The provisions in tax laws which have long recognized the requirements of petroleum operations are essential to the continued development of our oil resources and, in furtherance of the public interest, should be maintained.

The industry's ability to carry on an intensive and long-range search for new oil and gas fields has been greatly facilitated by Federal tax provisions for depletion and for deductions of intangible drilling, geophysical, and geological expenditures.

These provisions help provide the capital necessary for exploration. With the nation's demand for oil increasing, multiple efforts in oil finding should be stimulated to the fullest possible extent.

7. The petroleum resources of the lands beneath the marginal seas extending to the outer edge of the Continental Shelf can best be explored and developed under state, rather than Federal, control.

Substantial quantities of oil lie under the seas bordering the shores of several states. They constitute one of the most important sources of additional domestic oil supply remaining to be discovered and developed. A prudent oil policy would require that these resources be discovered and developed as soon as possible.

Years of experience have demonstrated that state laws and regulations, designed to provide the necessary incentives and proper conservation practices, and on-the-ground state administration encourage the risk taking vital to the discovery and development of petroleum resources. Federal laws and regulations, with final authority far removed from the scene of operations, have tended to discourage exploration for oil underlying Federal lands and to retard its discovery.

Furthermore, on historic and constitutional grounds and under judicial precedents, the abutting states should own the lands and the resources beneath the marginal sea to the outer edge of the Continental Shelf inasmuch as any area within or appurtenant to the continental United States is required, under our Federal system, to be included in one or more states of the Union. A sound national policy should prompt Congress to confirm in such abutting states the ownership of the lands and subsoil beneath such marginal seas.

8. Continued industry efforts to find and develop oil and gas on Federal public lands should be encouraged.

The policy of leasing the public domain for oil and gas exploration can contribute importantly to the efficient development of the nation's oil resources.

The statutes, rules, and regulations which govern these operations have in many instances retarded full development. They should be reviewed with the objective of stimulating further development. Points of improvement include the more expeditious leasing of the lands, the relaxation of acreage restrictions, and the issuance of leases which give management control to the lessee.

9. Conditions should be maintained under which the industry may continue to form the capital required to expand its operations to meet the nation's growing needs for petroleum.

All segments of the oil industry continually require capital to replace obsolete equipment and to expand their facilities and operations. These requirements are increasing as the population grows and the American standard of living is raised to higher levels. The bulk of the capital the industry employs has been created by the industry out of its own operations. Its future needs can best be met under a system of free markets and suitable tax provisions.

In addition, it is important that conditions be such as to encourage the thousands of small operators who are indispensable to a vigorous industry. When all segments of the industry are able to function in an atmosphere of confidence and stability, the extension of credits is facilitated and they are assured of sufficient capital to operate successfully.

10. Efficient marketing of oil and oil products is a major responsibility of the industry. It should continue to support and encourage a system of distribution under which thousands of independent marketers, integrated companies, and others compete to bring the industry's products to the consumer.

The oil distributor—both wholesaler and retailer—is the channel through which the industry serves the ultimate consumer.

Most oil distributors are independent businessmen who buy at wholesale. The marketing of petroleum is particularly suited to operations by individuals and small units, and the industry considers that the public interest will be served by continuing to encourage the existing competitive system.

The industry fully recognizes the interdependence of all units in the industry, large and small. It is important to the public and to the industry that the distribution system should be efficient, so that the benefits of progress in all branches of the industry will be passed on to the consumer.

Marketers should be encouraged to increase their service to the public through continued improvement in distribution methods, the opening of new facilities where needed, the introduction of new products, added conveniences, and courteous treatment.

The industry believes that competition for consumer preference is the best way to assure such service.

11. The oil industry is opposed to monopoly and believes that competition contributes to the public good.

The oil industry should operate on a basis which will contribute to the economic progress of the American people and provide needed supplies of oil. This objective requires an adequate productive effort and stable employment of hundreds of thousands of workers. It involves continued technological advance, elimination of waste, and avoidance of violent changes in output and employment.

The industry structure, which consists of many large and small enterprises and operations, has demonstrated its effectiveness under a competitive system which assures the attainment of these objectives.

The industry subscribes to the fundamental principles underlying the antitrust laws. It recognizes a continuing responsibility to maintain the rivalry in price, quality, and service which promotes technical progress and efficiency and passes on these benefits to the public.

II. NATURAL GAS

1. State and Federal laws should encourage, not impede, the development of natural-gas resources by industry.

Natural gas is closely associated with oil, and the production of both frequently coincides. Natural gas is assuming an increasingly important role as an energy source, not only for heating but in industrial processes .and as a future source of synthetic liquid fuels. It is in the public interest, therefore, that the conservation, efficient production, and use of natural gas should be fostered.

The several states should encourage by appropriate legislation arrangements among producers for the installation and operation of cycling and repressuring projects and other operating means for fostering the conservation and utilization of gas in and from oil and gas reservoirs.

The quantities of natural gas produced by many gas-producing states are in excess of the consumption of gas within those states. It is important, therefore, that the producers of gas have full opportunity to sell gas to interstate carriers for resale by them to local gas-distributing companies. Interstate transportation of natural gas and its sale in interstate commerce for resale are under Federal regulation. A threat exists that Federal regulation will be extended to include control over the production and gathering of gas and the price charged by producers and gatherers. This threat has the effect of discouraging the maximum development of facilities for gas utilization and the production and sale of gas in interstate commerce.

The proper sphere of regulation by Federal agencies is interstate commerce. Such agencies should have no authority to control directly or indirectly the production, gathering, and processing of gas or its price at or prior to its delivery into the main line of an interstate carrier or to control the local distribution of gas. In carrying out their proper function of regulating the transportation of natural gas in interstate commerce, Federal regulatory bodies should apply a formula which would allow an interstate carrier of natural gas to charge for gas delivered through its facilities a price which includes the price paid for the gas it purchased and the market value of the gas it produced.

End-use Control. It is not the function of the Federal government to control the end use of gas any more than it is its function to control the end use of coal, crude oil, cotton, wheat, or other commodities. The Constitution does not confer upon the Congress the power to control end use, and the exercise of such authority would be contrary to American principles. Control over the end use of gas would require control over the end use of other energy resources, which would lead to a vast bureaucracy involving a regimented industry and managed economy.

Gas is in open competition with coal, crude oil, and water power, the other energy resources. In a free economy, competition is the best regulator of the end use of gas. If Federal or state authority is extended into this area, private incentives would be restricted and development of the gas industry would be retarded. Furthermore, pressure groups would be encouraged to seek to establish standards or restrictions for their special advantage.

III. FOREIGN OIL

1. The participation of United States nationals in the development of world oil resources is in the interest of all nations and essential to our national security.

The importance of oil to economic and social progress is not confined to the United States. All nations need more oil for industrial development and to raise living standards.

Oil exists in many places in the world. Its efficient production is important both to the country where it is produced and to the world economy. The oil which a nation does not need for its own uses should find its way through the channels of international trade to other countries.

Oil from abroad should be available to the United States to the extent that it may be needed to supplement our domestic supplies. The availability of oil outside of the United States, in places well situated to supply our offshore requirements in time of emergency, is of importance to our national security.

Oil technology has been more highly developed by the United States than by any other nation. American methods and skills have made great contributions to the discovery, development, and conservation of oil resources in other countries. American interests today participate widely in international oil development. Conditions should be fostered that will further this participation but not to the extent that this involves preferential treatment of operations abroad at the expense of the domestic industry.

2. An effective oil policy should encourage access by our nationals to world oil resources on equal terms with other nationals and stable agreements between foreign governments and private industry on a basis which will promote development by free-enterprise methods.

A country's oil resources are best developed when all who are engaged in petroleum operations—its own nationals and those of foreign nations—compete on equal terms. Favored treatment of one group at the expense of another, state monopolies, and state competition in any phase of oil retard maximum development and are not in a nation's long-run interest.

The government of each country and its nationals should respect all valid concession contracts and lawfully acquired rights and should make no unilateral effort to interfere directly or indirectly with such contracts or rights.

Agreements between foreign governments and private enterprise should define the proper functions of each. They should provide to the companies operating in those countries security of title to the property or rights acquired; managerial control of operations; the opportunity to make a reasonable profit commensurate with the risks originally assumed and to form capital for expansion; and means for the prompt and fair settlement of disputes that may arise.

Foreign governments in return have a right to expect to participate in the benefits from ventures on their soil. Such participation includes payments of reasonable royalties and taxes. It is also reasonable that foreign countries should expect that their own requirements for oil be satisfied before any oil is exported, that waste be avoided, and that their people receive training and employment at fair wages.

3. The Federal government should encourage foreign oil development by American nationals by efforts directed through diplomatic channels to reduce political risks involved in such foreign operations and by permitting United States citizens to operate abroad in conformity with the laws and customs of other countries.

It is in the national interest that American oil companies should continue to take an active part in the development of petroleum resources in other countries.

The Federal government, therefore, by diplomatic representations, should exert its influence in behalf of a sound oil policy. It should seek to assure the observance of agreements made between foreign governments and American nationals and to minimize the political risks involved in foreign operations.

If American firms are to do business abroad, they must conform to the laws and customs of the countries in which they operate. American companies should not be penalized on occasions when such requirements conflict with the rules laid down for the conduct of business within this country, as long as these operations are consistent with the interests of the United States.

IV. IMPORTS

1. The nation's economic welfare and security require a policy on petroleum imports which will encourage exploration and development efforts in the domestic industry and which will make available a maximum supply of domestic oil to meet the needs of this nation.

The availability of petroleum from domestic fields produced under sound conservation practices, together with other pertinent factors, provides the means for determining if imports are necessary and the extent to which imports are desirable to supplement our oil supplies on a basis which will be sound in terms of the national economy and in terms of conservation.

The implementation of an import policy, therefore, should be flexible so that adjustments may readily be made from time to time.

Imports in excess of our economic needs, after taking into account domestic production in conformance with good conservation practices and within the limits of maximum efficient rates of production, will retard domestic exploration and development of new oil fields and the technological progress in all branches of the industry which is essential to the nation's economic welfare and security.

V. NATIONAL SECURITY

1. The maintenance of a vigorous oil industry in time of peace is the best way to assure the reserves and facilities needed in time of war.

The normal operations of the oil industry, under which oil is produced at optimum rates, provide the United States and other countries with a continuing reserve of potential productive capacity. In the event of a protracted national emergency, during which essential petroleum requirements might increase rapidly, this reserve productive capacity could be drawn upon to satisfy peak demands.

Civilian rationing of oil would be necessary under a war economy, as it would be for most commodities which are needed in large quantities by the armed services. Rationing would provide a large surplus of oil during the early stages of a conflict. Other measures could then be instituted as circumstances dictated. If storage facilities were provided, military stock piles could readily be accumulated out of the surplus to meet such sharply rising requirements as the armed services might anticipate with a mounting pace of operations. In the meantime, reserve productive capacity could be maintained through the continuation or expansion of exploratory efforts. If the need for additional quantities is anticipated, supplemental volumes could be obtained through synthesis of natural gas, oil shales, and coal, for which we have the necessary technological information, although very large requirements of steel and man power would be necessary.

It is clearly in the interests of national security that peacetime conditions which encourage the development of available reserves by private industry should be promoted. An active program of exploration by the industry is essential. High peacetime requirements for oil create high reserve productive capacity. They result, furthermore, in the competitive development of refining, transportation, and other facilities. The greater the civilian consumption at the outset of a war, the larger will be the supplies available through rationing.

Withholding from development the oil on public lands or in offshore areas, with the thought that it can be used in an emergency, is not sound policy in terms of national security. This oil can be made fully available only by continuous and prolonged peacetime development.

The "locking up" of proved reserves by arbitrarily curtailing existing production or by acquiring proven oil fields through purchase or condemnation is unnecessary and would retard the normal development of the industry. Importing oil and storing it in depleted or partly depleted oil or gas fields in the United States is also unnecessary as well as impractical.

A large expansion of reserves can be attained by the active development of foreign sources of supply, particularly those tributary to offshore requirement areas.

2. The government should accumulate such inventories of petroleum products in peacetime as would be needed by the armed services in the early stages of a conflict.

Stock accumulation by the government is desirable to the extent that adequate supplies of products of military specification may be assured for the initial period of a conflict. Stocks of such products should be stored in sufficient quantity to last until conversion of industry facilities or construction of additional facilities can be completed.

Special provision should be made for storing products such as aviation alkylates, which cannot be obtained by simple substitution or process change from civilian products, and products such as tetraethyl lead, for the production of which only a limited number of units now exist.

Stock piling on a massive scale in peacetime is unnecessary and impractical. If required, petroleum supplies could be accumulated through rationing during the early period of an emergency which, with additional supplies available through increased production and continued rationing, should be sufficient to meet the requirements of such an emergency.

3. Procedures for government-industry consultation should be maintained on a permanent basis so that plans to meet emergencies can be adjusted continually to changing conditions.

The problems of national security with respect to petroleum involve problems relating to our entire economy. They encompass not only military and civilian needs for oil but questions of supply of other commodities which affect the supply of petroleum.

It is impossible at this time to evaluate, except in general terms, the problems of an unknown future. Attempts to anticipate all the needs of protracted war would tend to establish rigid patterns which could seriously affect the economy and strength of the nation. Wise policies and appropriate actions must evolve out of constant study of changing factors.

The soundest procedure is to direct studies principally to the immediate and short-term requirements of an emergency. The existing Military Petroleum Advisory Board should continue to function. Among the problems for consideration are the time required to expand military supplies and contract civilian consumption; the rapidity of increase in requirements of particular military products in relation to expansion of special facilities to produce them; the interrelationship of production, refining, and transportation facilities under initial war conditions; the relative vulnerability of facilities for the production of particular products; the wartime availability of materials and man power required to sustain or increase production; and plans for providing storage capacity to accumulate military stock piles during the early period of a war.

Provisions to deal with these problems can be worked out in advance after careful study of alternatives so that unnecessary or uneconomic actions will be avoided.

In the event of another war, the experience of the Second World War will provide a basis for its successful prosecution. The pattern of government-industry cooperation through the Petroleum Administration for War and the Petroleum Industry War Council is suggested. An oil industry which has continued to progress under a sound national oil policy would again be prepared to throw all its resources, facilities, and man power to the nation's defense.

CONCLUSION

The American oil industry is distinctively a product of the American way of life. For many years it has operated under one of the most effective and efficient industrial policies in our economy.

The industry will continue to produce the optimum economic and social gains inherent in the nation's petroleum resources, granted the conditions of a free economy and continued recognition of the economic laws which direct its operations.

If, in addition, the United States government through diplomatic efforts is able to reduce the political risks inherent in foreign operations, American nationals with their capital, managerial skill, and technical knowledge can be counted on for increasingly important contributions to world recovery and peace.

Vigorous oil development under competitive conditions at home and abroad is the best way to assure our national security.

INDEX